The Analysis of Mortality
and Other Actuarial Statistics

The Analysis of Mortality and Other Actuarial Statistics

B. BENJAMIN PhD, FIA

and

J. H. POLLARD BSc, PhD, FIA, FASSA

*Published for the Institute of Actuaries
and the Faculty of Actuaries*

*Special edition for sale to members of the
Institute of Actuaries and members or students of the
Faculty of Actuaries*

HEINEMANN : LONDON

William Heinemann Ltd
10 Upper Grosvenor Street, London W1X 9PA

LONDON MELBOURNE TORONTO
JOHANNESBURG AUCKLAND

First published 1970
Second edition 1980
© Institute of Actuaries and the Faculty of
Actuaries in Scotland, 1970, 1980

434 90137 7

Filmset by Willmer Brothers Ltd, Birkenhead, Merseyside
Printed by Redwood Burn Ltd
Trowbridge & Esher

CONTENTS

PREFACE

This second edition retains the scope and purpose of the first edition in that it remains the official textbook of the Institute of Actuaries and the Faculty of the Actuaries in the field of study indicated by its title, which is unchanged. As before, the book, in some places, goes beyond the examination syllabuses of the two actuarial bodies. This is for the sake of completeness and in consideration of the needs of non-actuarial readers. Within these constraints the text has undergone major revision. Every chapter has been partially, and in some instances totally, rewritten; this is partly to correct defects in the first edition, which have been brought to light by teaching experience and partly to take account of new work in this field. The demographic content has been expanded to provide more complete and more balanced coverage of population methods. The treatment of graduation and of statistical methods generally has been brought more into line with modern practice; an entirely new chapter on stochastic processes has been added.

My original collaborator having died in the early stages of the preparation of 'Benjamin and Haycocks' I have been joined for this revision by John Pollard, Professor of Actuarial Studies at Macquarie University, Australia. This collaboration has been the source of intense pleasure to me because for many years now I have enjoyed the close friendship of the entire Pollard family and especially of his parents, Pearl and Alf Pollard. The latter was the first occupant of the Professorial chair which John now holds and was the first Professor to introduce a university degree covering what was then, in 1966, described as the Intermediate subjects of the Institute of Actuaries' syllabus. I owe John a special debt of gratitude for cheerfully responding to my every and frequent appeals for help and often for intellectual enlightenment.

We both owe a debt to our scrutineers, Barry Sherlock of the Institute of Actuaries and Colin Kirkwood of the Faculty of Actuaries. They were hard taskmasters who refused to allow any relaxation from rigour or clarity or completeness. But for their painstaking vigilance this book would have had many more defects than it may still have. We often grumbled; we usually complied; we always realized that in the process the text had been improved. Much help at this stage was derived from notes supplied by Jack Dyson of the ATS and David Wilkie, Chairman of the Examination Board of the Faculty. As on previous occasions I am deeply grateful to Jackie Millar of the ATS who operates as a very effective 'production manager' for the Textbook Committee of the two actuarial bodies. She helped in so many ways—hammering out and assembling copy, checking cross references and helping to make the book hang together, interceding with the publisher and not least encouraging a tiring author. Finally I wish to express my thanks to Pat Waugh who retyped many of the chapters from manuscript written in my own special microscopic hand, and to Coral Arter, John Pollard's secretary who typed the mathematical chapters and kept me supplied with 'good clean copy' from Australia with a promptness that made light of the distance.

Bernard Benjamin

CHAPTER ONE

MEASURES OF MORTALITY

General introduction

1.1 An important aspect of the science of financial planning, and one in which an actuary is especially skilled, lies in the ability to estimate the way in which contingent liabilities currently contracted, whether longer term, as in life insurance or pension business, or shorter term, as in motor, fire or marine insurance, are likely to emerge in the future as actual payments. This prediction is necessary to allow the institution accepting the contract, by charging appropriate premiums and by prudent investment of the proceeds, to make adequate provision to meet these payments as they fall due. This planning does not deal with the contract affecting a single individual or risk. It takes one contract with another and makes group predictions, as in all probability calculations, in order to ensure that in the long run, i.e. in the average, cash payments are adequately provided for. Fluctuations are inherent in natural experience of this kind. In some years the number of policy-holders in a life fund who die will be greater, if only by a small number, than that estimated, even if in the long run the estimates prove to be correct in total. There are other factors less tractable to predictive calculations than mortality, especially the future changes in the rate of interest earned on the reserves held against future liabilities; an assumption about this has to be made before discounting to the present the cash flows which are to take place in the future. Therefore, while past experience is used as a basis for estimating future changes in the population at risk, uncertainty about some of the factors compels the actuary to introduce margins of safety; to introduce an element of judgement into his calculations.

1.2 In estimating mortality the actuary traditionally employs the life table as a model but he knows that the past experience from which that table has been derived will never be exactly reproduced in the future. Mortality is itself constantly varying; there are fluctuations about an underlying trend (normally an improving trend). The actual observations from which the life table has been derived are a sample of total experience if only in terms of time, i.e. covering a short period of years. A certain random element of fluctuation will be inherent in the observations. The fluctuations, which we may regard as 'sampling errors', may be in different directions at different ages, and we shall discuss this feature later in relation to the subject of graduation. The mortality model ultimately adopted must incorporate assumptions about these sources of deviation from past experience, even if it is only an assumption that they can be ignored.

1.3 The purpose of these paragraphs is to put the use of mortality measurement in proper perspective in relation to actuarial calculations. This is not to suggest that measurement can be allowed to be inexact. On the contrary, if judgement has to be introduced in any final estimation, it is likely to be sounder when on the basis of adequate analysis of past experience.

Measures of mortality

1.4 The purpose of measuring mortality is to enable inferences to be drawn about the likelihood of death occurring within a specific population during a specific period of time. It is natural, therefore, for the basic measure to be expressed in proportional terms as a rate of mortality—the number of deaths occurring per unit of population in a particular interval of time. The unit of population may commonly be 1,000, 10,000, 100,000 or a million; it is a matter of arithmetical convenience. For example, the vital statistician may express 2,564 deaths in a general population of 216,342 persons in a year as an annual death rate of 1,185 deaths per 100,000 or 12 per 1,000, according to the number of significant figures he wishes to record. It is necessary to define not only the interval of time and the unit of population size but also to define what kinds of death (all or those from a particular cause) and what kind of population (the general population or those in a particular sex, age, etc., category).

1.5 The reason for this is that the risk of dying varies with a number of factors—sex and age, and other factors which influence the physical constitution or the environment of the people, such as birthplace, geographical locality of residence, occupation, marital condition. In calculating rates of mortality it is therefore necessary to differentiate the influence of these factors as well as to distinguish the contribution of different medical causes of death (types of disease or injury). Death rates may therefore be classified as general or specific, the first relating to all causes of death and to the general population, the second to special causes of death or to deaths in particular sections of the population, or both. In the latter event the extent of specificity must be carefully defined, e.g. the death rate from pneumonia among married males ages 40–44 last birthday, in England and Wales during 1976.

1.6 Whether general or specific death rates are under consideration it is important to be sure that the population used in the calculation is precisely that which produced the deaths used in the calculation; conversely the deaths must comprise all those occurring in this population and no others. The denominator of the rate (of which the numerator is the relevant number of deaths) is commonly referred to as 'the population at risk' or the 'exposed to risk'. In the example given above we should have, in the numerator of the rate, every death in 1976 of a married man aged 40–44 at death, resident in England and Wales and certified as due to pneumonia as the underlying cause; the denominator would include every married man aged 40–44 resident in England and Wales during 1976. This immediately raises the question of what we mean by 'during 1976'.

1.7 The population at risk in most vital statistical calculations is the mean population of the area (or, alternatively, class of person considered) over the period to which the rate relates. (It will be seen later that this kind of death rate is not the same concept as the age-specific rate of mortality used in life table calculations—though, except where mortality is changing rapidly with age, it is not numerically very different.) As a first approximation, the mid-year (or mid-interval) population is accepted as the mean population unless irregular or rapid changes in the population (as, for example, during a war) render it necessary to make more precise calculations of the number actually at risk. Death rates when calculated for a shorter period than a year are often expressed as an equivalent annual rate, viz. as the annual rate that would result from the persistence of the same mortality conditions for a full year.

1.8 This conversion is merely for convenience since it is often confusing to pass from annual to quarterly rates, and therefore desirable to work with rates of the same order of size throughout. The conversion, though convenient, may often be unrealistic. To assume that the mortality of a particular quarter which includes a widespread epidemic of influenza could persist for a whole year would not be justifiable but it is usually accepted that conversion is made without such implication. The shorter the interval, the more likely it is that the rate will be influenced by some epidemic occurrence or a spell of particularly inclement weather, so that while the rate for a very short period is a fact and a true statement of mortality for that period, extreme care should be exercised not to draw any inference about mortality at other times or over longer intervals.

1.9 It should also be borne in mind that where small numbers of deaths occur, chance fluctuations are likely to be relatively large. For example, suppose we have a population of only 1,000, with, over a long period of years, an average death rate of 13 per 1,000 per year. This means an average annual number of deaths of 13; but any elementary statistical textbook will tell us that the frequency distribution of the annual deaths will be such that fluctuations to fewer than 6 or to more than 20 will occur in each case as often as once in 40 years, and that, although the long run average will be 13, in any one year it is as likely as not that the number of deaths will be outside the range 11–15. Looking at the problem the other way round, we can see that a particular year when there was a chance occurrence of, say, 18 deaths would be a very misleading basis for calculating the underlying mortality. Where populations or rates are small, it is advisable to base calculations upon a group of years rather than upon a single year, in order to increase the number of deaths and thus to reduce the size of the possible error.

Variation of mortality with age and sex

1.10 Figure 1.1 shows the rates of mortality in England and Wales in 1971 in successive age groups for each sex (Scotland would show a similar differential at a slightly higher level of mortality). The actual rates are shown in Table 1.1. Mortality is highest at the extremes of age. Once the newborn infant has survived the hazards of the first few days of life, the rate of mortality falls rapidly, and during childhood the risk of death is very small, being very largely confined to that of the occasional lethal infection, which modern treatment with antibiotics or drugs has made extremely rare, and severe accidental injuries, to which childish recklessness or lack of adult care sometimes leads. In adolescence the impact and strain of industrial life bring a rise in mortality. These and other factors, inherent in the social and economic environment and individual ways of life, reacting upon constitutional weakness, where that exists, lead to a continuing increase in the risk of death as age advances. At later ages the wearing out of the human frame rather than inimical qualities of the

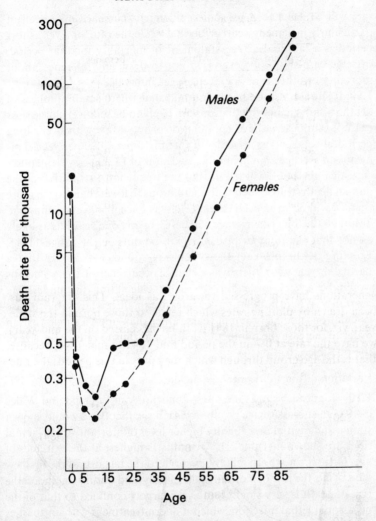

FIGURE 1.1

environment becomes the dominant cause of mortality. If this natural wearing out (true senility) were the only cause of death, the mortality rates shown in the diagram would take the form of J-shaped curves with rates maintained at insignificant levels until advanced ages, when there would be a steep upward rise, reflecting the approach of the wearing-out process. Figure 1.2 shows to what extent successive

Table 1.1 *England and Wales, 1971—rates of mortality per 1,000*

Age group	Males	Females
0–	19·78	15·12
1–4	0·76	0·64
5–9	0·44	0·29
10–14	0·37	0·23
15–19	0·90	0·38
20–24	0·94	0·42
25–34	0·98	0·61
35–44	2·32	1·59
45–54	7·12	4·34
55–64	20·3	10·1
65–74	51·8	26·5
75–84	118·7	77·8
85 and over	243·1	193·0

generations have progressed towards this ideal. This diagram has been drawn by plotting rates which relate to those born in the same year, viz. for those born in 1841 (with births centred on the mid-year) we have the rate at 0–4 in the period mid-1841 to mid-1846, because that is the age group through which they pass in this period: the rate

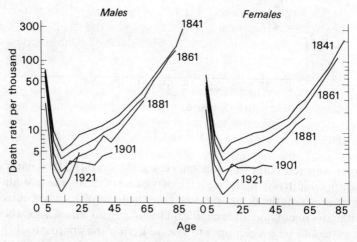

FIGURE 1.2

at 5–9 in the period mid-1846 to mid-1851, the rate at 10–14 in the period mid-1851 to mid-1856, and so on.

1.11 We have already shown in Figure 1.1 the difference between the patterns of mortality for the two sexes. The death rates for females are lower than those for males at all ages. Before 1890 there was an excess in the death rate of females at adolescence and early adult ages mainly associated with the heavier mortality from tuberculosis in girls; since that time the general level of tuberculosis mortality has fallen so much that this differential has no effect upon the comparison of rates from all causes. Briefly, the higher mortality of males may be explained in medical terms as follows:

1   In infancy and early childhood boys are generally more vulnerable to some birth hazards (prematurity, malformation, birth injury), to infection, possibly as a result of some biological factor, and to injuries, possibly as a result of more vigorous and venturesome activity; these are the principal causes of death at these ages.

2   In early and middle adult life the principal causes of death are accidents and violence, tuberculosis, heart disease and cancer, and the death rates are higher in men. The higher mortality from tuberculosis in men (except in very early adult life) is one indication of the generally greater vulnerability of men to respiratory disease of all kinds, not only tuberculosis but also bronchitis, influenza, pneumonia, cancer of the lung (and this greater vulnerability extends to advanced ages). The type of heart disease which is most responsible for deaths in this age group is arterial and described as cornonary thrombosis—there is still considerable controversy as to the relative weight of the factors operating to increase susceptibility to this disease, but an excessive diet, insufficient physical activity, nervous tension and hereditary predisposition, seem to play their part, and those with sedentary occupations appear to incur a higher risk, probably because the lack of physical activity tends to increase weight. The higher risk of accidents must be regarded as occupational in the broader sense of including, as compared with females, more outdoor movement in traffic etc., as well as greater industrial hazards.

3   At more advanced ages the process of physical deterioration and lessening resistance to disease associated with general wear and tear appear to proceed faster in men. Age for age, cerebral haemorrhages, arterial disease, cancer (especially of the lung) and

bronchitis take a heavier toll of males than females. Some, at least, of this excess mortality has been self-inflicted by cigarette smoking (Benjamin, 1977).

1.12 Enough is already known of the natural history of diseases and the social and environmental factors in their aetiology to render profitable the study of death rates specific, not only for age and sex, but also for cause—as certified by the medical practitioner in attendance before death, or by the coroner in cases necessitating inquest. The study of such rates over periods of time and in different areas may help to indicate the relative weight of various occupational and environmental factors in the different areas and the relative progress made in those areas towards reducing mortality. The contemporary increase, both in the United Kingdom and in the USA, of mortality from cancer of the lung and coronary arterial disease (especially in men) has been exercising considerable influence on the shape of the curve of death rates with age and provides an example of the need for cause analysis.

1.13 Finally there are ethnic factors to be taken into account. In the United States of America the mortality of the white population is considerably lighter than among the non-white at all except the extremely advanced ages. To what extent this difference is of truly racial origin or merely reflects different social and economic conditions is not clear but certainly the statistical separation is important. In England and Wales there are no separate statistics of the mortality of coloured people, but there have been and still are health problems associated with large-scale immigration.

Mortality indices

1.14 In 1961 the crude death rate (i.e. total deaths related to the total population) in Bournemouth was 13·2 per 1,000 living and the corresponding rate for Corby was only 5·2. These two figures do not indicate the real difference in the mortality risks of the population of the two towns at that time. Bournemouth is a coastal town attractive to older retired persons—in 1961, 22 per cent of the population was aged 65 or more—and this means the population was abnormal in that there was a relative shortage of young persons. The effect on the death rate was to reduce the denominator without proportionately reducing the numerator (because young people do not contribute many deaths) and thus to inflate the death rate. On the other hand, Corby was in 1961 a new town rapidly developing around an expanding steelworks; many young families had moved there and in consequence the population was short of old persons. This affected the numerator more than the denominator and deflated the crude death rate.

1.15 Consider Table 1.2.

Table 1.2

	Area A			Area B		
Age	Population	Deaths	Death rate per 1,000	Population	Deaths	Death rate per 1,000
	(000s)			(000s)		
0–4	280	1,400	5·00	220	2,200	10·00
5–24	900	900	1·00	810	1,215	1·50
25–44	910	2,730	3·00	900	2,970	3·30
45–64	720	14,400	20·00	780	11,700	15·00
65 and over	310	38,750	125·00	350	38,500	110·00
All ages	3,120	58,180	18·65	3,060	56,585	18·49

1.16 The crude death rates are 18·65 and 18·49 per 1,000 but their general similarity conceals the fact that the age-specific rates in area B are higher at young ages and lower at older ages than in area A, i.e. the age incidence of mortality is very different. But the age structure of the population of B is so much older than that of A that it produces an elevation of the crude death rate to compensate for the lighter age-specific mortality rates.

1.17 It must be borne in mind that the crude death rate is a weighted average of age-specific rates in which the weights are the numbers of the population in the respective age groups, i.e. if $m_{x,t}$ is the death rate at age x to $x + t$, and $E^c_{x,t}$ is the population in the same age group, the total deaths will be $\Sigma E^c_{x,t} . m_{x,t}$, where the summation is over all age groups, and the total population $\Sigma E^c_{x,t}$, so that the crude death rate is $[\Sigma E^c_{x,t} . m_{x,t}]/\Sigma E^c_{x,t}$.

1.18 Clearly if the values of $E^c_{x,t}$ are increased for older ages at the expense of the younger ages, then, notwithstanding the constancy of the age-specific rates of mortality, the crude death rate will rise. The weights used in such an average are therefore important. ($E^c_{x,t}$ is used here to symbolize the central or average population exposed to risk.)

The use of a single-figure index

1.19 Before taking this any further we should consider why it is that an average should be used at all. It ought to be evident that since mortality varies with age, and population age structure varies with area, then in comparing mortality in two different areas we ought to look at the individual age-specific rates. However, it is difficult mentally to assimilate a large number of rates, and for many purposes (e.g. for brevity in description, or ease in manipulation) it is desirable to have a summary measure to try to accomplish what the mind finds difficult to do unaided, i.e. to epitomize the whole experience. This is, of course, the fundamental object and justification of any type of average or index figure. It will be understood that this desire for a single measure or average is increased by virtue of the fact that mortality varies with many other characteristics, such as sex, marital condition, ethnic origin and social conditions, etc., so that for really thorough comparisons a very large number of refined specific rates may be necessary (though there is the dilemma that sub-division means smaller numbers and larger random errors). It has to be stressed that no one average is accepted as sufficient for all purposes.

Standardization

1.20 We have seen that the crude death rate is one such average but that it suffers from the defect that the weights used in its calculation are the local age group populations, i.e. they vary from area to area. Nevertheless this defect is not serious for the very large numbers of areas whose population have a structure of the same general character, and the crude death rate is indeed widely used in such circumstances. Where there is no precise knowledge of the population structure, i.e. where only the total deaths and the total population are known, there is, of course, no alternative to this procedure. Where the age structure is known, however, i.e. where the age-specific rates of mortality are known, there is no reason why in calculating the average death rate we should not avoid using weights which vary from area to area, by deciding to use a fixed set of weights, i.e. a standard population structure. Such an average rate then becomes a standardized mortality rate. Since populations can vary in their sex proportions at each age, it is usual to standardize rates for persons, i.e. for both sexes, for this source of variation also. The standardized mortality rate, then, is a weighted average of the age–sex specific mortality rates of a particular population under observation, the weights being the proportions in each age–sex group of a standard population (not the particular population under observation). This standard population structure is 'standard' in the sense that it is used for all the observed populations, the standardized rates of which can then be compared as rates which relate to a similar sex–age structure, i.e. any differences will arise from sources other than differences in sex–age structure.

Direct standardization

1.21 Employing the same notation as before but using the symbol $^sE^c$ to indicate the standard population and remembering that the rates are specific also for sex and the summation is over all ages (and, for 'persons' rates, i.e. for both sexes, is performed for the two sexes separately);

$$\text{Standardized mortality rate} = [\Sigma^sE^c_{x,t} \cdot m_{x,t}]/\Sigma^sE^c_{x,t}$$

Indirect standardization

1.22 Where, for example, a large number of local-authority rates of mortality require standardization on the basis of the national population, there will be difficulty in obtaining adequate data for the use of the direct method. First, except in census years, an age and sex analysis of the population will not normally be available. Second, an age and sex analysis of the deaths in local authorities is not normally available except for larger authorities. For most authorities, the number of deaths will not, in any one year, be large enough to support the calculation of reliable age and sex specific death rates.

1.23 It would avoid these difficulties if we could find a factor F such that, when the crude death rate of a district is multiplied by it, the result is equal to the standardized mortality rate, viz.

$$\left[\frac{\Sigma E^c_{x,t} \cdot m_{x,t}}{\Sigma E^c_{x,t}} \right] \times F = \left[\frac{\Sigma^sE^c_{x,t} \cdot m_{x,t}}{\Sigma^sE^c_{x,t}} \right]$$

where the values of the bracketed expressions are known but not necessarily the individual elements in the summations.

1.24 To calculate F we use the specific death rates for the standard population in this equation instead of the district rates (which may not be known).

$$F = \frac{\Sigma^s E^c_{x,t} \cdot {}^s m_{x,t}}{\Sigma^s E^c_{x,t}} \div \frac{\Sigma E^c_{x,t} \cdot {}^s m_{x,t}}{\Sigma E^c_{x,t}}$$

i.e. if the district population were subject at each age to the same mortality as in the standard population, its crude death rate would still be different from that of the standard population to the extent that the age structure of the district population differs from that of the standard population. If the district population is of an older age structure the crude rate will be inflated and F, to correct for this inflation, will be correspondingly less than unity. For example, if the inflation is $33\frac{1}{3}$ per cent, F will be $100/133\frac{1}{3}$ or 0.75. F will only apply to similar degrees of distortion, i.e. to circumstances where the general pattern of mortality is similar to that of the standard population, since we have assumed that the distortion is the same even though ${}^s m_{x,t}$ has been substituted for $m_{x,t}$, but it is usually valid to make this assumption. We still require $E^c_{x,t}$. These age group populations will be available at times of population census, and except when rapid population changes are taking place, it may be possible to assume that they remain sufficiently stable to permit the use of F, once calculated, throughout the intercensal period and until the next census makes it possible to recalculate F.

1.25 In the United Kingdom factors similar to F are used by the Registrars General to adjust local death rates to the national population structure (i.e. in this case the standard population death rates are the national rates for the current year) and these factors are then called 'Area Comparability Factors'.

1.26 For many comparisons the so-called 'standardized mortality ratio' is used. This does not need a standard population as such. It is a method familiar to actuaries—the comparison of actual deaths in a particular population with those which would be expected if 'standard' age-specific rates applied. In our symbols this is

$$[\Sigma E^c_{x,t} \cdot m_{x,t}]/[\Sigma E^c_{x,t} \cdot {}^s m_{x,t}]$$

which can be written

$$\frac{\Sigma E^c_{x,t} \cdot {}^s m_{x,t} \cdot \dfrac{m_{x,t}}{{}^s m_{x,t}}}{\Sigma E^c_{x,t} \cdot {}^s m_{x,t}}$$

i.e. it is a weighted average of the age-specific mortality differential $(m/^sm)$, where the weights are the expected deaths in each age group.

The development of standardized measures

1.27 The first reference to a standard rate occurs in Farr's report of 1856 (Sixteenth Annual Report of the Registrar General 1853). The reference is to a crude death rate of 17 per 1,000 expressing the level of mortality of certain 'healthy' districts. This concept was later used (Twentieth Annual Report) to calculate a standard 'natural' death rate for London in order to assess the excess mortality of the Metropolis. Essentially this represented 'indirect' standardization. It appears that the direct method was due to Ogle who read a paper on the subject to the International Statistical Institute in 1891, recommending the use of an international standard population (though the direct method had in fact been employed in the Annual Report of the Registrar General for 1885). Brownlee (1922) urged the use of the 'life table death rate', i.e. 'the ratio of the number of deaths of persons above any defined age to the number living above that age in a stationary population' (a population distributed on the basis of the L_x column of the relevant life table), i.e. $\Sigma d_x/\Sigma L_x$. But $\Sigma d_x = l_x$ and ΣL_x is T_x, so the rate becomes l_x/T_x. However T_x/l_x is $\mathring{e}_x$ and therefore the life table death rate is simply the reciprocal of the expectation of life, which is itself a widely used index. The standardized death rate as calculated by the direct method can be expressed as a weighted mean of ratios of age rates, with the deaths in the standard population age groups as the weights. It is not independent of the standard population. The direct method can also be criticized, since, in this case, the weights are not constant for all comparisons. Another possibility is the 'equivalent average death rate', i.e. a rate standardized by reference to a population with equal numbers in the age groups. This is thus an arithmetic mean of the rates for age groups up to some convenient limit, such as 65 (beyond which it becomes unrealistic).

1.28 Later Yerushalmy (1950) recalled that in normal direct standardized comparisons, the age ratios were weighted by the deaths in the standard population, with the result that undue representation was given to mortality at old age, where deaths were heavy and secular improvements slight, while little account was taken of mortality at younger ages, where deaths were few but improvement considerable. In order to give more representation to this important improvement at young ages he suggested weighting so that equal proportionate changes in age rates affect equally the mortality index (as the standardized rate now becomes) no matter at what ages these changes occur.

1.29 Starting with the normal expression for the standardized death rate we have:

$$\text{Standardized death rate} = \frac{\Sigma m_{x,t}\,{}^s E^c_{x,t}}{\Sigma {}^s E^c_{x,t}} \qquad (1.1)$$

$$= \frac{1}{{}^s E^c} \Sigma\left(\frac{m_{x,t}}{{}^s m_{x,t}}\right){}^s d_{x,t} \qquad (1.2)$$

where ${}^s d_{x,t}$ is the number of deaths in the standard population corresponding to ${}^s m_{x,t}$, and ${}^s E^c$ is the total standard population.

1.30 Yerushalmy effectively replaces ${}^s d_{x,t}$ by t, i.e. the age-specific mortality differentials are given equal weights. Kohn (1951) has proposed that if there is to be prior assessment of the weight to be given to a particular age group in averaging improvement, then there would be an advantage in separating the derivation of weights from the deaths or death rate of the age group for the disease in question, and in producing a system of weights which would be capable of universal application. Kohn suggests using the reciprocal of the age of death—in practice the reciprocal of the midpoint of the age interval of each age group, viz.

$$\text{Mortality index} = \frac{\Sigma m_{x,t}(t/a)}{\Sigma(t/a)}$$

where t = class interval, a = age at midpoint.

1.31 This, however, removes any reference to comparison with a standard mortality, and is a different kind of average from those considered above.

1.32 We may now summarize in Table 1.3 the various systems of weights in weighted averages of the age mortality rate ratios $(m_{x,t}/{}^s m_{x,t})$.

1.33 The life table is an effective model for summarizing mortality experience (see Appendix). It uses rates of mortality (q_x, the proportion of lives of exact age x who die before attaining exact age $x+1$) derived from that experience, to calculate the number of lives (l_x) who survive to exact age x out of an original cohort of births (l_0). Because mortality experience is different for males and females, the life table is always calculated separately for each sex. It provides a

Table 1.3

Index	Weights
Standardized—direct	Actual deaths in age group in standard population
Standardized—indirect	Approximation to above
Standardized mortality ratio	Actual deaths in age group in actual population
Yerushalmy	Equal

number of useful indices. For non-actuarial readers let us briefly recall that the symbols normally used, apart from l_x and q_x, include:

d_x The number dying between exact age x and age $x+1$, so that $l_{x+1} = l_x - d_x$.

m_x The central death rate or average mortality rate over the age interval x to $x+1$.

L_x The average number alive between x and $x+1$, or, alternatively, the number of years of life lived by l_x during the year of age x to $x+1$. $L_x = \int_0^1 l_{x+t} \, dt$.

$\mathring{e}_x$ By extension of this latter concept, the average life time after age x of l_x who survive to age x is $(\Sigma L_x)/l_x$, where the summation is to the limiting age beyond which the life table shows no survivors. It is referred to as the expectation of life at age x.

T_x This is written for ΣL_x and is the total population aged x and over in a stationary population generated by constant births and subject to the life table mortality.

p_x The proportion surviving at least one year after attaining exact age x. Thus $p_x = 1 - q_x$.

μ_x The force (or instantaneous rate) of mortality at age x defined as the ratio of the deaths in the infinitesimal interval of age x to $x+dt$ to the exposure time of the lives at risk between x and $x+dt$, i.e. $l_x dt$, so that

$$d_x = \int_{t=0}^{1} \mu_{x+t} \cdot l_{x+t} \cdot dt.$$

1.34   The central death rate $m_x = d_x/L_x$ is the average risk to which the population is subjected during its passage through the year of age x to $x+1$ and is a different concept from $q_x = d_x/l_x$, which represents the total effect of the mortality in terms of the proportion who fail to survive the whole year of age x to $x+1$ without reference to the variation of mortality risk over the course of that year. We shall return to this important difference later.

1.35 Group mortality rates, e.g.

$$\left[\sum_{t=0}^{4} d_{x+t}\right]\bigg/\sum_{t=0}^{4} L_{x+t}$$

are standardized in relation to the life table population. The expectation of life $\overset{\circ}{e}_x$ (and especially the expectation at birth $\overset{\circ}{e}$) is often used as a summary index for illustrating mortality improvements over time in a particular country or for comparing the mortality experiences of two countries.

Infant mortality

1.36 There has been no index of mortality more frequently used than the infant mortality rate—deaths of infants under 1 year of age per 1,000 live births. Most of the deaths after the first days are due to exogenous causes—mainly infections—and until recent times, when this component had shrunk to very small proportions, the rate was a sensitive index of social conditions and of public health progress. Like the expectation of life, it has the attraction of being a single figure index. One of John Graunt's principal 'observations' in 'Natural and political observations made upon the bills of mortality' (1662), related to the high mortality of infants. The infant mortality rate was then of the order of 300 per 1,000 live births. At the time of the institution of the General Register Office in 1837 the rate was still over 150 per 1,000 live births. The rate came into great prominence when, at the turn of the century, a really determined effort was made to develop the maternal and child welfare services as we now know them, and the early Medical Officers of Health of the towns were liable to be judged by what happened to the infant mortality rate. Better health services and the elimination of the grosser forms of poverty have changed the picture completely. In 1901 the pattern of infant mortality was as shown in Table 1.4.

1.37 At this time infections, much more associated with environment and less with congenital factors, predominated, and deaths were generally spread over the first year of life. As environmental causes diminished, interest was diverted to the residual and less tractable problem of endogenous causes of death. Such

Table 1.4 *England and Wales 1901—infant mortality (under 1 year per 1,000 live births)*

Cause	Rate
Measles	2
Whooping cough	5
Diarrhoeal diseases	34
Tubercular diseases	6
Meningitis and convulsions	19
Pneumonia	10
Bronchitis	13
Wasting disease	46
Other causes	16
All causes	151

Table 1.5 *England and Wales 1971—infant mortality per 1,000 related live births*

	In age period				
	Under 1 day	1 day and under 1 week	1 week and under 4 weeks	4 weeks and under 3 months	3 months and under 6 months	6 months and under 1 year
Maternal conditions unrelated to pregnancy, toxaemias of pregnancy, difficult labour, conditions of pregnancy and umbilical cord, birth injury, haemolytic disease of newborn, immaturity, congenital anomalies						
M	4·34	2·39	0·92	0·66	0·31	0·28
F	3·27	1·87	0·90	0·58	0·37	0·26
Pneumonia, bronchitis, gastroenteritis, other infective diseases, accidental mechanical suffocation, neglect and other violent causes						
M	0·09	0·29	0·60	1·64	1·31	0·81
F	0·09	0·20	0·44	1·26	1·08	0·75

causes are associated with the uterine development of the foetus and the birth process itself, congenital malformation, prematurity and birth injury. The figures for England and Wales in 1971 are illustrative (Table 1.5).

1.38 These two groups of causes, which account for about two-thirds of all deaths in the first year, differ widely in their age gradient. For the first group of constitutional and non-infective diseases nearly one-half of the infant deaths are in the first day and about four-fifths are in the first week; for the second group of infections and accidents only about one-twelfth of the infant deaths are in the first week, and about four-fifths occur after the first 4 weeks.

1.39 Partly from consideration of these differential age gradients and partly on grounds of simplicity it becomes customary to regard deaths in the first 4 weeks of life as attributable to neonatal mortality, as distinct from later deaths, which are classed as post-neonatal. The neonatal mortality rate is calculated in the same way as the infant mortality rate, viz. per 1,000 live births. The tremendous reduction in infant mortality since the turn of the century has been more attributable to reduction in post-neonatal mortality (infections—diarrhoeal or respiratory—and accidents) than in neonatal mortality. Mortality from prematurity, congenital malformations or injury at birth has been more resistant to improvement.

1.40 More recently there has been a tendency to distinguish even more clearly the true natal deaths from those attributable to post-natal environmental influences by reference to deaths in the first week of life, and such deaths per 1,000 related live births provide an early neonatal mortality rate. These deaths combined with still-births and rated to a 1,000 total births can be regarded as measuring mortality at a period of time surrounding birth and may be described as perinatal mortality.

1.41 The perinatal mortality rate has the advantage that, unlike its components, the still-birth and early neonatal rates, it is not likely to be disturbed by variations in the practice of recording or in the actual timing of foetal deaths. If a foetus is regarded as surviving beyond intra-uterine existence, a death is transferred from the still-birth to the early neonatal category though the actual reality of the situation—death around the point of delivery—is unaffected. This is quite an important point, as the precise fixation of the time of foetal death is often difficult. Study of the perinatal mortality rate is now a widely used method of monitoring the level of obstetric and paediatric care in health services (Chamberlain *et al.*, 1975).

Longitudinal studies—survival factors

1.42   At the beginning of this century a new problem had emerged: tuberculosis was killing large numbers of adults and most of them died young. In the early days little could be done to arrest the relentless progress of the disease, and efforts were concentrated upon the detection of cases and on the isolation of the infectious patients. Later, as the possibility of curative treatment began to be probed, it was necessary to establish careful systems of surveillance to measure the risks of relapse or death in different treatment groups. Orthodox actuarial methods were employed, the deaths in each year of duration of treatment being related to the number surviving in that year of duration. The main problem was to reduce to a minimum the number of patients 'lost sight of' and, in respect of these, to make appropriate deductions from the exposed to risk, which formed the denominator of the death rate in any year of duration. The index prepared for each group was the proportion surviving at the end of x years.

1.43   Later the method was developed as a means of assessing the effects of treatment of cancer, another disease following a comparatively slow course which presented a problem of growing proportions as the average length of life increased. The method has also been widely used both for the assessment of the prognosis following cardiovascular or cerebrovascular accidents (e.g. myocardial infarctions or strokes) and in longitudinal studies of initially healthy lives, for the evaluation of the factors that operate to produce such incidents.

Generation mortality tables

1.44   The continuing improvement in mortality from almost all causes of death at most ages, together with the wealth of mortality experience by then accumulated, led actuaries, especially in the period between the two World Wars, to turn seriously to the problem of forecasting the future changes in mortality. In this process emphasis was given to the fact that comparison of successive life tables might be misleading. The normal life table, based on the deaths of a limited period, is not likely to be reproduced in the future; it mixes the experience of a number of different generations—the lives who contribute to the death rates at advanced ages were born many decades before those who contribute to the rates at young ages, and they have lived through conditions which are unlikely to be replicated for later generations. This defect can be remedied when mortality records have been maintained over a long period, and a life table can be based on the experience of a single generation, following it through from birth to extinction.

Years of life lost

1.45 The movement of the impact of preventable mortality to middle life, and the new problem of the lack of improvement in the mortality of older men, have led to the development of another method of presenting mortality, which serves to impress on the public conscience the loss of active life that occurs.

1.46 The aim is to consider the years of life lost by each death rather than simply to count the number of persons whose lives were terminated; the underlying concept being that a man dying at the age of, say, 30 might but for the 'accident' of death have lived to the remainder of his normal span, and that it might be a greater achievement to prevent his death than to save the life of a man aged 90, who cannot have much longer to live.

Table 1.6 *Years of life lost per 1,000 population—England and Wales*

	Persons		Males		Females	
	15–64	total*	15–64	total	15–64	total*
1848–72	497	1,004	542	1,047	455	964
1952	76	238	92	266	61	211
1952, per cent of 1848–72	15	24	17	25	13	22

*Total to age 85 (males) and 88 (females). Standardized on the 1952 population.

1.47 There is the problem of the choice of the 'normal span of life' to be used in measuring years lost on death. There is no precise or absolute measure, since a current life table is necessarily based upon the mortality of the lives now dying and is never exactly reproduced. Any projected life table would be entirely arbitrary and speculative. We may take refuge in the fact that the assessment of mortality improvement requires relative indices rather than absolute measures, and simply and arbitrarily adopt as the limit of 'normal' life that age in the life table at which the number of lives surviving is less than 10 per

Table 1.7 *England and Wales—mortality in 1848-72 and 1952*

Period	Mean population (000s)	Death rate per thousand	Males						Females					
			Under 1	1-14	15-44	45-64	65 +	All ages†	Under 1	1-14	15-44	45-64	65 +	All ages†
1848–72	20,029	25·73*	202·66	16·21	9·81	23·94	95·63	23·45	162·28	15·80	9·64	20·62	86·27	21·42
1952	43,940	11·32	31·74	0·78	1·81	13·70	79·43	12·21	24·74	0·58	1·31	8·06	58·79	10·50
1952 per cent of 1848-72	–	44	16·0	5·0	18·0	57·0	83·0	52·0	15·0	4·0	14·0	39·0	68·0	49·0

* Standardized on the 1952 population.
† Crude rate, unstandardized.

cent of the original entrants, viz. the maximum span within which 90 per cent of persons die and is survived only by an abnormally longeval 10 per cent. For males this is 85 and for females 88 years of age in round numbers and at current levels of mortality. The Registrar General in calculating the index for England and Wales, which is published in the *Quarterly Return* for the second quarter of each year, has used 85 for both sexes. He distributes the years of life between the working age period, 15 to 64, and the remainder. For a man dying at age 20 it would therefore be assumed that a total potential loss of years of life (for index purposes only) of 65 years is incurred, and 45 of those years would be in the working age range. On this basis the mortality of 1952 represented a total loss of 238 years, and a loss of 76 working years per 1,000 population. If the specific mortality rates of 1848–72 were applied to the 1952 population, these losses would be raised to 1,004 and 497 respectively. Comparable figures are shown in Tables 1.6 and 1.7, taken from a paper by Logan and Benjamin (1953).

Senescence

1.48   Another possible index is the life span that can be attained under optimal conditions. Actuaries have always been profoundly interested in the variation in the incidence of mortality with age, since many of their calculations of contingencies depend upon this variation. The study of this age variation in mortality has given rise to a number of hypothetical 'laws' of mortality based on theories about the exertion on the human body of deleterious influences or about the wearing out of components of the body and the exhaustion of living resources. These theories date from Gompertz (1825), who argued on physiological grounds that the intensity of mortality (in his terms the average exhaustion of man's power to avoid death) gained equal proportions in equal intervals of age, giving rise to an increasing force of mortality viz. $\mu_x = Bc^x$. Later Makeham (1867) introduced a constant component as well as an exponentially increasing component of the force of mortality as a reflexion of the division of causes of death into two kinds, those due to chance and those due to deterioration, giving $\mu_x = A + Bc^x$.

1.49   It was soon evident that such a relatively simple law would not represent mortality experience throughout life, and subsequent developments led to the proposal of more complex mathematical relationships between age and the force of mortality and even of different parts of the age range. Thiele (1872), for example, proposed

$$\mu_x = a_1 \exp[-b_1 x] + a_2 \exp[-\tfrac{1}{2}b_2(x-c)^2] + a_3 \exp[b_3 x]$$

in which the last term is a Gompertz curve to represent old age mortality, the first a decreasing Gompertz curve to represent the mortality in childhood, and the middle term a normal curve. Perks (1932) introduced a new family of curves in the general form

$$\mu_x = \frac{A + Bc^x}{Kc^{-x} + 1 + Dc^x}$$

and rationalized this procedure with some interesting speculations on the theory of mortality. He found an analogy between the 'inability to withstand destruction' of Gompertz and the then current physical concept of entropy change—the measure of the time progression of a statistical group from organization to disorganization. There was also the previous work of Karl Pearson, who fitted overlapping curves not to the force of mortality but to the curves of deaths, the curves being intended to represent the mortality of old age, middle life, youth, childhood, and infancy, the causes of death being different in these different periods of life. This method of analysis throws light upon the problem of cause of death classification. Conversely, an analysis of the curve of deaths into a number of separate curves for different medical causes yields the total chance of dying from a particular cause.

1.50 While further work continued on the fitting of mathematical functions to the force of mortality, μ_x, attention was focused on the curve of deaths (i.e. of $\mu_x l_x$) as an alternative operand by a paper by Phillips (1935). Later Clarke (1950) returned to the analysis of the curve of deaths. He argued that mortality improvements had not extended the natural lifespan but had only allowed more to achieve it. He distinguished between 'anticipated' and 'senescent' deaths; the ages at death in the latter group were measures of natural lifespans and had a frequency distribution like other animal characteristics. Beard (1950) also paid attention to the curve of deaths, using the incomplete gamma function as the basic analytical function.

1.51 Clarke's hypothesis was that every individual carried with him from birth a genetically endowed term of life beyond which it was impossible for him to survive, and that if we knew these terms for every member of the population we could form a frequency distribution similar to that of any other biometric quantity. This distribution would represent a limiting form of the curve of deaths. Clarke went further and supposed that this distribution would not shift as a whole toward later ages, i.e. that the modal span of life was invariant; he rejected the possibility as 'intangible speculation' outside the practical framework of his study, namely the relatively short-term trend of mortality. Deaths were then divided into two categories: those which happened because the term of the lifespan had run out—senescent deaths—and all others, whether from accident or disease, which were in fact a cutting short of the lifespan—anticipated deaths. He first obtained, therefore, a limiting curve of deaths by constructing a table of mortality in which the q_x (probability of deaths between age x and $x + 1$) column would consist of values (q_x^s) appropriate only to causes of death which could be regarded as senescent. The next stage was to predict the pace at which actual rates of mortality would in a given future period approach those of the limiting table.

1.52 If we can regard the terminal peak in the age distribution of deaths in the life table (the 'curve of deaths') as the centre of a distribution of senescent deaths, we observe the change in the age of this peak and the proportion of total deaths falling in this senescent area (Benjamin, 1959) as we move from the earliest to the latest national life table (Table 1.8).

1.53 The main change in the hundred years or so has been the increase in the proportion of people attaining the currently modal term of lifespan, from about 40 to 70 per cent, while the shift in the peak has been a mere 3 or 4 years for men and 7 years for women. Nevertheless the modal span is increasing.

Table 1.8   *Senescent deaths*

| Life table | Period of deaths | Males | | Females | |
		Peak age (years)	Senescent deaths as a percentage of total deaths	Peak age (years)	Senescent deaths as a percentage of total deaths
ELT 1	1841	72.0	39.9	73.5	41.0
ELT 8	1910–12	73.5	51.5	76.0	55.3
ELT11	1950–2	75.7	69.4	80.3	70.3
ELT12	1960–2	74.8	74.5	80.6	72.3

1.54 To sum up, we see that there are many different kinds of mortality rate or index, each of them specific to a particular purpose, though they are all interrelated and all dependent upon a basic measurement of a death rate over some interval of time. It is important to give some thought to what one is trying to measure or compare and to choose the most appropriate rate.

Relation between rates and frequency distributions

1.55 All statisticians, whether actuaries, medical practitioners or public health workers, when examining their data make use of the concept of the frequency distribution and its descriptive parameters. In many texts on vital statistics there may be a tendency to hide this by stressing that the basic measure is a rate or ratio, leaving it unrelated to frequency distributions. However, if a simple rate of decrement such as the rate of mortality is considered, it is easy to see that it is connected with a frequency distribution.

1.56 The annual rate of mortality q has been identified with the proportion of a given population P that dies during an interval of one year. Thus, if θ denotes the number of deaths, then $q = \theta/P$. But we could argue in the following alternative way. Of an indefinitely large population P, a proportion q die during the year and a proportion $p = 1 - q$ survive, the two cases being mutually exclusive and no third case being possible. Designating a death by 1 and a survival by 0, the following distribution of the number of deaths of an individual in the population can be written down:

Variable	Relative frequency	Variable × Relative frequency
0	p	0
1	q	q
mean =	$0 + q = q$	
variance =	$(0 - q)^2 p + (1 - q)^2 q$	
=	pq	

[handwritten margin note: Bernoulli with p, q changed ∴ mean $= q$]

From this we deduce that the mean and variance of the proportion of deaths in a sample of size E from the population would be qE and pq/E respectively. This also explains why the test of a difference between actual (θ) and expected (Eq) deaths in a population E is a test of the

$$\chi^2$$

difference between two distributions. The values of x^2 are $(\theta - Eq)^2/Eq$ and $(E - \theta - Ep)^2/Ep$ or in total $(\theta - Eq)^2/Epq$.

1.57 When the term 'rate' is used in the above simple sense, that is in cases where only two alternative events are possible and a simple ratio results, the associated frequency distribution concept is easy to see. Unfortunately this is not always so; there is a good deal of confusion and ambiguity in the terminology of vital statistics, in particular in the use of such terms as ratios, rates and probabilities, and as a result there is a lack of any obvious relationship to the frequency distribution concept.

1.58 Thus for mortality we have the ratio of the number experiencing the event to the number exposed to the risk of the event; but in the case of the birth rate the ratio is between the number of births and the number of the total population, all of whom cannot be considered liable to the risk, so that a third 'event' is possible. The gross reproduction rate is the sum, for all the child-bearing ages, of the ratios at each age of the number of girl babies born in a year to the population of women during the year, so that again all are not liable to the risk and the rate is not itself a direct ratio (though a notional meaning as a ratio exists). There is no readily discernible generalization common to these rates, and only in mortality is any direct analogy with probability distributions feasible. Again, consider the sickness rate for a specified population. There is more than one type of sickness rate, as we shall see later, but at this stage we shall define it as the ratio of the number of weeks' sickness experienced by the population during an interval of one year to the number of the population at the beginning of the year. It is assumed that there are no new entrants into the population during the year and that the only exits are by death. Clearly this ratio is not similar to the rate of mortality. A more comparable ratio would be the proportion who are sick at any time during the year.

1.59 The sickness rate as defined is connected with the following multi-variable distribution:

Number of days of sickness	Frequency
0	P_0
1	P_1
2	P_2
.	.

$$
\begin{array}{ll}
\cdot & \phantom{P_{365}}\cdot \\
365 & P_{365} \\
366 & P_{366}
\end{array}
$$

P_r being the number of lives with a sickness claim of r days' duration.

1.60 The sickness rate (adjusting the variable to weeks) is the mean of this distribution, and the variance of the sickness rate is approximately the variance of this distribution divided by the total mean population. Expressed in this way, it is easy to see how the sickness rate differs from a simple ratio, such as the rate of mortality. Moreover, taking the simple ratio of the proportion sick at any time during the year ($\bar{p}$) mentioned in the last sentence of para. 1.58, we have

$$
\bar{p} = \frac{\sum\limits_{1}^{366} P_r}{\sum\limits_{0}^{366} P_r}
$$

and $\bar{r}$, the mean duration of a sickness claim $= \dfrac{\sum\limits_{1}^{366} r \cdot P_r}{\sum\limits_{1}^{366} P_r}$

As the rate of sickness (S) is proportional to $\dfrac{\sum\limits_{1}^{366} r \cdot P_r}{\sum\limits_{0}^{366} P_r}$

$$
S = \frac{\sum\limits_{1}^{366} P_r}{\sum\limits_{0}^{366} P_r} \cdot \frac{\sum\limits_{1}^{366} r \cdot P_r}{\sum\limits_{1}^{366} P_r} = \bar{p} \cdot \frac{\sum\limits_{1}^{366} r \cdot P_r}{\sum\limits_{1}^{366} P_r}
$$

$$
= \bar{p} \cdot \bar{r}
$$

a relationship which throws light on the complex nature of the index and will be used when dealing with sickness data.

Terminology

1.61 On this basis there is a temptation to suggest that the present terminology for rates should be replaced by one based on frequency distribution terms. There are arguments against this, however. A minor one is that the present terminology is widespread and well understood by students; but the important reason is that the term rate implies a time interval which is not suggested by a frequency distribution. The important characteristic of a rate is that it is derived from a frequency distribution arising during a specified time interval, and if any terminology is to be generally acceptable, it should make this clear. If the time interval were to be changed, then the parameters would be affected and a different frequency distribution would result. Thus for some purpose it might be desirable to obtain rates of decrement in each half year rather than the normal rates. Further, in constructing a mathematics of the life or decrement table, it is convenient to introduce a concept based on the operation of diminishing the time interval without limit. This concept, the force of decrement, is a mathematical notion, and it could not be measured directly from any data; we must always measure some form of rate or ratio with reference to a finite interval of observation.

1.62 The outcome of this discussion is that the terminology of 'rate', 'proportion', 'ratio' must be retained. Generally we shall use the word 'rate' when the ratio refers to a time interval (as, for instance, in the case of the rate of mortality or the rate of birth), and for the relative extent to which a group is married or is aged x, at a given point of time we shall use the word 'proportion'. This terminology could not, however, be used consistently without making a departure from common actuarial usage. In the case of sickness the 'proportion sick' usually means the proportion who have some sickness during a given time interval and not the proportion sick at a given point in time. We have decided against making any alteration but the context will make clear which usage is meant. The sickness rate, however, is based on a multi-variable frequency distribution, as explained above.

1.63 Another difficulty arises in connection with the term 'probability'. As is well known, of the several possible definitions of probability, one is based on relative frequency. For this reason the rate of mortality is often referred to as the probability of dying. We should prefer to use the word probability only when we are concerned with statistical or scientific inference, that is when we wish to make probability statements about specified hypotheses. However, again common usage may prevent us from adopting this course consistently, and in cases of doubt it is hoped that the context will make our meaning clear. In general we shall use the words 'ratio', 'rate' and 'proportion', but when it is felt that it is better to use some other term, the meaning will be defined.

1.64 It is important to understand clearly the nature of the rates and the ratios that are used, and to be able to relate them to frequency distributions characterizing a given population over an interval of time or on a given date. This point of view is particularly important, as will be seen, when it is a case of comparing two or more rates or proportions. The known relevant factors influencing these measures must then be considered, and it is illuminating to enquire how changes in each of the factors influence the shape of the frequency distributions. For instance, two sickness rates may be very similar in magnitude and yet the different shapes of the two frequency distributions may be important.

Exposed to risk

1.65 A rate might be defined as 'the relative number in an aggregate who acquire the characteristic x during the interval of time h', but this is not precise, since the size of the given aggregate may change during the time interval h by the operation of other factors than that being measured. In calculating a death rate (x is death) we generally find that not only is the population under investigation subject to decrement other than by death but that it is also subject to increment. For example, in the investigation of mortality by life offices there are new policies as well as surrenders, lapses and maturities of existing policies; and in the investigation of the general mortality of the population of a country there are births, emigrants and immigrants. In order to obtain a measure of the death rate for a population or aggregate of this type it is necessary to approximate, and it is in this way that the concept of 'risk time' or 'exposed to risk' arises.

The need for graduation

1.66 The concept of the frequency distribution is useful in another sense. Most mortality experiences are samples from much larger experiences, and at individual ages the deaths and the rates derived therefrom are thus subject to sampling error. These errors (deviations from the true underlying rates) may be assumed to be random and to fluctuate from age to age both in size and sign. It would be possible to calculate the confidence intervals for any specified probability level and to portray the progression of age rates of mortality not in linear form but as a band, i.e. an area between two lines connecting respectively the upper and lower bounds of the confidence intervals. These could not be of any practical value to actuarial calculations, which require the application at any stage of a specific rate of mortality and not a range of rates. It is possible with the aid of a computer to explore the effects of using rates of mortality drawn from a range, and some risk calculations might require this, but for rating purposes this kind of exercise is not generally appropriate. It is usually necessary to estimate within the confidence interval the true rate at each age point. In doing so we can obtain some help from the observed rates at neighbouring ages. This type of inference is called graduation.

1.67 It is assumed that if the experience were large enough, and the random errors were insignificant, the observed rates of mortality would exhibit a smooth progression with age and that graduation, which uses the rates collectively or in several groups to achieve a smooth progression, is thus justified as a method of estimating the true trend. There are three main types of graduation process:

1   The graphical method, in which a hypothetical curve is drawn, by inspection, through the area bounded by the confidence intervals. There is clearly, and may rightly be, an element of subjective judgement. Use is made of experience as to what a curve of death rates should look like.

2   Finite difference methods, which depend on the principle that the standard error of the weighted mean of two or more independent (or imperfectly correlated) random errors is less than the sum of the correspondingly weighted individual standard errors. This is the well-known process of moving averages employed extensively in time series analysis. $var(w_1 e_i + w_2 e_j) = w_1^2 var e_i + w_2^2 var e_j < w_1 v$

3   Curve-fitting methods, which are based on the assumption that the underlying values have a particular mathematical form whose parameters may be estimated from the observed values.

1.68 So far we have considered only random deviations from a true underlying smooth progress of rates with age. The underlying progression may not be smooth; there may be real or intrinsic irregularity, and, depending on its source and likely reproducibility in the future, it may be desired to retain it. Methods 2 and 3 will tend to smooth out those true irregularities if applied too automatically. The investigator, as in method 1, must first inspect the data and make decisions as to the type of irregularity he wishes to retain, and to modify his application of the methods accordingly—for example, by applying separate graduation processes on either side of the irregularity. We shall deal with graduation more fully in later chapters.

REFERENCES

Beard, R. E. (1950). Some experiments in the use of the incomplete gamma function for the approximate calculation of actuarial functions. *Proc. Centen. Assembly Inst. Actu.*, **8**, 89.

Benjamin, B. (1959). *Ciba Foundation Symposium on Life span of Animals*, 2. In Ciba Foundation Colloquia on Ageing Vol. 5 (Wolstenholme, G. E. W. and O'Connor, M. eds) J. A. Churchill, London.

Benjamin, B. (1977). Trends and differentials in lung cancer mortality. *World Health Statistics Report*, Vol. 30, No. 2, W.H.O., Geneva.

Brownlee, J. (1922). The use of death rates as a measure of hygienic conditions. *Medical Research Council Special Reports Series*, No. 60.

Chamberlain, R., Chamberlain, G., Howlett, B., Claireaux, A. (1975). *British Births 1970*, Heinemann Medical Books, London.

Clarke, R. D. (1950). A bio-actuarial approach to forecasting rates of mortality. *Proc. Centen. Assembly Inst. Actu.*, **2**, 12.

Farr, W. (1856) *Sixteenth Annual Report of the Registrar General 1853*, p. xvi, H.M.S.O.

General Register Office (1875). *Supplement to 35th Annual Report*, H.M.S.O.

General Register Office (1936). *Decennial Supplement England and Wales, 1931*, Part I: *Life tables*, H.M.S.O.

Gompertz, B. (1825). On the nature of the function expressive of the law of human mortality; and on a new mode of determining the value of life contingencies. *Phil. Trans. R. S.*, **115**, 513.

Graunt, J. (1662). Natural and political observations made upon bills of mortality. Reprinted in *J. Inst. Actu.*, **90**, 1.

Kohn, R. (1951). An objective mortality indicator. *Canadian J. Pub. Health*, **42**, 375.

Logan, W. P. D. and Benjamin, B. (1953). Loss of expected years of life. *Monthly Bulletin of Min. of Health and Pub. Health Lab. Service*, December, 244.

Makeham, W. M. (1867). On the law of mortality. *J. Inst. Actu.*, **13**, 325.

Perks, W. (1932). On some experiments in the graduation of mortality statistics. *J. Inst. Actu.*, **63**, 12.

Phillips, E. W. (1935). The curve of deaths. *J. Inst. Actu.*, **66**, 17.

Thiele, P. N. (1872). On a mathematical formula to express the rate of mortality throughout the whole of life. *J. Inst. Actu.*, **16**, 313.

Yerushalmy, J. (1950). A mortality index for use in place of the age-adjusted death rate. *American J. Pub. Health*, **41**, 907.

EXERCISES FOR CHAPTER ONE

1   The data in Table 1.9 are available for males in two areas A and B and for the whole country C.

Table 1.9

Age	Population (000s)			Annual deaths (all causes)		
	A	B	C	A	B	C
0–14	150	100	1,450	600	400	3,190
15–44	300	350	2,700	600	520	4,050
45–64	150	100	1,600	3,000	1,500	24,000
65–84	120	75	1,200	10,200	5,550	88,000
85+	10	5	60	3,000	1,280	15,360
	730	730	7,010	17,400	9,250	134,600

(i) Calculate the death rates by age for each area.

(ii) Standardize the all-ages death rates for areas A and B directly by reference to the population of C. How do the mortality levels of A and B compare (a) with each other, (b) with the country, C, as a whole?

2   It has been suggested that for making world-wide international comparisons of cancer mortality, the all-ages death rates would be rendered incomparable by variations in age structure between one country and another, and that the rates for each sex, should be age-standardized. It has been further suggested that for this particular cause of death a special standard age structure should be used. Comment on these suggestions. If you agree with the second suggestion, what kind of age structure would you use?

3   It has been suggested that one way of demonstrating the effect of preventing coronary heart disease would be to calculate the expectation of life on the basis of the total elimination of this cause of death. Comment on this suggestion. How would you make this calculation?

4   Given notifications of whooping cough by age and sex during a year of average incidence, how would you estimate the proportion of boys in the population who suffer from the disease before attaining the age of 10?

5   How is the published birth rate for the United Kingdom calculated? Indicate its defects, if any, as a measure of fertility

6   How is the 'life table death rate' defined? Is it a useful measure of mortality?

7 Explain how the 'years of life lost' rate is calculated and comment on the usefulness of this measure.

8 In what way is the age death rate which appears in published national vital statistics different from the rate of mortality of a life table?

9 Explain the link between the concept of a rate of mortality and the concept of a frequency distribution.

10 What is a generation life table and for what purposes might it be advantageous to have such a table?

11 What is the 'curve of deaths'? Can you suggest particular features of mortality patterns that would be readily demonstrated by such a curve?

CHAPTER TWO

RATES AND EXPOSED TO RISK

Introduction

2.1 Chapter 1 comprised a wide-ranging discussion of mortality and other indices of various types as an introduction to the subject of mortality and demographic measurement. We can now begin to consider the real kernel of the problem of mortality measurement—the correspondence of deaths and the population (the exposed to risk) forming the denominator of the rate. Let us first recapitulate a little.

2.2 We have noted in the previous chapter that a rate is a measure of proportion expressing the relative frequency of occurrence of an event, e.g. birth, death, marriage or passing an examination, or of a characteristic, e.g. left-handedness or obesity. If we say that 6 per million of the total population of the United Kingdom die each year from progressive muscular atrophy, such a statement has two purposes: (1) it immediately conveys the comparative rarity of dying from this cause, and (2) it enables us to calculate the expected annual number of such deaths in a population of a given size. Before the second purpose can be fulfilled, however, two further pieces of information must be given, and their importance will be underlined as this textbook proceeds. We must know what kind of population and what period of time the rate applies to. If this rate were calculated from the experience of a special section of the population, e.g. children or males only, or of a population of a particular racial origin, it would not necessarily apply to any other (the rate in the total population of the United Kingdom is 7 per million for males and 5 for females). If the rate were measured over the years, say, 1915–18, it is highly probable that as a result of medical advances or improvements in health since that time, the rate applicable to the present time would be much smaller.

The crude death rate

2.3 If we take the number of deaths from all causes occurring in, say, the United Kingdom in the 3 years 1970–72 inclusive, and divide this number by three times the total of the populations of the component countries as enumerated at censuses held in 1971, we obtain an annual rate which may be regarded as representing the average mortality of the United Kingdom during these years. As we have seen, such a rate cannot be compared with similar rates for other countries because the populations of the countries are not similar in respect of characteristics (population structure especially) which affect mortality. We would not be comparing like with like in respects other than mortality risks. Mortality rates vary with sex, age, occupation and other factors, so that it becomes necessary to analyse rates in accordance with these factors.

2.4 Another criticism of the crude death rate is that it is not precise. The deaths are recorded over 3 years whilst the population is measured at only the middle of the period. A better measure of the population generating the deaths would be the mean population over the 3 years if this could be obtained.

The rate of mortality

2.5 Let us look at a more narrowly defined rate which avoids the lack of specificity about sex and age, and about the population from which the deaths are derived. This is a rate with which readers may already be familiar, namely q_x, the life table rate of mortality. This rate is defined (see para 1.33) as d_x/l_x, where l_x is the number of lives attaining the exact age x, and d_x is the number of deaths occurring in these lives between exact age x and exact age $x + 1$. Thus q_x is the rate of decrease in the life table population between age x and age $x + 1$ (in proportion to the population aged x), since individuals, by definition of the life table, leave the population only by death.

2.6 In order to construct a life table, a set of rates q_x for all integral ages x is required, and, if the life table is to serve any useful purpose, the set of rates q_x must be derived from measurement of an actual population. At this stage the reader should ask himself how he would obtain such a set of rates if he had full particulars about a population over a specified period of time. The procedure may seem intuitively simple, since it would appear that all that is required is a method of counting. For example, why not simply count all the lives that attain age x during the period, denoted by $\overset{\circ}{l}x$, and all the deaths that occur between age x and $x + 1$, denoted by θ_x? Then the ratio $\theta_x/\overset{\circ}{l}_x$ is clearly an estimate of q_x. Let us, however, consider this procedure more

closely to decide whether it is satisfactory. Suppose that the period is
1 January 1970 to 31 December 1974 and the population is composed
of the policy-holders of a Life Office. Some of the lives will attain age x
before January 1970 and age $x+1$ after this date. They will not be
included in $\overset{\circ}{l}_x$ but if any of them die on or after 1 January 1970 and
before attaining $x+1$, they will be included in θ_x. Furthermore some
of the lives will attain age x during 1974 and therefore will attain age
$x+1$ after the end of the investigation period. Any deaths among them
occurring in 1975 will not be included in θ_x. We also have to consider
what to do about new entrants and withdrawals during the 5 years.
Withdrawals will occur by surrenders and by claims other than those
arising on death. Some new entrants will occur between age x and age
$x+1$ and will thus not be included in $\overset{\circ}{l}_x$ but the deaths out of these new
entrants between age x and age $x+1$ will be included in θ_x. Some
withdrawals will occur between age x and age $x+1$ and they will be
included in $\overset{\circ}{l}_x$; yet any deaths that occur after withdrawal but before
age $x+1$ is attained will not be included in θ_x. These 'errors' are in
different directions, and at some ages may approximate in the
aggregate to zero, but such a result would be accidental and could not
be relied upon. There is therefore no way of knowing how close the
ratio $\theta_x/\overset{\circ}{l}_x$ is to the true value of q_x.

2.7 Some of these difficulties could be overcome by making the
period of observation run from the birthday in 1970 to the birthday in
1974 and by excluding new entrants until they attain the birthday
immediately following entry. Thus the lives attaining age x in 1970
would be counted and the deaths out of these lives between age x and
$x+1$ would be counted. Similarly the number of lives attaining age x in
1971 would be counted and also the deaths out of these lives between
age x and age $x+1$, and similarly for 1972 and 1973. The only
difficulty left would arise from the withdrawals between age x and age
$x+1$. They cannot simply be omitted because if any of them had died
after age x but before withdrawal, they would have been included in
θ_x. They have been at risk of dying and hence of being included in θ_x
for part of the age interval x to $x+1$. A possible solution would be to
count a withdrawal as a fraction of an individual, the fraction being
the proportion of the age interval x to $x+1$ for which the life was at
risk. If this solution is accepted, however, there is no reason why the
same procedure should not be adopted for new entrants between age x
and age $x+1$ or for those who attained age x in 1969 and therefore age
$x+1$ in 1970.

Assumptions made in estimating risk time

2.8 The solution, suggested in the previous paragraph, can be examined theoretically in order to ascertain what assumptions can be made. Let

$\mathring{l}_x$ = number attaining exact age x during the investigation period.

n_{x+r} = number of new entrants at exact age $x + r$ during the period, $0 < r < 1$

w_{x+r} = number of withdrawals at exact age $x + r$ during the period, $0 < r < 1$

θ_x = number of deaths occurring out of these groups of lives between exact age x and exact age $x + 1$ while they are under observation, i.e. within the investigation period; deaths of new entrants after entry are included but deaths of withdrawals after withdrawal are excluded.

$\mathring{q}_x$ = observed rate of mortality between exact age x and exact age $x + 1$.

then, if $_{1-r}\mathring{q}_{x+r}$ is the rate of mortality at age $x + r$ for the time period $1 - r$, i.e.

$$_{1-r}\mathring{q}_{x+r} = \frac{\mathring{l}_{x+r} - \mathring{l}_{x+1}}{\mathring{l}_{x+r}},$$

then

$$\theta_x = \mathring{l}_x\mathring{q}_x + \sum_r n_{x+r} \cdot {_{1-r}\mathring{q}_{x+r}} - \sum_r w_{x+r} \cdot {_{1-r}\mathring{q}_{x+r}}$$

2.9 In order to solve this equation it is necessary to make some simple assumption about the form $_{1-r}\mathring{q}_{x+r}$. Usually it is assumed that $_{1-r}\mathring{q}_{x+r} = (1-r)\mathring{q}_x$, which implies that

$$(l_{x+r})^{-1} = r \cdot (l_{x+1})^{-1} + (1-r)(l_x)^{-1}$$

and this is justifiable at most points of the life table. The reader should test this graphically for various values of $r(0 < r < 1)$ and of x. We may then write

$$\theta_x = \mathring{q}_x \left[\mathring{l}_x + \sum_r (1-r)n_{x+r} - \sum_r (1-r)w_{x+r} \right].$$

Note that this assumption concerning $_{1-r}\mathring{q}_{x+r}$ implies that new entrants and withdrawals experience the same mortality as do the lives forming $\mathring{l}_x$, so that $\mathring{q}_x$ is not affected. It will be seen later that this is not always the case. In Chapter 5 on select tables the treatment of new entrants, when their mortality differs from that of the general average, will be demonstrated. Withdrawals from life assurance cannot be dealt with so easily. There are grounds for believing that age for age their average mortality is lower than the general average. Obviously lives that are in very bad health will not surrender their policies if they can avoid taking such action. However, in order to test this belief it would be necessary to estimate mortality rates according to age in respect of lives who withdraw, after the date of withdrawal. Such data do not exist and in practice the assumption is made that withdrawals experience the mortality of the general population.

2.10 Now $\sum_r (1-r)n_{x+r}$ is the sum of the fractional parts of the year of age during which the new entrants were at risk. Similarly the deduction of $\sum_r (1-r)w_{x+r}$ means that the withdrawals are also dealt with in a similar way, since they will have been included in either $\mathring{l}_x$ or $\sum_r n_{x+r}$, and have to be removed from risk for those parts of the year of age x to $x+1$ after the dates of withdrawal. The expression in brackets in para. 2.9 then is the sum of the risk time contributed by the $(\mathring{l}_x + \sum_r n_{x+r})$ lives during the interval of age x to $x+1$. Alternatively it can be regarded as the equivalent number of lives aged exactly x and observed to age $x+1$ or previous death (equivalent, that is, in the number of deaths generated). θ_x can then be regarded as the deaths from the equivalent number of lives and

$$\mathring{q}_x = \frac{\theta_x}{\mathring{l}_x + \sum_r (1-r)n_{x+r} - \sum_r (1-r)w_{x+r}} \tag{2.1}$$

2.11 The denominator is denoted by E_x and is called the initial exposed to risk. The use of the word 'initial' indicates that E_x is equivalent to the number of 'starters' at exact age x that would generate the θ_x deaths on the assumption that there were no withdrawals or new entrants between exact age x and exact age $x+1$. Thus it is analogous to l_x lives generating d_x deaths in the life table. In actuarial literature it is frequently stated that in calculating E_x the deaths are given a full year's exposure in the year of death, i.e. they contributed a full unit to E_x in respect of the year of death. That this is true should be clear from the explanation given above.

The concept of m_x

2.12 An alternative rate to consider is m_x, the central death rate. This is a concept introduced in para 1.33 of Chapter 1, where it was defined as the average mortality rate over the age interval x to $x+1$. In life table terms this is

$$m_x = \frac{dx}{\displaystyle\int_0^1 l_{x+t} \cdot dt}.$$

$\int_0^1 l_{x+t} dt$ is the total risk time contributed by the l_x lives of the life table to the age interval x to $x+1$, the risk time for the deaths d_x being calculated only to the age of death and not to age $x+1$ as for q_x. If this notion is now transferred to a real, rather than a life table, population, we can write

$$\mathring{m}_x = \frac{\theta_x}{\bar{l}_x + \sum_r (1-r)n_{x+r} - \sum_r (1-r)w_{x+r} - \sum_r (1-r)\theta_{x+r}} \qquad (2.2)$$

where the deaths are dealt with in the same manner as the withdrawals.

2.13 This denominator is known as the central exposed to risk and is denoted by E_x^c.

Derivation of rates from an actual population

2.14 In this section the procedure for obtaining a set of $\mathring{q}_x$ from an actual population according to the principles of paragraphs 2.5–2.11 will be considered in some detail. Essentially the procedure is the very simple one of counting. Suppose that a set of $\mathring{q}_x$ is required, based on the mortality experienced during 1 January 1970 to 31 December 1974, and that the population comprises the policy-holders of a Life Office. Suppose that the following information is given on a card for each life that was at risk at any time during the period of investigation:

Date of birth
Date of entry into assurance
Date of withdrawal ⎱ if this occurred between 1 January 1970
Date of death ⎰ and 31 December 1974.

We then proceed to schedule the data in the working sheet shown below.

Age Interval

Lives ... $x-2/x-1, x-1/x, x/x+1, x+1/x+2, x+2/x+3, ...$

A

B

C

.

.

.

Each card is inspected and the exact period at risk for each interval inserted in the appropriate place in the table. For simplicity we shall now assume that the population is limited to the fourteen lives listed in Table 2.1 (though we should not in practice base rates on such a small number). Consider, for example, life A, born on 1 April 1918 entering assurance on 1 July 1954 and withdrawing on 1 October 1973. This life was at risk from 1 January 1970 to 1 October 1973, i.e. for 3·75 years. On 1 January 1970 this life was aged 51 years 9 months, so that the life was at risk for $\frac{1}{4}$ years during the age interval 51 to 52. During each of the age intervals 52/53, 53/54 and 54/55 the life was at risk for the full year, and during the age interval 55/56 for $\frac{1}{2}$ years. Hence the table can be entered as follows:

$$A \dots 50- \quad 51- \quad 52- \quad 53- \quad 54- \quad 55- \quad 56-$$
$$- \quad \tfrac{1}{4} \quad 1 \quad 1 \quad 1 \quad \tfrac{1}{2} \quad -$$

Next consider a life D born on 1 July 1919, entering assurance on 1 May 1971 and dying on 1 November 1974. He was a new entrant during the period of investigation and he was at risk from 1 May 1971 to 1 November 1974, i.e. 3·5 years. His age at entry was 51·8$\dot{3}$ years, so that he was at risk for 0·1$\dot{6}$ years during the age interval 51 to 52, and for one year during each of the age intervals 52/53, 53/54 and 54/55. He died during the age interval 55/56 at age 55·3 years, so that the amount of risk time during this age interval would depend on whether E_{55}^c or E_{55} is being calculated. For E_{55}^c the amount would be 0·3 years while for E_{55} it would be 1 year (because in calculating $\mathring{q}_x$ all the θ_x must be exposed for a full year, since q_x relates to l_x who *enter* the year of age). The table entries would be

	50–	51–	52–	53–	54–	55–	56–
E_{55}	–	0·1$\dot{6}$	1	1	1	1	–
E_{55}^c	–	0·1$\dot{6}$	1	1	1	0·3	–

2.15 In practice there will be several thousand lives under observation, and it would be possible to calculate the exact fractional exposures only if a computer were to be available and the computer were programmed to carry out the logical steps set out in para. 2.14. Most life offices and a number of consulting firms do have computer facilities, but at this stage in our discussion it is assumed that a computer is not available. In these circumstances (and to a large extent in practice) some approximations must be made, and it is generally assumed that the average contribution of all lives who do not contribute a full year to E_x or E_x^c is $\frac{1}{2}$ year except that those who die, as already stated, are exposed for a full year in the calculation of E_x. These assumptions would always need to be checked and modified if necessary. If the assumptions could be accepted as valid, then instead of entering the exact fraction of risk time in the working sheet we would enter $\frac{1}{2}$.

2.16 The procedure is illustrated in Tables 2.1 and 2.2 for the fourteen cases. For simplicity in the text of para. 2.14 the dates of cases A and D have been taken as the first day of the relevant month, though this is an unlikely combination.

Table 2.1 *Period of investigation 1 January 1970 to 31 December 1974*

Case	Date of Birth		Date of entry to Assurance		Date and mode of exit from observation		
A	1 April	1918	1 July	1954	1 October	1973	Withdrawal
B	27 January	1919	25 June	1959	31 December	1974	Existing
C	25 December	1915	26 December	1971	25 June	1972	Withdrawal
D	1 July	1919	1 May	1971	1 November	1974	Death
E	1 December	1916	2 February	1953	31 December	1974	Existing
F	7 June	1920	2 January	1970	31 December	1974	Existing
G	9 September	1916	10 November	1960	26 January	1972	Death
H	1 March	1917	7 April	1969	10 March	1970	Withdrawal
I	21 October	1917	28 August	1973	6 February	1974	Death
J	18 February	1913	10 May	1964	31 December	1974	Existing
K	10 October	1918	17 November	1973	31 December	1974	Existing
L	15 April	1917	16 April	1970	10 November	1974	Withdrawal
M	25 January	1915	4 October	1969	3 April	1970	Withdrawal
N	20 June	1919	22 July	1974	31 December	1974	Existing

NOTE: In the final column of the table 'Existing' means existing at 31 December 1974 and passing out of observation at that date (the end of the period of investigation). This is denoted by the symbol e_x (x being the age classification) and the individual is sometimes referred to as an 'ender'. Similarly those who were under observation at 1 January 1970 (the beginning of the period of investigation) are referred to as 'beginners' and (see Table 2.2) are denoted by b_x (x being the age classification).

Table 2.2   *Aggregate experience. Life-year. Central exposed to risk*

	Classification		49	50	51	52	53	54	55	56	57	58	59	60	61
A	b_{51}	w_{55}			½	1	1	1	½						
B	b_{50}	e_{55}		½	1	1	1	1	½						
C	n_{56}	w_{56}								½-½ = 0					
D	n_{51}	θ_{55}			½	1	1	1	½						
E	b_{53}	e_{58}					½	1	1	1	1	½			
F	n_{49}	e_{54}	½	1	1	1	1	½							
G	b_{53}	θ_{55}					½	1	½						
H	b_{52}	w_{53}				½	½								
I	n_{55}	θ_{56}							½	½					
J	b_{56}	e_{61}								½	1	1	1	1	½
K	n_{55}	e_{56}							½	½					
L	n_{53}	w_{57}					½	1	1	1	½				
M	b_{54}	w_{55}						½	½						
N	n_{55}	e_{55}							½-½ = 0						
	Totals	E_x^c	½	1½	3	4½	6	7	5½	3½	2½	1½	1	1	½

2.17 The sum of the columns of Table 2.2 gives the total central exposed to risk for the fourteen cases. If the exact fractional exposures were to be inserted instead of counting fractions as ½ in every case, the final row of Table 2.2 would read

49	50	51	52	53	54	55	56	57	58	59	60	61
0·42	1·07	2·42	4·16	6·54	6·63	5·85	3·18	2·57	1·16	1·00	1·00	0·84

and the total exposures would be 36·84. The reader should check this as an exercise. The total exposures in Table 2.2 add to 38, so that the assumption of uniform distribution of movements over the year of age clearly introduces a large error in such a small sample.

Exposed to risk formulae

2.18 If a computer is not available, there is a simple counting procedure which can be used. It can be inferred very easily from the form of Table 2.2. Suppose E_y^c is required. The rate interval, i.e. the interval of age within which risk time is to be calculated and within which the risk of death (death rate) is to be estimated, is in this case 1 year, the life year y to $y+1$. The number living at the start of the rate interval of 1 year, i.e. those that attain their yth birthday during the period 1 January 1970 to 31 December 1974, has already been denoted by $\overset{\circ}{l}_y$. Each of these lives will contribute 1 year to E_y^c unless they pass out of observation before $y+1$, i.e. unless they are included in the withdrawals at age y last birthday w_y, the deaths at age y last birthday θ_y or the 'enders' e_y, i.e. those existing at age y last birthday at 31 December 1974 who pass out of observation at that date (the end of the period of investigation). If the dates of all these exits are, on the average, midway between y and $y+1$, then an estimate of the contribution of $\overset{\circ}{l}_y$ to E_y^c is

$$\overset{\circ}{l}_y - \tfrac{1}{2}(w_y + \theta_y + e_y)$$

2.19 We must, in addition, bring in the contributions to E_y^c of the beginners b_y who existed at 1 January 1970 at age y last birthday, and the new entrants at age y last birthday during the investigation period n_y, since part of their life year y to $y+1$ falls within the period of investigation.

2.20 If we can assume again that, on the average, the contribution of each of these lives is half a year

$$E_y^c = \overset{\circ}{l}_y + \tfrac{1}{2}b_y + \tfrac{1}{2}n_y - \tfrac{1}{2}\theta_y - \tfrac{1}{2}w_y - \tfrac{1}{2}e_y \tag{2.3}$$

2.21 If the data are classified as in Table 2.2, it is easy to derive $\overset{\circ}{l}_y$. These are all the lives for which entries will have been made in the table for ages prior to y, less all those lives for which entries ceased to occur prior to age y. The lives for which there are entries will be all those existing on 1 January 1970 and whose age at that time was less than age y plus all those who entered during the investigation period at ages less than y. This gives $\sum\limits^{y-1} b_x + \sum\limits^{y-1} n_x$, the summation being taken from the youngest age. The lives for which entries ceased to occur before age y will consist of all those lives who withdrew or died before age y plus all the lives existing at 31 December 1974 at ages below age y, i.e.

$$\sum^{y-1} w_x + \sum^{y-1} \theta_x + \sum^{y-1} e_x,$$

thus

$$\overset{\circ}{l}_y = \sum^{y-1} b_x + \sum^{y-1} n_x - \sum^{y-1} w_x - \sum^{y-1} \theta_x - \sum^{y-1} e_x \tag{2.4}$$

the summation being taken from the youngest age.

2.22 If we remember that every life who enters observation must pass out of observation, i.e. every b or n must also be included in w, θ, or e, then

$$\sum b_x + \sum n_x = \sum w_x + \sum \theta_x + \sum e_x$$

and

$$0 = \sum b_x + \sum n_x - \sum w_x - \sum \theta_x - \sum e_x \qquad (2.5)$$

2.23 If we subtract (2.5) from (2.4) we obtain

$$\mathring{l}_y = -\sum_y b_x - \sum_y n_x + \sum_y w_x + \sum_y \theta_x + \sum_y e_x$$

where the summations are from age y to the oldest age, as an alternative expression for $\mathring{l}_y$.

2.24 Substituting (2.4) in (2.3) we have

$$E_y^c = \sum^{y-1} (b_x + n_x - w_x - \theta_x - e_x) + \tfrac{1}{2}b_y + \tfrac{1}{2}n_y - \tfrac{1}{2}w_y - \tfrac{1}{2}\theta_y - \tfrac{1}{2}e_y \quad (2.6)$$

and

$$\mathring{m}_y = \theta_y / E_y^c \qquad (2.7)$$

2.25 If we wish to calculate E_y, we must remember that, by definition, all the deaths θ_y are to be given a full year of exposure. We must also remember that, as indicated in equation (2.6), θ_y have been given one half of a year of exposure in E_y^c. We must therefore add a further $\tfrac{1}{2}\theta_y$ to E_y^c to obtain E_y. Thus

$$E_y = \sum^{y-1} (b_x + n_x - w_x - \theta_x - e_x) + \tfrac{1}{2}b_y + \tfrac{1}{2}n_y - \tfrac{1}{2}w_y - \tfrac{1}{2}e_y \qquad (2.8)$$

$$\mathring{q}_y = \theta_y / E_y \qquad (2.9)$$

2.26 For working purposes it is better to difference these formulae

$$E_y^c - E_{y-1}^c = \tfrac{1}{2}(b_{y-1} + b_y) + \tfrac{1}{2}(n_{y-1} + n_y) - \tfrac{1}{2}(w_{y-1} + w_y)$$

$$- \tfrac{1}{2}(\theta_{y-1} + \theta_y) - \tfrac{1}{2}(e_{y-1} + e_y) \qquad (2.10)$$

$$E_y - E_{y-1} = \tfrac{1}{2}(b_{y-1} + b_y) + \tfrac{1}{2}(n_{y-1} + n_y) - \tfrac{1}{2}(w_{y-1} + w_y)$$

$$- \tfrac{1}{2}(e_{y-1} + e_y) - \theta_{y-1} \qquad (2.11)$$

If x_0 is the youngest age in the table, E_{x_0} can be obtained from the general formula and E_{x_0+1}, E_{x_0+2} obtained successively by applying the difference formula.

2.27 Let us now use this approach to obtain E_{55}^c from the data of Table 2.2

$$E_{55}^c = \sum_{x}^{54}(b_x + n_x - w_x - \theta_x - e_x) + \tfrac{1}{2}b_{55} + \tfrac{1}{2}n_{55} - \tfrac{1}{2}w_{55} - \tfrac{1}{2}\theta_{55} - \tfrac{1}{2}e_{55}$$

$$= (6 + 3 - 1 - 0 - 1) + 0 + \tfrac{3}{2} - 1 - 1 - 1$$

$$= 5\tfrac{1}{2}$$

which agrees with the value at the foot of the age 55 column in Table 2.2 $(E_{55} = E_{55}^c + \tfrac{1}{2}\theta_{55} = 6\tfrac{1}{2})$.

A direct approach to the difference formula

2.28 The difference formula can be obtained directly in tabular form (Table 2.3), showing the contribution of each item to E_{x-1}^c and E_x^c (or to E_{x-1} and E_x) in turn.

Table 2.3

Item	E_{x-1}^c	E_x^c	$E_x^c - E_{x-1}^c$
b_{x-1}	$\tfrac{1}{2}$	1	$\tfrac{1}{2}b_{x-1}$
b_x	—	$\tfrac{1}{2}$	$\tfrac{1}{2}b_x$
n_{x-1}	$\tfrac{1}{2}$	1	$\tfrac{1}{2}n_{x-1}$
n_x	—	$\tfrac{1}{2}$	$\tfrac{1}{2}n_x$

2.29 The first column gives those b and n which contribute different average amounts of risk time to E_{x-1}^c and E_x^c, and the figures under E_{x-1}^c and E_x^c show these average amounts of risk time per individual assuming that n_x and b_x are uniformly distributed over the age interval x to $x+1$ and that there are no exits before age $x+1$. Then

$$E_x^c = E_{x-1}^c + \tfrac{1}{2}(b_{x-1} + b_x) + \tfrac{1}{2}(n_{x-1} + n_x)$$

less a correction for exits before age $x+1$.

2.30 The correction can be obtained as in Table 2.4.

Table 2.4

Item	$E^c_{x-1} + \frac{1}{2}(b_{x-1}+b_x) + \frac{1}{2}(n_{x-1}+n_x)$	E^c_x	Difference
w_{x-1}	$\frac{1}{2}$	—	$-\frac{1}{2}w_{x-1}$
w_x	1	$\frac{1}{2}$	$-\frac{1}{2}w_x$
e_{x-1}	$\frac{1}{2}$	—	$-\frac{1}{2}e_{x-1}$
e_x	1	$\frac{1}{2}$	$-\frac{1}{2}e_x$
θ_{x-1}	$\frac{1}{2}$	—	$-\frac{1}{2}\theta_{x-1}$
θ_x	1	$\frac{1}{2}$	$-\frac{1}{2}\theta_x$

2.31 The first column shows those w, e and θ which contribute different average amounts of risk time to $E^c_{x-1} + \frac{1}{2}(b_{x-1}+b_x) + \frac{1}{2}(n_{x-1} + n_x)$ and E^c_x, and the second and third columns show the average amount per individual, again assuming a uniform distribution of w, e and θ over the age interval (see para 2.34). The final column gives the correction and indicates that

$$E^c_x - E^c_{x-1} - \frac{1}{2}(b_{x-1} + b_x + n_{x-1} + n_x) =$$
$$-\frac{1}{2}(w_{x-1} + w_x + e_{x-1} + e_x + \theta_{x-1} + \theta_x)$$

whence

$$E^c_x = E^c_{x-1} + \frac{1}{2}(b_{x-1} + b_x + n_{x-1} + n_x) -$$
$$\frac{1}{2}(w_{x-1} + w_x + e_{x-1} + e_x) - \frac{1}{2}(\theta_{x-1} + \theta_x)$$

2.32 Once the logic of the procedure is appreciated a single table (Table 2.5) will be sufficient.

Table 2.5

Item	E^c_{x-1}	E^c_x	$E^c_x - E^c_{x-1}$
b_{x-1}	$\frac{1}{2}$	1	$\frac{1}{2}b_{x-1}$
b_x	—	$\frac{1}{2}$	$\frac{1}{2}b_x$
n_{x-1}	$\frac{1}{2}$	1	$\frac{1}{2}n_{x-1}$
n_x	—	$\frac{1}{2}$	$\frac{1}{2}n_x$
w_{x-1}	$\frac{1}{2}$	—	$-\frac{1}{2}w_{x-1}$
w_x	1	$\frac{1}{2}$	$-\frac{1}{2}w_x$
e_{x-1}	$\frac{1}{2}$	—	$-\frac{1}{2}e_{x-1}$
e_x	1	$\frac{1}{2}$	$-\frac{1}{2}e_x$
θ_{x-1}	$\frac{1}{2}$	—	$-\frac{1}{2}\theta_{x-1}$
θ_x	1	$\frac{1}{2}$	$-\frac{1}{2}\theta_x$

2.33 Note that for E_{x-1} and E_x the lines for death will read as in Table 2.6, so that

$$E_x = E_{x-1} + \tfrac{1}{2}(b_{x-1} + b_x + n_{x-1} + n_x)$$
$$- \tfrac{1}{2}(w_{x-1} + w_x + e_{x-1} + e_x) - \theta_{x-1}$$

Table 2.6

	E_{x-1}	E_x	$E_x - E_{x-1}$
θ_{x-1}	1	–	$-\theta_{x-1}$
θ_x	1	1	–

2.34 The average contributions per individual are calculated on the assumptions that

1 entrants to the period of investigation are under observation to age $x+1$;
2 exits from the period of investigation are under observation at age $x-1$.

2.35 If it is not clear which ages of any item will appear in the table, ages on either side of those thought necessary can be tested. For example, b_{x-2} would contribute 1 to both E^c_{x-1} and E^c_x and need not appear in the difference table. Similarly b_{x+1} would not contribute to either E^c_{x-1} or E^c_x, and again need not appear.

2.36 It will be seen later, when complicated examples are considered, that this method is very powerful.

An example of an application of the formulae

2.37 In order to use these formulae the following data are required for each age x:

b_x a census at 1 January 1970 of the lives then existing at age x last birthday.

n_x, w_x, θ_x schedules of the new entrants, withdrawals and deaths between 1 January 1970 and 31 December 1974 according to age x last birthday at entry, withdrawal or death.

e_x a census at 31 December 1974 of the lives then existing at age x last birthday.

2.38 For illustrative purposes E^c_x is obtained in Table 2.7 for the fourteen cases given in Table 2.1. The reader should check this derivation against the procedure of para. 2.32. The final column will be seen to agree with the bottom line of Table 2.2. Note also that, in the table, each life appears *once* under b_x or n_x and *once* under w_x, θ_x or e_x.

Table 2.7

Age last birthday	b_x	n_x	w_x	θ_x	e_x	E_x^c
49		F				$\frac{1}{2}$
50	B					$1\frac{1}{2}$
51	A	D				3
52	H					$4\frac{1}{2}$
53	EG	L	H			6
54	M				F	7
55	–	I,K,N	A,M	D,G	B,N	$5\frac{1}{2}$
56	J	C	C	I	K	$3\frac{1}{2}$
57			L			$2\frac{1}{2}$
58					E	$1\frac{1}{2}$
59						1
60						1
61					J	$\frac{1}{2}$

Important characteristics of mortality rates

2.39 A practical method for obtaining mortality rates from an actual population has now been described. At this stage it is important to consider just what these measures mean. $\mathring{q}_x$ is a rate of diminution between age x and age $x+1$ by death alone. It refers to a specified population (in this chapter a Life Office population has been assumed). Clearly the same method could be used for the members of a Pension Fund or for the members of a Friendly Society and for any other defined population for which the appropriate data could be obtained. Populations are rarely homogeneous with regard to the risk of death. A rate $\mathring{q}_x$ calculated from data of the whole of a population would not necessarily apply to a particular sub-group of that population. For example, the Life Office population could be divided according to sex, type of policy or county of residence. All these groups may show significantly different values of $\mathring{q}_x$.

2.40 The degree of sub-division in any investigation will depend on its purpose and on what is practical having regard to the number of lives in the population. The smaller the group, the greater will be the relative random errors in the deaths and the less reliable will be the resulting $\mathring{q}_x$. Further, the rates $\mathring{q}_x$ depend on the date of the investigation. For a specified population, $\mathring{q}_x$ for a given age varies over time. The variation depends on changes in climatic conditions, prevalence of epidemics, and unexplained random variation; and also there is usually a secular declining trend, due to improvements in medical care and general living conditions. An investigation over 5 years will give a reasonable average of climatic conditions and possibly of the effects of epidemics, so that the resulting set of $\mathring{q}_x$ can be described as indicating the level of age mortality for the specified population at, say, the midpoint of the period of investigation.

Intervals of time—an important distinction

2.41 The two important time periods should be noted:

1   The rate interval i.e. the interval of age for which the risk of death is to be estimated and which therefore determines the age to which each death is assigned. In this chapter the rate interval has been the year of age, or life-year, as it is usually called; deaths have been classified by their actual age last birthday at death. In later chapters it will be seen that the form of the data sometimes requires some alternative rate interval, but that rates according to age can still be derived.

2   The period of investigation which 'dates' the set of $\mathring{q}_x$ obtained (i.e. defines the point of time at which the lives were observed and at which the estimated age-specific $\mathring{q}_x$ values were applicable). When the period of investigation is several years, it cannot be confused with the rate-year. But obviously mortality can be investigated in respect of a single calendar year, and then it is quite possible for some confusion to arise.

An alternative method of obtaining the formulae

2.42 So far in this chapter E_x^c or E_x has been obtained by a simple counting procedure. We shall now idealize the situation so as to make use of the concepts of the calculus. In the theory of life contingencies this procedure is followed in manipulating or applying the life table, for which purpose it is assumed that l_x is a continuous function of x. Similarly it can be assumed that such functions as $\mathring{l}_x$ are continuous.

2.43   Let $f(x+r, t)dr$ denote the number of lives between age $x+r$ and $x+r+dr$ at time t. Then

$$\int_0^1 f(x+r, t)dr$$

will be the number of lives aged x last birthday at time t. Denote these by $P_x(t)$ so that

$$P_x(t) = \int_0^1 f(x+r, t)dr$$

2.44   Consider a period of investigation 0 to T and assume that E_x^c is required in respect of this period. At any time t the population at risk for the age interval x to $x+1$ is that population such that if a member died at time t he would be included in θ_x, the deaths during 0 to T at age x last birthday. Obviously this population is $P_x(t)$, the lives age x last birthday at time t. At time t each life in this population will contribute an element of risk time dt to E_x^c, and hence, the total risk time for age x to age $x+1$ during the period 0 to T is

$$\int_0^T P_x(t)dt = \int_0^T \int_0^1 f(x+r, t)dr\, dt.$$

2.45   We can now find usable formulae for E_x^c by obtaining simple approximations to this integral. The approximation will depend on the order of integration, since the double integral must be reduced to a single integral before an approximation can be obtained.

2.46   At this stage consider the result of first integrating with respect to t. Since $f(x+r, t)dr$ are the number of lives at time t between age $x+r$ and age $x+r+dr$, $f(x+r, t)dt$ must be the number of lives attaining age $x+r$ during the time interval t to $t+dt$. Hence

$$\int_0^T f(x+r, t)dt$$

must be the sum of all the lives who attain exact age $x+r$ during the period 0 to T, that is to say

$$\int_0^T f(x+r, t)dt = \mathring{l}_{x+r}$$

Hence $$E_x^c = \int_0^1 \mathring{l}_{x+r}dr$$

2.47 If it is now assumed that $\mathring{l}_{x+r}$ is approximately linear over the age interval x to $x+1$, it follows that

$$E_x^c = \tfrac{1}{2}(\mathring{l}_x + \mathring{l}_{x+1})$$

If $\mathring{l}_x$ and $\mathring{l}_{x+1}$ are expressed in terms of b_x, n_x, w_x, θ_x, and e_x in accordance with equation (2.4), then (2.6) is obtained. It should be noted that a single global assumption has been made about the form of the population at risk over the rate interval. In the continuous formula (2.10) separate assumptions are made about the distribution of the various components and circumstances sometimes warrant the use of different fractions for different components. Examples will be given in later chapters.

The census formula

2.48 If the order of integration is first with respect to r, another type of formula can be obtained.

2.49 In para. 2.44 we had

$$E_x^c = \int_0^T P_x(t)\, dt$$

and if $P_x(t)$ is approximately linear in t over each calendar year it follows that

$$E_x^c = \tfrac{1}{2}P_x(o) + \sum_1^{T-1} P_x(t) + \tfrac{1}{2}P_x(T) \qquad (2.12)$$

In other words, E_x^c can be obtained approximately if the only data available are censuses according to age last birthday at each 1 January. It is not, of course, essential that annual censuses should be available, but in the case of Life Offices and Pension Funds such tabulations are usually required for many other purposes, and it would be convenient to use them also for an investigation into mortality experience.

2.50 If, alternatively, the period of investigation were a single calendar year, then it would be reasonable to take as an estimate of E_x^c the population at the middle of the calendar year who were aged x last birthday. This approach is commonly employed in respect of national populations to produce national life tables.

2.51 It should be noticed that the use of the double integral can be avoided. Either time t can be considered and the population at risk then is $P_x(t)$, giving

$$E_x^c = \int_0^T P_x(t)dt,$$

or age $x + r$ can be considered, and the population at risk then is $\overset{\circ}{l}_{x+r}$, giving

$$E_x^c = \int_0^1 \overset{\circ}{l}_{x+r} dr.$$

2.52 We have now obtained two practical methods to give appropriate formulae for E_x^c. The method of paras 2.42 to 2.51 is generally known as the 'census method', since E_x^c is calculated from censuses only. The method of paras 2.18 to 2.26 is usually called the 'continuous method', because when applying the difference formula, the exposed to risk is calculated continuously from age to age, i.e. E_x is derived from E_{x-1} by making the appropriate adjustments. We shall continue to use this terminology, though it must not be confused with the mathematical concept of 'continuity', an assumption which has been used to develop both methods.

2.53 The main point of paras 2.42 to 2.52 is to show that the continuous and census methods are related and both result in formulae which are approximations to the exact counting of the risk time contributed by each life. If in the continuous method illustration of Table 2.7 a larger sample of lives had been used (say, several hundred), the approximation to exact counting must have been very close; and if for the census method daily censuses were available, this would clearly provide the basis for calculating an almost exact value of the integral of para. 2.49, and therefore of the exact total risk time.

2.54 In this chapter the reader has been introduced to basic concepts in the estimation of the rate of mortality from the analysis of data from lives observed for varying lengths of time during an investigation of the experience of, for example, a Life Office or a national population. These concepts are important to the calculation of correct lengths of exposure for individual lives. The chapter also introduced the reader to formulae which, using these concepts, greatly facilitate the summation of the individual exposures, though with some approximation. At this point the reader might wonder why, since computer programs can be written to apply the basic concepts, it is necessary to consider exposed to risk formulae. There are two reasons. The first, purely practical, reason is that it may quite often not be possible to use a computer either because a computer is not available, or because the experience may be too small to justify its use, or because the data are in a format which cannot, except with difficulty, be transformed to be compatible with computer use. The second, and more important, reason is that the discipline of constructing exposed to risk formulae is a very important aid to the clear understanding and application of the basic concepts. Even where a computer is to be used, both the input and the program may be incorrect if these basic concepts are not clearly understood. To write down the correct exposed to risk formula is, in effect, to write down sure guidelines for the whole operation of the mortality investigation. The reader will appreciate this more fully as the subject is further developed in Chapters 3 to 5.

EXERCISES FOR CHAPTER TWO

1 Explain the difference between the rate interval and the period of investigation. Define both.
2 What is the difference in concept between m_x and q_x?
3 If $P_{x,t}$ denotes the population living on 30 June in year t aged x last birthday on that date, and $\theta_{x,t}$ denotes the deaths at age x last birthday in year t, derive expressions for $\mathring{m}_x$ and $\mathring{q}_x$ in terms of $P_{x,t}$ and $\theta_{x,t}$ where the period of investigation starts on 1 January in year t, and ends on 31 December in year t.

From Table 2.8 calculate $\mathring{m}_{55}$, $\mathring{m}_{56}$, $\mathring{m}_{57}$, $\mathring{q}_{55}$, $\mathring{q}_{56}$, $\mathring{q}_{57}$

Table 2.8

Age last birthday	In force on 30 June			Deaths in		
	1976	1977	1978	1976	1977	1978
55	4,214	4,535	4,751	49	55	58
56	4,124	4,197	4,479	51	53	56
57	3,971	4,168	4,361	53	54	58

4 In an investigation which runs from 1 January 1974 to 31 December 1978, the lives in Table 2.9 are involved, among others.

Table 2.9

Case	Date of birth	Date of entry to assurance	Date and mode of exit from observations	
A	1 May 1918	1 July 1960	31 Dec. 1978	Existing
B	20 Jan. 1920	20 Aug. 1970	1 Oct. 1975	Withdrawal
C	5 July 1915	5 Jan. 1976	15 June 1976.	Withdrawal
D	1 Oct. 1918	20 May 1968	1 Sept. 1977.	Death
E	10 Aug. 1920	1 Sept. 1972	31 Dec. 1978.	Existing
F	16 April 1915	10 Oct. 1704	10 Nov. 1974.	Withdrawal
G	9 Sept. 1918	31 Jan. 1973	1 June 1974.	Death

Draw up a table in the form of Table 2.2, showing the elements to which these lives contribute and their contributions to E_x^c for the range of values of x involved.

5 Use the method of paras 2.24 to 2.36 to check the values derived in question 4, and draw up a table in the form of Table 2.7 to illustrate these results.

6 Derive the census formula for E_x^c. What is the advantage of the census formula? Show how the continuous and census formulae are related.

7 In the use of the exposed to risk formulae when the rate interval is the year of age, what assumptions are usually made in estimating the risk time contributed by entrants and exits?

CHAPTER THREE

OTHER RATE INTERVALS

The calendar year rate interval: continuous method

3.1 In the previous chapter the two basic and distinct time periods, the rate interval and the period of investigation, were defined and given special emphasis. In that chapter the rate interval was the year of age, that is to say q_x was the rate of diminution from death alone between exact age x and exact age $x+1$.

3.2 Suppose a population is classified according to age, say nearest age x at 1 January of a particular year, i.e. between exact age $x - \frac{1}{2}$ and exact age $x + \frac{1}{2}$. Let $P_{(x)}$ denote this population, and suppose that it is observed over the whole calendar year and that the deaths denoted by $\theta_{(x)}$, are counted; then if there are no new entrants or withdrawals, the ratio $\theta_{(x)}/P_{(x)}$ is a q type annual rate, since it measures the rate of diminution by death of $P_{(x)}$ over a year. Let us denote this rate by $\mathring{q}_{(x)}$. Clearly a set of such rates would show the correlation between mortality and age just as effectively as a set of $\mathring{q}_x$ obtained by the methods of previous chapters. In practice this procedure is frequently followed. In the case of Pension Funds and Friendly Societies data are obtained in this form for other purposes, and it is convenient to use the same data in connexion with mortality or sickness investigations. This procedure of deriving mortality rates has often been referred to as the calendar year method. This description is intended to indicate that the rate interval is the calendar year (for it is really only the rate interval that is different, not the method). It is important to realize that the underlying principle is no different from that discussed in Chapter 2. In each case a group of lives classified according to some age definition is observed over a period of 12 months (the rate interval) and the deaths occurring among them are counted. It is only the definitions of the group and the rate interval which are different. In this present case the group is classified according to some age definition on a specified date, often 1 January of a particular year. The deaths must be those occurring in the succeeding 12 months, tabulated according to the same age classification as at the same specified date previous to death. Again, as before, adjustments have to be made for entrants and exits to the group (also defined by age at the same date) during the period of investigation.

Exposed to risk formulae

3.3   The simplest type of tabulation for the calendar year method is that in which all the items are recorded according to some age definition on 1 January. For example, consider a period of investigation over a single calendar year so that the rate interval and the period of investigation coincide. Let

$P_{(x)}$ be the population nearest age x on 1 January, and

$n_{(x)}$, $w_{(x)}$ and $\theta_{(x)}$ be the new entrants, withdrawals and deaths during the calendar year who were nearest age x on 1 January.

Then assuming that $n_{(x)}$, $w_{(x)}$ and $\theta_{(x)}$ are uniformly distributed over the calendar year (see para. 3.43)

$$E_{(x)} = P_{(x)} + \tfrac{1}{2}n_{(x)} - \tfrac{1}{2}w_{(x)} \tag{3.1}$$

and

$$E^c_{(x)} = P_{(x)} + \tfrac{1}{2}n_{(x)} - \tfrac{1}{2}(w_{(x)} + \theta_{(x)}) \tag{3.2}$$

$$\mathring{q}_{(x)} = \frac{\theta_{(x)}}{E_{(x)}}, \quad \mathring{m}_{(x)} = \frac{\theta_{(x)}}{E^c_{(x)}}$$

3.4   At first sight this approach seems to differ from the procedure described in Chapter 2. Suppose, however, that the period of investigation was the 5 calendar years 1 January 1970 to 31 December 1974. The above formula could be applied to each calendar year and the resulting $E_{(x)}$ could be added together. This would require that new entrants, withdrawals and deaths had been tabulated separately for each calendar year. Censuses on each 1 January would not be needed, since if a census, say $_0P_{(x)}$ at 1 January 1970, were available and the new entrants, withdrawals and deaths during the rth calendar year are denoted by $_{r-1}n_{(x)}$, $_{r-1}w_{(x)}$ and $_{r-1}\theta_{(x)}$ respectively, then censuses on each 1 January can be obtained by means of the relationship

$$_{r-1}P_{(x)} + {_{r-1}n_{(x)}} - {_{r-1}w_{(x)}} - {_{r-1}\theta_{(x)}} = {_rP_{(x+1)}}$$

3.5   However, it is not necessary to obtain the intermediate censuses in this way. It is sufficient to have data as follows:

$_0P_{(x)} \equiv b_{(x)} = $ number of lives at 1 January 1970 who were nearest age x;

$n_{(x)}$, $w_{(x)}$ and $\theta_{(x)}$ = the new entrants, withdrawals and deaths during 1 January 1970 to 31 December 1974 who were nearest age x at the 1 January before entry or exit;

$_5P_{(x)} \equiv e_{(x)}$ = number of lives at 31 December 1974 who were nearest age x.

3.6 The first requirement is $\sum\limits_{r=0}^{4} {_rP_{(x)}}$, which will be denoted by $\overset{\circ}{l}_{(x)}$ (i.e. the total of the numbers of lives under observation, who were nearest age x on each 1 January during the period of investigation). Thus $\overset{\circ}{l}_{(x)}$, like $\overset{\circ}{l}_x$ in the previous chapter, represents the total of the numbers of lives at the beginning of each defined rate-year (x) to $(x+1)$ during the period of investigation.

3.7 Using the same reasoning as for the life-year rate interval, all the beginners at nearest age x or at younger ages will attain nearest age x on a 1 January during the period of investigation, provided they do not pass out of observation before that 1 January is reached. The same statement applies to all new entrants who were nearest age $x-1$ or less on 1 January before entry. Hence

$$\overset{\circ}{l}_{(x)} = \sum^{x} b_{(y)} + \sum^{x-1} n_{(y)}$$

less the appropriate exits (including enders).

3.8 The required exits are withdrawals and deaths who were nearest age $x-1$ or less on 1 January before withdrawal or death and the enders on 31 December 1974 who were then nearest age x or less, and

$$\overset{\circ}{l}_{(x)} = \sum^{x} b_{(y)} + \sum^{x-1} n_{(y)} - \sum^{x-1} w_{(y)} - \sum^{x-1} \theta_{(y)} - \sum^{x} e_{(y)}$$

and, applying formulae (3.1) and (3.2),

$$E_{(x)} = \sum^{x} b_{(y)} + \sum^{x-1} n_{(y)} + \tfrac{1}{2}n_{(x)} - \sum^{x-1} w_{(y)}$$
$$- \tfrac{1}{2}w_{(x)} - \sum^{x-1} \theta_{(y)} - \sum^{x} e_{(y)} \tag{3.3}$$

and

$$E^c_{(x)} = \sum^{x} b_{(y)} + \sum^{x-1} n_{(y)} + \tfrac{1}{2}n_{(x)} - \sum^{x-1} w_{(y)}$$
$$- \tfrac{1}{2}w_{(x)} - \sum^{x-1} \theta_{(y)} - \tfrac{1}{2}\theta_{(x)} - \sum^{x} e_{(y)} \tag{3.4}$$

3.9   There are no fractional elements for b and e, since the beginners came under observation at the beginning of a rate-year and the enders passed from observation at the end of a rate-year. The new entrants, deaths and withdrawals, however, are assumed to be uniformly distributed over the rate-year (i.e. in this case the calendar year) as for the life-year rate interval, and hence the form of the expression for these items is the same for both methods.

3.10   A table similar to Table 2.2 can be constructed, showing the contribution of each life to individual rate-years. Table 3.1 illustrates this procedure for the fourteen cases used in Chapter 2. As before, all fractions are shown as $\frac{1}{2}$.

Table 3.1   *Aggregate experience. Calendar year Central exposed to risk*

Case	Classification		Age nearest on 1 January											
			50	51	52	53	54	55	56	57	58	59	60	61
A	b_{52}	w_{55}			1	1	1	$\frac{1}{2}$						
B	b_{51}	e_{56}		1	1	1	1	1						
C	n_{55}	w_{56}						$\frac{1}{2}$	$\frac{1}{2}$					
D	n_{51}	θ_{54}		$\frac{1}{2}$	1	1	$\frac{1}{2}$							
E	b_{53}	e_{58}				1	1	1	1	1				
F	n_{50}	e_{55}	$\frac{1}{2}$	1	1	1	1							
G	b_{53}	θ_{55}				1	1	$\frac{1}{2}$						
H	b_{53}	w_{53}				$1-\frac{1}{2}$ $=\frac{1}{2}$								
I	n_{55}	θ_{56}						$\frac{1}{2}$	$\frac{1}{2}$					
J	b_{57}	e_{62}								1	1	1	1	1
K	n_{54}	e_{56}					$\frac{1}{2}$	1						
L	n_{53}	w_{57}				$\frac{1}{2}$	1	1	1	$\frac{1}{2}$				
M	b_{55}	w_{55}						$1-\frac{1}{2}$ $=\frac{1}{2}$						
N	n_{55}	e_{56}						$\frac{1}{2}$						
	Totals E_x^c		$\frac{1}{2}$	$2\frac{1}{2}$	4	7	7	7	3	$2\frac{1}{2}$	1	1	1	1

3.11   In Table 3.1 the integral ages indicate nearest age on 1 January and the interval between x and $x+1$ is also therefore the calendar year at the beginning of which a life was nearest age x. For example, case A was a beginner on 1 January 1970 at nearest age 52 and he withdrew during the calendar year 1973, at the beginning of which he was nearest age 55. He therefore contributes 1 year during each of the calendar years, which according to the above definition corresponds to (nearest) age intervals 52/53, 53/54, 54/55 and a fraction of year 55/56. The average fraction of $\frac{1}{2}$ (which of course would only apply to a group) rather than the exact fraction is allocated in the table, to show the procedure that would be followed for dealing with larger numbers. Case I was a new entrant during 1973, and at the beginning of this year he was nearest age 55. He died during 1974 and at the beginning of this year he was nearest age 56. He is therefore allocated $\frac{1}{2}$ year in respect of $E^c_{(55)}$ or $\mathbf{E}_{(55)}$ and $\frac{1}{2}$ year in respect of $E^c_{(56)}$ or 1 year in respect of $E_{(56)}$.

3.12 As before, the total of the columns give the total exposed to risk in respect of the rate-year shown at the head of the column.

The difference formula

3.13 The formula obtained by differencing formula (3.4) is

$$E^c_{(x)} = E^c_{(x-1)} + b_{(x)} + \tfrac{1}{2}(n_{(x-1)} + n_{(x)})$$
$$- \tfrac{1}{2}(w_{(x-1)} + w_{(x)}) - e_{(x)} - \tfrac{1}{2}(\theta_{(x-1)} + \theta_{(x)}) \quad (3.5)$$

$$\mathring{m}_{(x)} = \frac{\theta_{(x)}}{E^c_{(x)}} = \mathring{m}_{x+f}, \text{ where } -\tfrac{1}{2} < f < \tfrac{1}{2}$$

3.14 We write $\mathring{m}_{x+f}$ because we have to determine the age to which $\mathring{m}_{(x)}$ applies. In para. 3.6 we defined $\mathring{l}_{(x)}$ as the total number of lives at the beginning of the rate interval (x) to $(x+1)$, so that $x+f$ depends on the distribution of the exact ages of those lives which were then nearest age x. We know that (x) cannot be less than $x-\tfrac{1}{2}$ or more than $x+\tfrac{1}{2}$ and we can safely write $-\tfrac{1}{2} < f < \tfrac{1}{2}$. If the distribution of ages is approximately rectangular between $x-\tfrac{1}{2}$ and $x+\tfrac{1}{2}$, then f may be taken as zero. However, this assumption of an even age distribution must be tested, since it may not always be tenable. It would be possible for changes in the volume of new life-assurance business or in the predilection of new entrants about the nearness of their birthdays on entry, to introduce periodicities to the distribution of x within (x), though this is unlikely in large experiences.

3.15 The difference formula can be obtained directly by the same tabular method that was used for the life-year formula. See Table 3.2. Remembering that $E^c_{(x)}$ is the risk time in terms of the calendar year interval, it is clear that $b_{(x)}$ coming under observation on 1 January 1970 will each contribute 1 year during 1970 to $E^c_{(x)}$, provided they do

Table 3.2

Item	Average contribution to $E^c_{(x-1)}$	$E^c_{(x)}$	$E^c_{(x)} - E^c_{(x-1)}$
$b_{(x)}$	—	1	$b_{(x)}$
$n_{(x-1)}$	$\frac{1}{2}$	1	$\frac{1}{2}n_{(x-1)}$
$n_{(x)}$	—	$\frac{1}{2}$	$\frac{1}{2}n_{(x)}$
$w_{(x-1)}$	$\frac{1}{2}$	—	$-\frac{1}{2}w_{(x-1)}$
$w_{(x)}$	1	$\frac{1}{2}$	$-\frac{1}{2}w_{(x)}$
$e_{(x)}$	1	—	$-e_{(x)}$
$\theta_{(x-1)}$	$\frac{1}{2}$	—	$-\frac{1}{2}\theta_{(x-1)}$
$\theta_{(x)}$	1	$\frac{1}{2}$	$-\frac{1}{2}\theta_{(x)}$

not die or withdraw during 1970. Similarly $e_{(x)}$ who pass out of observation just before 1 January 1975 will contribute 1 year to $E^c_{(x-1)}$, provided they were under observation on 1 January 1974 when they were nearest age $(x-1)$. The treatment of n, w and θ is similar to that for the life-year interval.

3.16 For $E_{(x)}$ the only difference is in the treatment of $\theta_{(x)}$, as in Table 3.3.

Table 3.3

	$E_{(x-1)}$	$E_{(x)}$	$E_{(x)} - E_{(x-1)}$
$\theta_{(x-1)}$	1	—	$-\theta_{(x-1)}$
$\theta_{(x)}$	1	1	—

So that
$$E_{(x)} - E_{(x-1)} = b_{(x)} + \tfrac{1}{2}(n_{(x)} + n_{(x-1)})$$
$$-\tfrac{1}{2}(w_{(x-1)} + w_{(x)}) - \theta_{(x-1)} - e_{(x)} \quad (3.6)$$

3.17 The procedure is simple, provided that the definition of the rate interval is kept clearly in mind. It is then necessary to interpret the mortality rate which results from the process.

3.18 We can illustrate the examination of para. 3.15 in diagrammatic form. Figure 3.1 shows clearly that $b_{(x)}$ represented by ABCD contributes a whole year to $E^c_{(x)}$ (the shaded area of exposure is equal in area to a square of 1 year); that $n_{(x)}$, represented by points within the parallelogram EFGH, contributes a $\frac{1}{2}$ year to $E^c_{(x)}$, since, if

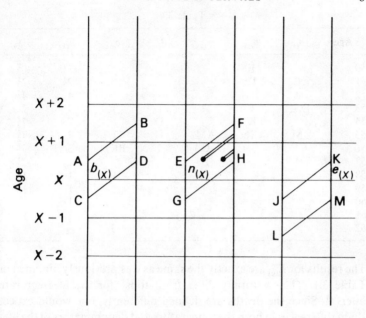

FIGURE 3.1

This is a Lexis diagram (named after the mathematician who is regarded as having first introduced its use). In this diagram, time (the period of investigation) extends horizontally. At the same time, age (measured vertically) must be increasing, so that the observation or exposure of an individual life is along a line moving upwards at 45°. The shaded areas ABCD and JKLM represent the exposure of all $b_{(x)}$ and $e_{(x)}$ respectively and the shaded elements in EFGH represent two members of $n_{(x)}$. See para. 3.18.

the points of entry are evenly distributed and if each point contributes an element of infinitesimal width along the line parallel to EF and joining the point to FH, the average area will be half the parallelogram EFGH and this is equal to $\frac{1}{2}$ a year; and that $e_{(x)}$, represented by KM contributes a whole year to $E^c_{(x-1)}$ (from JL) but no risk time to $E^c_{(x)}$.

Example

3.19 As an illustration of the use of the procedure of paras 3.15 and 3.16, the formulae have been applied in Table 3.4 to the fourteen cases of Table 2.1.

Table 3.4

Age	$b_{(x)}$	$n_{(x)}$	$w_{(x)}$	$\theta_{(x)}$	$e_{(x)}$	$E^c_{(x)}$	$E_{(x)}$
50		F				$\frac{1}{2}$	$\frac{1}{2}$
51	B	D				$2\frac{1}{2}$	$2\frac{1}{2}$
52	A					4	4
53	EGH	L	H			7	7
54		K		D		7	$7\frac{1}{2}$
55	M	CIN	AM	G	F	7	$7\frac{1}{2}$
56			C	I	BKN	3	$3\frac{1}{2}$
57	J		L			$2\frac{1}{2}$	$2\frac{1}{2}$
58					E	1	1
59						1	1
60						1	1
61						1	1
62					J	—	—

The results for $E^c_{(x)}$ are exactly the same as was previously obtained in Table 3.1. They naturally differ from those for the life-year rate interval. Since the deaths are defined differently, one would expect slight differences in both the numerators and denominators of the life-year and calendar-year mortality rates, but if several thousand lives had been in question the resulting rates would be almost identical.

The census formula for a calendar year

3.20 It will be remembered that a census formula was obtained by first considering the population at risk at time t. To obtain $E^c_{(x)}$ when using the calendar year as the rate interval, the population at risk will clearly comprise those lives then in the experience who were nearest age x on 1 January before time t. Suppose that the point of time t falls in the rth calendar year at time k from 1 January and let the population then at risk be denoted by $_{r-1}P_{(x)}(k)$. Then the risk time for the rth calendar year will be

$$\int_0^1 {}_{r-1}P_{(x)}(k)dk \doteqdot \tfrac{1}{2}({}_{r-1}P_{(x)}(0) + {}_{r-1}P_{(x)}(1))$$

which is similar in form to formula (2.12).

3.21 The expression $_{r-1}P_{(x)}(0)$ refers to the population at 1 January of the rth calendar year who were then nearest age x. We shall denote this simply as $_{r-1}P_{(x)}$. Similarly $_{r-1}P_{(x)}(1)$ refers to the population at the end of the rth calendar year who were nearest age x at the beginning of that year. They were therefore nearest age $x+1$ at the end of the year, and if we remember that the end of the rth year is also the beginning of the $(r+1)$th year, we can denote this population as $_rP_{(x+1)}$. Hence in these symbols

$E^c_{(x)}$ in respect of the rth calendar year

$$= \tfrac{1}{2}(_{r-1}P_{(x)} + _rP_{(x+1)}) \tag{3.7}$$

3.22 The change of symbols makes the formula look in form different from that for the life-year rate interval, but this is apparent only since we are merely expressing formula (2.12) in different symbols.

3.23 $E^c_{(x)}$ for the whole period of investigation is

$$\tfrac{1}{2}(\sum_{r=0}^{4} {}_rP_{(x)} + \sum_{r=1}^{5} {}_rP_{(x+1)}) \tag{3.8}$$

3.24 Consider again formula (3.2)

$$E^c_{(x)} = {}_0P_{(x)} + \tfrac{1}{2}(n_{(x)} - w_{(x)} - \theta_{(x)})$$

But

$$_0P_{(x)} + n_{(x)} - w_{(x)} - \theta_{(x)} = {}_1P_{(x+1)}$$

or

$$n_{(x)} - w_{(x)} - \theta_{(x)} = {}_1P_{(x+1)} - {}_0P_{(x)}$$

Substituting above

$$E^c_{(x)} = \tfrac{1}{2}({}_0P_{(x)} + {}_1P_{(x+1)})$$

and if we remember that (3.2) related to only one year of investigation, we must sum this expression over 5 years. We then obtain a formula identical to (3.8). Thus the continuous and census formulae give identical amounts of exposure.

3.25 In the case of the calendar-year rate interval both the continuous and census formulae imply the observation of a group of lives $l_{(x)}$ (or $P_{(x)}$, since they are identical) over the calendar year and estimating $E^c_{(x)}$ on the assumption that new entrants' deaths and withdrawals are distributed uniformly over the calendar year. The results must therefore be identical.

The policy-year rate interval

3.26 We now consider the procedure to be adopted when the rate interval is the policy year, i.e. the period from one policy anniversary to the next, and, as for the calendar-year rate interval, in order to obtain rates according to age the lives must be classified in age groups at the beginning of the rate-year, i.e. at a policy anniversary.

• **3.27** For example, suppose that a rate was required for the policy year beginning in 1970, then one procedure would be to record all lives existing at their policy anniversaries in 1970, or effecting new policies, according to nearest age on their policy anniversary, or at entry. Denote these lives by $\overset{\circ}{l}_{(x)}$. Each $\overset{\circ}{l}_{(x)}$ is then observed until the policy anniversary in 1971 and the deaths among them, $\theta_{(x)}$, are counted. If there were no withdrawals (there cannot be new entrants during a policy year), then $\theta_{(x)}/\overset{\circ}{l}_{(x)}$ would be a q-type rate for the groups of lives $\overset{\circ}{l}_{(x)}$, and it would measure the rate of decrement by death over a policy year. Adjustments for withdrawals can be made by adopting the same principles as those adopted for the life- and calendar-year methods. If there were $w_{(x)}$ withdrawals and they are assumed to be distributed uniformly over the policy year, then $E_{(x)} = \overset{\circ}{l}_{(x)} - \frac{1}{2}w_{(x)}$.

3.28 It will be noted that this situation resembles both the life-year and the calendar-year rate interval concepts. In all cases the rate-year is from one anniversary to the next, the anniversary being, for the life-year, the birthday; for the policy year, the 'birthday of a policy'; and for the calendar year, the beginning of that year. For all three rate intervals (life-year, calendar-year, policy-year), in order to obtain age rates the lives must be grouped according to some age definition (in the life-year it is exact age x, while in the policy year and calendar year it may be, for example, nearest age or age last birthday at the beginning of the rate-year). If the reader concentrates on remembering which rate-year he is using—life, calendar or policy—there are no other differences to worry about. The same principles of tabulation and derivation of exposure apply to each type of rate interval.

Tabular representation

3.29 Again it is possible in principle to obtain the exposed to risk by constructing a table or matrix which shows the contribution of each life to each rate interval. Table 3.5 has been constructed for the fourteen cases given in Table 2.1. Each row represents a life and each column a policy year. For example, the column headed 50 represents the policy year at the beginning of which a life was nearest age 50. Case A came under observation on 1 January 1970 when he was nearest age 51 at the previous policy anniversary, and he withdrew during the policy year at the beginning of which he was nearest age 55; he therefore contributes a fraction of a year to policy year 51 ($\frac{1}{2}$ has been entered in the table for all fractional cases on the assumption of a

Table 3.5 *Aggregate experience. Policy year. Central exposed to risk*

Case	Classification		Nearest age at beginning of policy year											
		50	51	52	53	54	55	56	57	58	59	60	61
A	$b_{(51)}$ $w_{(55)}$		$\frac12$	1	1	1	$\frac12$						
B	$b_{(50)}$ $e_{(55)}$	$\frac12$	1	1	1	1	$\frac12$						
C	$n_{(56)}$ $w_{(56)}$							$1-\frac12$ $=\frac12$					
D	$n_{(52)}$ $\theta_{(55)}$			1	1	1	$\frac12$						
E	$b_{(52)}$ $e_{(57)}$			$\frac12$	1	1	1	1	$\frac12$				
F	$n_{(50)}$ $e_{(54)}$	1	1	1	1	$\frac12$							
G	$b_{(53)}$ $\theta_{(55)}$				$\frac12$	1	$\frac12$						
H	$b_{(52)}$ $w_{(52)}$			$\frac12-\frac12$ $=0$									
I	$n_{(56)}$ $\theta_{(56)}$							$1-\frac12$ $=\frac12$					
J	$b_{(56)}$ $e_{(61)}$							$\frac12$	1	1	1	1	$\frac12$
K	$n_{(55)}$ $e_{(56)}$						1	$\frac12$					
L	$n_{(53)}$ $w_{(57)}$				1	1	1	1	$\frac12$				
M	$b_{(55)}$ $w_{(55)}$						$\frac12-\frac12$ $=0$						
N	$n_{(55)}$ $e_{(55)}$						$1-\frac12$ $=\frac12$						
	Totals $E^c_{(x)}$	$1\frac12$	$2\frac12$	$4\frac12$	$6\frac12$	$6\frac12$	$5\frac12$	4	2	1	1	1	$\frac12$

uniform distribution of entrants over a year of entry), 1 year to each of policy years 52, 53 and 54, and a fraction of a year (again counted as $\frac12$ on the assumption of a uniform distribution of exits over the policy year) to policy year 55. The total of each column gives an estimate of $E^c_{(x)}$. As we have already stated, in practice the assumption as to the uniform distribution of entrants or exits could only be made for a sufficiently large experience and in any case would have to be tested.

Exposed to risk formulae

3.30 The procedure above makes use of only part of the information available from the period 1 January 1970 to 31 December 1974, since deaths (and corresponding exposure) before the policy anniversary in 1970 and after the policy anniversary in 1974 are excluded. If, instead, the full period of observation is used, the simplest method of tabulation would be to record all data according to nearest age at the previous policy anniversary (i.e. anniversary of entry), and new entrants would be recorded according to nearest age at entry:

$b_{(x)}$ = number of lives at 1 January 1970 who were nearest age x at the previous policy anniversary;

$n_{(x)}$ = new entrants during 1 January 1970 to 31 December 1974 who were nearest age x at entry;

$w_{(x)}$ and $\theta_{(x)}$ = withdrawals and deaths during 1 January 1970 to 31 December 1974 who were nearest age x at the previous policy anniversary;

$e_{(x)}$ = number of lives at 31 December 1974 who were nearest age x at the previous policy anniversary.

3.31 If $\mathring{l}_{(x)}$ denotes the number of lives who were nearest age x on any policy anniversary between 1 January 1970 and 31 December 1974, then

$$\mathring{l}_{(x)} = \sum^{x-1} b_{(y)} + \sum^{x} n_{(y)} - \sum^{x-1} (w_{(y)} + \theta_{(y)} + e_{(y)})$$

The summations are taken from the youngest age in each case. $n_{(y)}$ is summed to x, since $n_{(x)}$ enter at the beginning of the policy year (x) to $(x+1)$ and therefore must be included in $\mathring{l}_{(x)}$. $b_{(y)}$ is summed to $x-1$, since by definition $b_{(x-1)}$ will be (x) at this anniversary in 1970.

3.32 To obtain $E_{(x)}$, adjustments must be made to $\mathring{l}_{(x)}$ in respect of $b_{(x)}$, $w_{(x)}$ and $e_{(x)}$. It is again assumed that these elements are distributed uniformly over the rate-year, i.e. over the policy year. For example, it is assumed that for $b_{(x)}$ the average time to the next policy anniversary is 6 months, so that the addition to $\mathring{l}_{(x)}$ is $\frac{1}{2}b_{(x)}$. Similarly the deduction in respect of w and e is $\frac{1}{2}(w_{(x)} + e_{(x)})$. Since new entrants, of necessity, enter at the beginning of the rate-year, no adjustment is required. Hence

$$E_{(x)} = \sum^{x-1} b_{(y)} + \tfrac{1}{2}b_{(x)} + \sum^{x} n_{(y)} - \sum^{x-1} (w_{(y)} + \theta_{(y)} + e_{(y)})$$
$$- \tfrac{1}{2}(w_{(x)} + e_{(x)}) \tag{3.9}$$

$$\mathring{q}_{(x)} = \frac{\theta_{(x)}}{E_{(x)}}$$

$$= \mathring{q}_{x+f} \text{ where} -\tfrac{1}{2} < f < \tfrac{1}{2}$$

3.33 If E_x^c is required and we assume uniform distribution of $\theta_{(x)}$, then the final term would be $-\frac{1}{2}(w_{(x)} + \theta_{(x)} + e_{(x)})$ and

$$\mathring{m}_{(x)} = \frac{\theta_{(x)}}{E_x^c} = \mathring{m}_{x+f} \tag{3.10}$$

Table 3.6

Item	Average contribution to $E^c_{(x-1)}$	$E^c_{(x)}$	Difference
$b_{(x-1)}$	$\frac{1}{2}$	1	$\frac{1}{2}b_{(x-1)}$
$b_{(x)}$	–	$\frac{1}{2}$	$\frac{1}{2}b_{(x)}$
$n_{(x)}$	–	1	$n_{(x)}$
$w_{(x-1)}$	$\frac{1}{2}$	–	$-\frac{1}{2}w_{(x-1)}$
$w_{(x)}$	1	$\frac{1}{2}$	$-\frac{1}{2}w_{(x)}$
$e_{(x-1)}$	$\frac{1}{2}$	–	$-\frac{1}{2}e_{(x-1)}$
$e_{(x)}$	1	$\frac{1}{2}$	$-\frac{1}{2}e_{(x)}$
$\theta_{(x-1)}$	$\frac{1}{2}$	–	$-\frac{1}{2}\theta_{(x-1)}$
$\theta_{(x)}$	1	$\frac{1}{2}$	$-\frac{1}{2}\theta_{(x)}$

3.34 If the average age is approximately x, i.e. $f \doteqdot 0$, then

$$\mathring{q}_{(x)} \doteqdot q_x \quad \text{and} \quad \mathring{m}_{(x)} \doteqdot m_x$$

The difference formula

3.35 Differencing formula (3.10) gives

$$E^c_{(x)} - E^c_{(x-1)} = \tfrac{1}{2}(b_{(x-1)} + b_{(x)}) + n_{(x)} - \tfrac{1}{2}(w_{(x-1)} + w_{(x)}$$
$$+ e_{(x-1)} + e_{(x)}) - \tfrac{1}{2}(\theta_{(x-1)} + \theta_{(x)}) \qquad (3.11)$$

3.36 This formula can also be obtained directly, as in Table 3.6, and the sum of the last column is equal to $E^c_{(x)} - E^c_{(x-1)}$.

Table 3.7

Nearest age	$b_{(x)}$	$n_{(x)}$	$w_{(x)}$	$\theta_{(x)}$	$e_{(x)}$	$E^c_{(x)}$	$E_{(x)}$
50	B	F				$1\frac{1}{2}$	$1\frac{1}{2}$
51	A					$2\frac{1}{2}$	$2\frac{1}{2}$
52	EH	D	H			$4\frac{1}{2}$	$4\frac{1}{2}$
53	G	L				$6\frac{1}{2}$	$6\frac{1}{2}$
54					F	$6\frac{1}{2}$	$6\frac{1}{2}$
55	M	KN	AM	DG	BN	$5\frac{1}{2}$	$6\frac{1}{2}$
56	J	CI	C	I	K	4	$4\frac{1}{2}$
57		L			E	2	2
58						1	1
59						1	1
60						1	1
61					J	$\frac{1}{2}$	$\frac{1}{2}$

3.37 The application of this formula and the corresponding formula for $E_{(x)}$ to the fourteen cases in Table 3.1 is shown in Table 3.7.

The census formula

3.38 The deaths are those occurring during the period of observation who were nearest age x at the policy anniversary previous to the date of death. Considering any time t during the period of observation, the population at risk must be the population nearest age x on the policy anniversary before t. Denote this population by $P_{(x)}(t)$ and therefore

$$E^c_{(x)} = \int_0^T P_{(x)}(t)dt$$

where T is the time length of the period of observation. Assuming that $P_{(x)}(t)$ is approximately linear over unit time intervals

$$E^c_{(x)} = \tfrac{1}{2}P_{(x)}(0) + \sum_1^{T-1} P_{(x)}(t) + \tfrac{1}{2}P_{(x)}(T) \qquad (3.12)$$

If the unit period is 1 year, then for a practical solution annual censuses are required on, say, each 1 January according to nearest age at the previous policy anniversary.

3.39 The reader should note the similarity to the life-year formula. The form is the same but the definitions of P are different. In the life-year method the census population P_x is according to age x at previous birthday, while in the policy-year method the census population $P_{(x)}$ is according to nearest age at the previous 'birthday' of the policy held by the life in question.

3.40 We are almost at the end of this chapter, which has been concerned with different rate intervals. Before we leave this discussion let us reiterate what was said in para. 3.28, because it cannot be said too often. The different rate intervals do not necessitate different methods or principles. A rate-year runs from one 'anniversary' to the next; lives are grouped according to a defined age as at the beginning of the rate year. The anniversary and possibly the age definitions are different for different rate-years but not the general methods of tabulation of exposure and derivation of rates.

Rate-year	Anniversary	Age at beginning of rate year
Life-year	Birthday	Exact age x

Calendar year	1 January	Nearest age or age last birthday or age next birthday or difference between calendar year of exposure and calendar year of birth, etc.
Policy year	Policy anniversary	Same options as for calendar-rate year.

The logical procedure therefore is (1) define the rate interval, (2) choose the age definitions, and (3) develop the exposed to risk formulae (either continuous or census, which give identical results) by the general principles of Chapter 2.

Lives and policies

3.41 In discussing the policy-year method no distinction has been drawn between lives and policies. This would not matter if each life had only one policy. In practice a life may have several policies, either taken out at the same time or at different times, and it is usual to base a mortality investigation on policies, often eliminating all but one policy of those effected at the same time. Thus a life that takes out say three policies at time t_1, two policies at time t_2 and one policy at each of times t_3 and t_4 would be counted as four 'lives', one in respect of each of the times t_1 to t_4. The resulting rates are therefore not strictly based on 'lives' in the sense considered in the previous sections. They are rates in respect of policies, subject to the restriction described above. It should be borne in mind that these rates and the associated life tables and monetary values are used in the financial operations of Life Offices and that these operations are concerned with the financial contracts, so that it is appropriate to base these rates on policies. Furthermore each policy entrant is usually subject to medical examination or strict health enquiry, so that each policy entry for the same person is similar, from a mortality risk point of view, to that of a new life; this is an added reason for regarding 'policies' as more important than 'lives'. There is, however, an overriding practical point that the exclusion of duplicates would be a complication in data collection that would not be acceptable unless there were a strong justification for it.

3.42 It is a well-known statistical phenomenon that if a sample is chosen by selecting, say, households rather than individuals, the variance of the sample is increased, for the simple reason that if one member of a household is deviant from average, the other members

Table 3.8 C.M.I. Bureau—Sample distribution of deaths over year of age

Age last birthday at death	Number of complete months from last birthday to death												Total
	0	1	2	3	4	5	6	7	8	9	10	11	
15–19					1								1
20–29	2	5	1	2	2	2	4	2	1	3	1	4	29
30–39	3	5	6	5	4	4	5	7	6	7	3	2	57
40–49	11	13	14	11	10	8	9	9	13	16	16	16	146
50–59	24	36	32	30	33	33	21	33	34	28	21	27	352
60–64	16	18	11	12	12	10	10	13	9	11	7	12	141
65–69	3	6	4	6	5	7	8	11	4	5	9	2	70
70–74	1	6	5	8	5	7	4	7	4	7	1	8	63
75–79	3	3	5	3	7	3	2	10	4	6	6	9	61
80–84	4	4	10	2	4	4	8	–	2	1	2	2	42
85–89	4	1	4	3	3	3	3	2	6	3	3	3	39
90+	–	–	3	1		2	2	1	–	1	–	1	14
Total	71	97	95	83	90	82	76	95	83	88	69	86	1,015

are likely to be similarly deviant (if one is in the top social stratum the other members are likely to be in the same stratum of the population). The inclusion of duplicate lives in insurance data is a similar form of 'clustering' and will increase the sampling variance of the rates. This strengthens the need for graduation, the purpose of which is to remove this variance. It should be stressed that this discussion and that of the previous paragraph applies to all investigations whatever the rate interval and not just to the use of the policy year.

The assumption of uniform distribution of decrements over the rate interval

3.43 Some observers have noted that deaths are not uniformly distributed over the year of age but show a distinct hump immediately following the attainment of a birthday. Table 3.8 shows the distribution of deaths of males by month of age for specified age groups in a random sample drawn from the records of the C.M.I. On the whole the assumption of uniform distribution seems to be justified. There is no particular concentration, certainly not in the first month after the birthday; 518 deaths occurred in the first half of the year of age and 497 in the second half. The mean number of deaths in a month was 85 and the fluctuations about that mean were -14, $+12$, $+10$, -2, $+5$, -3, -9, $+10$, -2, $+3$, -16, $+1$. It is possible to fit a regression line to the monthly figures, and it does descend over the year of age, but taking the unit of time as 1 month, the slope is $-\cdot42$, which is a very gradual decline in relation to the mean of 85 and can probably be accounted for by the wastage of the exposures over the year of age.

EXERCISES FOR CHAPTER THREE

1   It is desired to obtain values of $\mathring{q}_x$ from a large pension fund experience for which the period of investigation was 1 January 1976 to 31 December 1978. The age range is 25 to 65 and the data are tabulated as below:

b_x = number of members at 1.1.76, then aged x *next* birthday;

e_x = number of members at 31.12.78, then aged x *next* birthday;

n_x = number of members joining the fund whose age was x *next* birthday on 1 January preceding entry;

w_x = withdrawals of members whose age was x *next* birthday on 1 January preceding exit;

θ_x = deaths of members whose age was x *next* birthday on 1 January preceding death.

Persons under 25 are not eligible to join the fund. You may assume that all members are of the same sex.

(i)   What is the rate interval you will adopt and why?
(ii) Derive a formula for $E_x - E_{x-1}$ stating any assumptions you wish to make.
(iii) To what age does the $\mathring{q}_x$ obtained from (ii) apply? What assumptions are implied?
(iv) Given the following extract from the data, calculate θ_x/E_x for three values of x:

Age x	b_x	n_x	w_x	θ_x	e_x
25	0	17,623	3,330	32	0
26	5,782	3,153	2,612	73	5,093
27	6,059	3,249	2,646	88	4,334

2   $_0P_x$ and $_1P_x$ represent the numbers exposed to risk of death at age x on 1 January 1976 and 31 December 1976 respectively for a large group of assured lives. For each method of calculating E_x^c given below, select the most appropriate definition of age at death from (a) age next birthday at death, and (b) age last birthday on 31 December 1976, for use in determining $\mathring{m}_x$. In each case give reasons for your choice and state the age to which the calculated rates of $\mathring{m}_x$ would apply.

		Definition of x	
Method	E_x^c	$_0P_x$	$_1P_x$
1	$\frac{1}{2}(_0P_x + {}_1P_x)$	1976 minus calendar year of birth	1977 minus calendar year of birth
2	$\frac{1}{2}(_0P_x + {}_1P_{x+1})$	1976 minus calendar year of birth	1977 minus calendar year of birth

3   The following is a summary of part of the data from two separate investigations, each made between 1.1.76 and 31.12.77.

Investigation A
Number of lives under observation on 1.1.76 then aged 50 last birthday = 1,162
Number of lives under observation on 1.1.77 then aged 50 last birthday = 1,128
Number of lives under observation on 1.1.77 then aged 51 last birthday = 1,169
Number of lives under observation on 1.1.78 then aged 50 last birthday = 1,140
Number of lives under observation on 1.1.78 then aged 51 last birthday = 1,145
Number of lives under observation on 1.1.78 then aged 52 last birthday = 1,180
Number of deaths aged 50 last birthday at date of death = 21.

Investigation B
Number of lives under observation on 1.1.76 then aged 50 nearest birthday = 2,761
Number of lives under observation on 1.1.77 then aged 50 nearest birthday = 2,587

Number of lives under observation on 1.1.77 then aged 51 nearest birthday
= 2,839
Number of lives under observation on 1.1.78 then aged 50 nearest birthday
= 2,689
Number of lives under observation on 1.1.78 then aged 51 nearest birthday
= 2,753
Number of lives under observation on 1.1.78 then aged 52 nearest birthday
= 2,801
Number of deaths aged 50 nearest birthday on the 1st January preceding the
date of death = 58.

For each investigation use the data supplied to make an estimate of $\mathring{q}_{50}$.
State any assumptions made. (You may not need to use *all* the data given in
the question.)

4   For the following classifications of data, derive equations for $(E_x - E_{x-1})$.
Assume the only information available is that given below and state
any assumptions you make in deriving your equations. In each case the
period of investigation is 1.1.74 to 31.12.78 and b_x, e_x, n_x, w_x, θ_x, are
respectively the numbers of beginners (at 1.1.74), enders (at 31.12.78), new
entrants, withdrawals and deaths at age x, where x is as defined below.

Investigation A
b_x where x is age last birthday on 1.1.74.
e_x where x is age last birthday on 31.12.78.
n_x where x is age last birthday at entry.
w_x where x is age last birthday at withdrawal.
θ_x where x is age last birthday at death.

Investigation B
b_x where x is age next birthday on 1.1.74.
e_x where x is age next birthday on 31.12.78.
n_x where x is calculated as calendar year of entry minus calendar year of
   birth.
w_x where x is calculated as calendar year of withdrawal minus calendar year
   of birth.
θ_x where x is calculated as calendar year of death minus calendar year of
   birth.

(a) State briefly with reasons whether your answer in each case would
need to be modified if all new entrants entered on 1 April. (You are not
required to produce a revised formula.)
(b) State briefly with reasons whether your answer in each case would
need to be modified if all new entrants entered 3 months before a birthday.
(You are not required to produce a revised formula.)
(c) State briefly with reasons whether your answer for investigation *A*
would need to be modified if *deaths* were classified according to age nearest
birthday at death, instead of as shown. (You are not required to produce a
revised formula.)

CHAPTER FOUR

OTHER AGE GROUPINGS AND SOME SPECIAL PROBLEMS

Introduction

4.1 In the previous chapters the treatment of exposed to risk formulae has been presented in the simplest possible terms so that the general principles for deriving formulae could be clearly demonstrated. The rate-year has been clearly defined in each case and all the data were assumed to be capable of tabulation according to a simple age classification as at the beginning of the rate year during which the life or policy entered or passed from observation. The age classification adopted automatically defined the 'age' to which the resulting rate related. For the life-year rate interval this 'age' was exact age x, while for the calendar-year and policy-year rate intervals we were concerned with groups of lives or policies which, at the beginning of the interval, were at nearest age x, and were assumed to be, on the average, aged exactly x. Thus, for each rate interval used, rates for integral age x were obtained directly from the ratio of θ_x to E_x as tabulated.

4.2 The principles followed in deriving exposed to risk formulae are quite general and do not depend on the particular age classification used. Further, they do not depend on the assumption of a uniform distribution of entrants or exits over the rate-year, although information is required on which to base this or any other assumption before a formula can be derived. In this chapter examples will be given of the treatment of other age tabulations and other distributions of entrants and exits over the rate-year. It is hoped that readers will realize that they could have dealt with these problems themselves by means of the principles that have already been learned. Indeed it would be good practice to try to solve each problem before reading the solution given in the text.

THE LIFE-YEAR RATE INTERVAL

(1) Alternative age groupings

4.3 In Chapter 2 the tabulation used consisted of a grouping by age last birthday at entry to or exit from observation. Suppose, however, that all these events had been tabulated according to nearest age instead of age last birthday. Denote the events by $b_{(x)}, n_{(x)}, w_{(x)}, \theta_{(x)}, e_{(x)}$. Consider $\theta_{(x)}$; they are the deaths during the age interval $x - \frac{1}{2}$ to $x + \frac{1}{2}$, hence if this age interval is taken as the rate-year, the deaths $\theta_{(x)}$ are the correct numerator for deriving $\mathring{q}_{x - \frac{1}{2}}$. It will be appreciated that $x - \frac{1}{2}$ to $x + \frac{1}{2}$ is just as much a life-year as x to $x + 1$ is, and the reasoning used in Chapter 2 can be applied to this life-year. The age at the beginning of the rate year is $x - \frac{1}{2}$ and

$$\mathring{l}_{x - \frac{1}{2}} = \sum^{x-1} b_{(y)} + \sum^{x-1} n_{(y)} - \sum^{x-1} w_{(y)} - \sum^{x-1} \theta_{(y)} - \sum^{x-1} e_{(y)}$$

and $\quad E_{x - \frac{1}{2}} = \mathring{l}_{x - \frac{1}{2}} + \frac{1}{2}b_{(x)} - \frac{1}{2}w_{(x)} - \frac{1}{2}e_{(x)} + \frac{1}{2}n_{(x)}$

4.4 This will be recognized as the same as the E_x form of (2.3) except that the age definition is different. The reader should not be confused by the presence in the same formula of two suffixes $x - \frac{1}{2}$ and (x): the symbol (x) is a convention for tabulation; in the formula it can be read as '$x - \frac{1}{2}$ at commencement of rate interval'.

4.5 The resulting rate, of course, is $\mathring{q}_{x - \frac{1}{2}}$ and rates for integral ages would have to be obtained by interpolation, though this itself may be part of the graduation process, a subject which is dealt with in later chapters.

4.6 As our next example we suppose that only $b_{(x)}$ and $e_{(x)}$ were tabulated according to nearest age x and that n_x, w_x and θ_x were tabulated according to age last birthday. On the assumption that, generally, b_x and e_x are linear functions of x, over short ranges of x, it will be possible to estimate b_x and e_x from tabulated values of $b_{(x)}$ and $e_{(x)}$ on the basis that

$$b_x \doteqdot \frac{1}{2}[b_{(x)} + b_{(x+1)}] \quad \text{and} \quad e_x \doteqdot \frac{1}{2}[e_{(x)} + e_{(x+1)}]$$

and therefore

$$\mathring{l}_x = \sum^{x-1} b_{(y)} + \frac{1}{2}b_{(x)} + \sum^{x-1} n_y - \sum^{x-1} w_y - \sum^{x-1} \theta_y - \sum^{x-1} e_{(y)} - \frac{1}{2}e_{(x)}$$

4.7 To obtain E_x, the adjustment required in respect of lives existing at the beginning of the investigation is an addition of the contribution to E_x from the $\frac{1}{2}b_{(x)}$ aged x to $x + \frac{1}{2}$ and the $\frac{1}{2}b_{(x+1)}$ aged $x + \frac{1}{2}$ to $x + 1$ not included in $\mathring{l}_x$, since they come under observation between age x and age $x + 1$. Assuming that on the average the former were age $x + \frac{1}{4}$

and the latter age $x + \frac{3}{4}$ at the beginning of the period of investigation, then the addition is $\frac{3}{4}(\frac{1}{2}b_{(x)}) + \frac{1}{4}(\frac{1}{2}b_{(x+1)})$. Similarly $\frac{3}{8}e_{(x)} + \frac{1}{8}e_{(x+1)}$ must be deducted. Hence,

$$E_x = \overset{\circ}{l}_x + \tfrac{3}{8}b_{(x)} + \tfrac{1}{8}b_{(x+1)} + \tfrac{1}{2}n_x - \tfrac{1}{2}w_x - \tfrac{3}{8}e_{(x)} - \tfrac{1}{8}e_{(x+1)}$$

$$= \sum^{x-1} b_{(y)} + \tfrac{3}{8}b_{(x)} + \tfrac{1}{8}b_{(x+1)} + \sum^{x-1} n_y + \tfrac{1}{2}n_x - \sum^{x-1} w_y - \tfrac{1}{2}w_x$$

$$- \sum^{x-1} \theta_y - \sum^{x-1} e_{(y)} - \tfrac{7}{8}e_{(x)} - \tfrac{1}{8}e_{(x+1)}$$

and

$$E_x - E_{x-1} = \tfrac{1}{8}(b_{(x-1)} + 6b_{(x)} + b_{(x+1)}) + \tfrac{1}{2}(n_{x-1} + n_x)$$

$$- \tfrac{1}{2}(w_{x-1} + w_x) - \tfrac{1}{8}(e_{(x-1)} + 6e_{(x)} + e_{(x+1)}) - \theta_{x-1}$$

4.8 In practice $b_{(x)}$ and $e_{(x)}$ would probably be substituted for the b and e expressions respectively, giving

$$E_x - E_{x-1} = b_{(x)} + \tfrac{1}{2}(n_{x-1} + n_x) - \tfrac{1}{2}(w_{x-1} + w_x) - e_{(x)} - \theta_{x-1}$$

4.9 This is equivalent to assuming that the lives $b_{(x)}$ are on average aged x exactly and hence exposed for the full year of age x to $x + 1$ (a more restrictive assumption than that of para. 4.6). Without the knowledge of the distribution of the birthdays of $b_{(x)}$ over the calendar year for successive values of x it is not possible to say which approximation is the more accurate. In general when assumptions of this kind are being used they should be tested. Sometimes this may mean actual examination of the data. At other times the fact that the data are already grouped may preclude examination. In the latter case general reasoning must be used. The reader should not assume that the more complicated formula is always the more accurate; apparent precision may be spurious, especially where numbers are small.

4.10 As a third example consider a tabulation in which b_x, n_x, w_x and e_x are given according to age x last birthday, but the deaths are given for nearest age at death. The simplest procedure would be to assume that the deaths θ_x at age x last birthday are equal to $\frac{1}{2}(\theta_{(x)} + \theta_{(x+1)})$ and then use formula (2.11) to obtain the exposed to risk for rates for integral ages. An objection that is sometimes raised against this procedure is that because the number of deaths at a single age is small, the averaging of them might produce serious error in allocation between adjacent ages. This seems to be unlikely. The number of deaths is always small compared with the exposed, so a simple averaging procedure applied to the irregular numbers of deaths should not cause much distortion. Moreover, if the rates are going to be graduated (smoothed) for the purpose of constructing a life table, the objection is even less serious. However, it is undesirable to risk creating irregularities in the progression of the rates if this can be avoided. Further, if the rates are required for some purpose that depends on accuracy at individual ages, it might be better not to average the deaths, but to average all the other items, assuming that the resultant percentage error in E will be small. Thus

$$b'_{(x)} = \tfrac{1}{2}(b_{x-1} + b_x)$$

$$n'_{(x)} = \tfrac{1}{2}(n_{x-1} + n_x) \text{ etc.}$$

Using $b'_{(x)}$, $n'_{(x)}$, $w'_{(x)}$, $e'_{(x)}$ and $\theta'_{(x)}$, rates for half ages would be obtained directly. There is no certainty that the second method will produce smoother rates, but it is probable that it will.

(2) Non-uniform distributions

4.11 In obtaining formula (2.11) it was assumed that all the groups of lives b_x, n_x, w_x and e_x were distributed uniformly over the life-year. For example, for b_x it was assumed that birthdays were distributed uniformly over the calendar year so that these lives entered the investigation on the average half-way through the life-year x to $x+1$, contributing $\tfrac{1}{2}b_x$ to E_x. A similar assumption was made for each of the other groups of lives, i.e. that dates of entry to or exit from exposure were evenly distributed over the rate-year. In practice this assumption should be tested by means of a sample of the data. Suppose that a sample of new entrants showed that on the average they entered 3 months before the next birthday. The addition in respect of new entrants to $\overset{\circ}{l}_x$ to obtain E_x would now be $\tfrac{1}{4}n_x$ and not $\tfrac{1}{2}n_x$. If the remaining assumptions are unchanged, the difference formula would be

$$E_x - E_{x-1} = \tfrac{1}{2}(b_{x-1} + b_x) + \tfrac{1}{4}(3n_{x-1} + n_x)$$

$$- \tfrac{1}{2}(w_{x-1} + w_x) - \tfrac{1}{2}(e_{x-1} + e_x) - \theta_{x-1}$$

If, alternatively, it was stated that new entrants entered on the average on 1 October of each year, this would not help to define their exposure, since at that date they could still be distributed uniformly over the age interval x to $x + 1$. It will be seen later, however, that this information would affect a formula based on the calendar year as the rate-year. The important aspect on which to focus attention is the distribution over the rate interval.

THE CALENDAR-YEAR RATE INTERVAL

(1) Alternative age groupings

4.12 In Chapter 3 the use of the calendar-year rate interval was illustrated, given a tabulation according to nearest age on 1 January. Other age classifications could, however, be used. For example, consider the classification according to age x last birthday on 1 January. The rate $\mathring{q}_{(x)}$ can now be assumed to be an estimate of the rate for the average age of this group at 1 January, i.e. q_{x+k}, $0 < k < 1$. In practice k is usually taken as $\frac{1}{2}$, but such an assumption should be tested against an actual distribution.

4.13 A tabulation sometimes encountered in practice is that based on nearest age at entry into assurance and the calendar year of entry or exit. Thus, for a period of investigation 1 January 1970 to 31 December 1974, we have

$b_{(x)}$ $x = (1970 - \text{year of entry}) + \text{nearest age at entry};$

$e_{(x)}$ $x = (1975 - \text{year of entry}) + \text{nearest age at entry};$

$n_{(x)}$ $x = \text{nearest age at entry};$

$\left. \begin{array}{l} w_{(x)} \\ \theta_{(x)} \end{array} \right\}$ $x = (\text{year of exit} - \text{year of entry}) + \text{nearest age at entry}.$

4.14 Consider $\theta_{(x)}$. These are the deaths during a calendar year, the age scheduled being the nearest age on the policy anniversary falling in that calendar year. Hence the rate-year is the calendar year and $\mathring{q}_{(x)}$ measures the rate of diminution by death, over a calendar year, of a group of lives that existed on 1 January and were nearest age x on the next policy anniversary. $E_{(x)}$ is the initial exposed to risk measured in calendar-year units, the age being nearest age on the policy anniversary falling in the calendar year and not nearest age x on 1 January as illustrated in Chapter 3. The point to be stressed is that this is a group of lives being traced over a calendar year or until death. The manner in which the group is classified depends on the form of the data, e.g. age last birthday on 1 January, nearest age on 1 April, nearest age on date of marriage anniversary or, as in the present illustration, nearest age on policy anniversary. Whatever the classification, the resulting $\mathring{q}_{(x)}$ can then be regarded as an estimate of q_{x+k}, where $x + k$ is the average age of the group on 1 January. Using the definition of deaths given in 4.13, i.e. classifying by nearest age x on policy anniversary falling in the calendar year of death, and assuming that the average age on the policy anniversary is x and that the average policy anniversary is 1 July, then the average age on 1 January is $x - \frac{1}{2}$, for here $k = -\frac{1}{2}$, and

$$\mathring{q}_{(x)} \doteqdot q_{x-\frac{1}{2}}$$

4.15 The exposed to risk formula is indentical in form to (3.6). The difference formula can be obtained directly as follows:

	$E_{(x-1)}$	$E_{(x)}$	$E_{(x)} - E_{(x-1)}$
$b_{(x)}$	—	1	$b_{(x)}$
$n_{(x-1)}$	$\frac{1}{2}$	1	$+\frac{1}{2}n_{(x-1)}$
$n_{(x)}$	—	$\frac{1}{2}$	$+\frac{1}{2}n_{(x)}$
$w_{(x-1)}$	$\frac{1}{2}$	—	$-\frac{1}{2}w_{(x-1)}$
$w_{(x)}$	1	$\frac{1}{2}$	$-\frac{1}{2}w_{(x)}$
$e_{(x)}$	1	—	$-e_{(x)}$
$\theta_{(x-1)}$	1	—	$-\theta_{(x-1)}$

$$E_{(x)} - E_{(x-1)} = b_{(x)} + \tfrac{1}{2}(n_{(x-1)} + n_{(x)}) - \tfrac{1}{2}(w_{(x-1)} + w_{(x)}) - e_{(x)} - \theta_{(x-1)}$$

$$\mathring{q}_{(x)} = \frac{\theta_{(x)}}{E_{(x)}} \doteqdot \mathring{q}_{x-\frac{1}{2}}$$

(2) Non-uniform distribution of increments and decrements

4.16 We may now consider the actual distributions of new entrants, withdrawals and deaths over the calendar year. In deriving formula (3.3) it was assumed that these numbers were distributed uniformly. Hence, for example, $n_{(x-1)}$ contributed on the average $\frac{1}{2}$ each to $E_{(x-1)}$ and 1 each to $E_{(x)}$ provided that they did not withdraw or die before the end of either the calendar years of entry or the following year. Suppose that we are told that entrants enter on 1 September, then the addition to $\mathring{l}_{(x)}$ to derive $E_{(x)}$ would be $\frac{1}{3}n_{(x)}$. Considering the difference formula, $n_{(x-1)}$ will contribute $\frac{1}{3}$ each to $E_{(x-1)}$ and 1 each to $E_{(x)}$, while $n_{(x)}$ will contribute nil to $E_{(x-1)}$ and $\frac{1}{3}$ each to $E_{(x)}$, and the term for new entrants in the difference formula will be $+\frac{1}{3}(2n_{(x-1)}+n_{(x)})$. It is worth noting that any distribution for which the average time of entry or exit is the middle of the calendar year will give the same formula as that based on a uniform distribution.

THE POLICY-YEAR RATE INTERVAL

(1) Alternative age groupings

4.17 No new principles come into play. In Chapter 3 the age grouping used was the nearest age on the policy anniversary, which is the beginning of a rate-year. As in the calendar-year method, age last birthday or age next birthday could be used and the resulting $\mathring{q}_{(x)}$ would refer to the average of such an age group, say $x+\frac{1}{2}$ and $x-\frac{1}{2}$ respectively.

4.18 Nearest age at the previous policy anniversary is the same as nearest age at entry plus curtate duration. Suppose, however, that $b_{(x)}$ and $e_{(x)}$ are tabulated according to nearest age at entry plus nearest duration. With no further information, the most reasonable assumption would be that $\frac{1}{2}b_{(x)}$ were nearest age $x-1$ and $\frac{1}{2}b_{(x)}$ nearest age x at the previous policy anniversary, but when making adjustments, it must be remembered that this assumption implies that the former will enter during the second half of the policy year $(x-1)$ while the latter will enter during the first half of the policy year (x). Hence the table for deriving the difference formula would read as Table 4.1,

Table 4.1

	Age on previous policy anniversary	$E_{(x-1)}$	$E_{(x)}$	$E_{(x)}-E_{(x-1)}$
$\frac{1}{2}b_{(x-1)}$	$(x-2)$	1	1	nil
$\frac{1}{2}b_{(x-1)}$	$(x-1)$	$\frac{3}{4}$	1	$\frac{1}{8}b_{(x-1)}$
$\frac{1}{2}b_{(x)}$	$(x-1)$	$\frac{1}{4}$	1	$\frac{3}{4}b_{(x)}$
$\frac{1}{2}b_{(x)}$	(x)	—	$\frac{3}{4}$	
$\frac{1}{2}b_{(x+1)}$	(x)	—	$\frac{1}{4}$	$\frac{1}{8}b_{(x+1)}$
$\frac{1}{2}b_{(x+1)}$	$(x+1)$	—	—	nil

giving for the b-term

$$+\tfrac{1}{8}(b_{(x-1)}+6b_{(x)}+b_{(x+1)})$$

Similarly the e-term would be

$$-\tfrac{1}{8}(e_{(x-1)} + 6e_{(x)} + e_{(x+1)})$$

4.19   If all the items were tabulated according to nearest age at entry plus nearest duration, then the deaths $\theta_{(x)}$ would be distributed over a year stretching from the middle of policy year $(x-1)$ to the middle of policy year (x), i.e. the policy anniversary on which nearest age was attained would fall in the middle of the rate-year. This rate-year is still a 'policy year' in the same sense as $x - \tfrac{1}{2}$ to $x + \tfrac{1}{2}$ was regarded as a 'life-year'. As indicated below in para. 4.20, $n_{(x)}$ must now be regarded as entering half-way through this 'policy' rate-year. Formula (3.9) must therefore be adjusted for this (in the difference formula the term will be $\tfrac{1}{2}(n_{(x-1)} + n_{(x)})$) and for the different definitions of $b_{(x)}$, $e_{(x)}$, $w_{(x)}$ and $\theta_{(x)}$. The resulting $\mathring{q}_{(x)}$ will refer to the average age at the start of the rate-year, i.e. at the midpoint of the policy year $(x-1)$, say $x - \tfrac{1}{2}$. The reader should work this out in detail for himself using the methods of Chapter 3.

(2) Non-uniform distributions

4.20   As before, we are interested in the distribution of entries and exits over the rate interval, in this case the policy year. New entrants must always enter at the same point in the rate-year; for example, at the start when the age is given as nearest age at entry plus curtate duration, and at the midpoint of the rate year when the age is given as nearest age at entry plus nearest duration. Clearly in the latter case the new entrants will enter half-way through the rate-year, which might be denoted by $(x) - \tfrac{1}{2}$ to $(x) + \tfrac{1}{2}$.

4.21   Consider the normal policy-year method, where the rate year is the policy year (x), i.e. the deaths $\theta_{(x)}$ are nearest age x at the beginning of the policy year of death. Suppose that we are told that all lives enter on 1 October. Since new entrants must enter at the beginning of a policy year, they are not affected. Also the information does not restrict the distribution of withdrawals, so that they will not be affected. However, $b_{(x)}$ and $e_{(x)}$ are affected, since the previous policy anniversary will be 1 October, and hence, for example, $b_{(x-1)}$ will contribute $\tfrac{3}{4}$ each to $E_{(x-1)}$ and 1 each to $E_{(x)}$, and $b_{(x)}$ will contribute nil to $E_{(x-1)}$ and $\tfrac{3}{4}$ each to $E_{(x)}$. The b-term in the difference formula will then be $\tfrac{1}{4}(b_{(x-1)} + 3b_{(x)})$ instead of $\tfrac{1}{2}(b_{(x-1)} + b_{(x)})$. The addition to $\mathring{l}_{(x)}$ to obtain $E_{(x)}$ will be $\tfrac{3}{4}b_{(x)}$. Similarly the corresponding e-terms will be $-\tfrac{1}{4}(e_{(x-1)} + 3e_{(x)})$ and $-\tfrac{3}{4}e_{(x)}$ respectively.

4.22 If withdrawals are not to be assumed to be uniformly distributed, then we require some information about the distribution. (We ought not to make any presumption of uniformity without some knowledge of distribution.) Generally suppose that withdrawals on the average withdraw at time f from the policy anniversary prior to withdrawal, $0 \leq f < 1$. Then the difference table would read as Table 4.2,

Table 4.2

	$E_{(x-1)}$	$E_{(x)}$	$E_{(x)} - E_{(x-1)}$
$w_{(x-1)}$	f	—	$-f w_{(x-1)}$
$w_{(x)}$	1	f	$-(1-f) w_{(x)}$

giving $-(f w_{(x-1)} + (1-f) w_{(x)})$ for the w-term in the difference formula.
4.23 The mechanics of these methods are very simple, and the student should have no difficulty in dealing with any special case that may arise. Some readers may find it helpful to represent the exposures in diagrammatic form, as in the simple case illustrated in Chapter 3. As an example, the form of tabulation described in para. 4.18 is demonstrated in Figure 4.1.

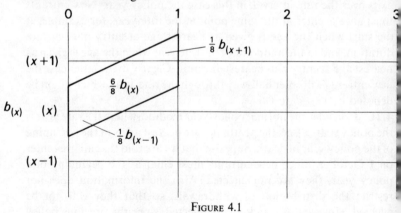

FIGURE 4.1

The Period of Investigation

4.24 Hitherto the period of investigation has been taken as an integral number of calendar years, often 5.
4.25 In the case of the life-year method a period that has sometimes

been used is one ranging from the birthday in, say, calendar year K to the birthday in, say, calendar year $K + T$—for example, from the birthday in 1970 to the birthday in 1975. The term b_x would now be the lives existing on their xth birthday in 1970, while e_x would be those existing on their xth birthday in 1975; n_x, w_x and θ_x would be tabulated as before according to age last birthday at entry or exit, but they would be limited to entrants or exits between the xth birthday in 1970 and the xth birthday in 1975, i.e. their xth birthday will fall in any of the calendar years 1970 to 1974 inclusive. However, although these items would be numerically smaller than if all the movements in the full 6 years were recorded, they appear with the same coefficients in the difference formula, since the age tabulation is unchanged. The only items in the formula which require different coefficients from those derived in Chapter 2 are b_x and e_x, since they now enter at the start of the life-year x or leave at the end of the life-year $x - 1$. Hence, for b and e, the difference table would read as Table 4.3,

Table 4.3

	E_{x-1}	E_x	$E_x - E_{x-1}$
b_{x-1}	1	1	nil
b_x	—	1	b_x
e_{x-1}	—	—	nil
e_x	1	—	$-e_x$

and the difference formula would be

$$E_x - E_{x-1} = b_x + \tfrac{1}{2}(n_{x-1} + n_x) - \tfrac{1}{2}(w_{x-1} + w_x) - e_x - \theta_{x-1}$$

4.26 If E_x is obtained directly from $\mathring{l}_x$, then

$$\mathring{l}_x = \sum^x b_y + \sum^{x-1} n_y - \sum^{x-1} w_y - \sum^{x-1} \theta_y - \sum^x e_y$$

and to obtain E_x only $\tfrac{1}{2}(n_x - w_x)$ must be added.

This formula is similar in form to the calendar-year formula, since the definitions of b, n, w, θ and e are the same *in relation to the rate-year*.

4.27 A similar tabulation can arise from the use of the policy year as the rate-year if the period of observation is taken from the policy anniversary in 1970 to the policy anniversary in 1975; $b_{(x)}$ will now be all the lives existing on their policy anniversary in 1970 when they were nearest age x. Similarly $e_{(x)}$ will be those existing on the policy anniversary in 1975 when they were nearest age x. The terms $n_{(x)}$, $w_{(x)}$

and $\theta_{(x)}$ will again be tabulated according to nearest age at entry or nearest age at the policy anniversary previous to exit, but they will be limited to those for whom the policy anniversary on which they were nearest age x fell in the calendar years 1970 to 1974 inclusive. Care must be exercised over the new entrants during 1970, since they could be included in either $b_{(x)}$ or $n_{(x)}$. They must not be counted twice.

4.28 The difference formula is

$$E_{(x)} - E_{(x-1)} = b_{(x)} + n_{(x)} - \tfrac{1}{2}(w_{(x-1)} + w_{(x)}) - e_{(x)} - \theta_{(x-1)}$$

The reader is again advised to derive this formula in detail by means of the methods from Chapter 3.

Example 4.1

It is required to investigate the mortality experience of a large Assurance Office over the calendar year 1978, and the tabulations and formulae for $E^c_{(x)}$ scheduled below are suggested for obtaining m-type rates of mortality.

The number of policies in force on 1 January 1978 are denoted by $_0P_x$ and those on 31 December 1978 by $_1P_x$. The number of policies in force on the birthday of lives who attain exact age x during 1978 are denoted by $\mathring{l}_x$ and the number of policies in force on lives who attain the policy anniversary at which they were nearest age x by $\mathring{l}_{(x)}$. Death claims during 1978 are denoted by θ_x.

		Exposed to risk	
Code	$E^c_{(x)}$	Definition of x	
		$_0P_x$	$_1P_x$
A	$\tfrac{1}{2}(_0P_x + {_1P_x})$	1978 minus calendar year of birth	1979 minus calendar year of birth
B	$\tfrac{1}{2}(_0P_x + {_1P_{x+1}})$	1978 minus calendar year of birth	1979 minus calendar year of birth
C	$\tfrac{1}{2}(_0P_x + {_1P_x})$	Nearest age on 1 January 1978	Nearest age on 31 December 1978
D	$\tfrac{1}{2}(_0P_x + {_1P_{x+1}})$	Nearest age on 1 January 1978	Nearest age on 31 December 1978
E	$\tfrac{1}{2}(_0P_x + {_1P_x})$	Nearest age on policy anniversary in 1977	Nearest age on policy anniversary in 1978
F	$\tfrac{1}{2}(_0P_x + {_1P_{x+1}})$	Nearest age on policy anniversary in 1977	Nearest age on policy anniversary in 1978
G	$\mathring{l}_x$		
H	$\mathring{l}_{(x)}$		

Deaths

Code	Definitions of x in θ_x
1	1978 minus calendar year of birth
2	Nearest age at entry plus curtate duration at death
3	Age next birthday at death
4	Nearest age on 1 January 1978
5	Nearest age at death
6	Nearest age at entry plus curtate duration at 1 January 1978
7	Nearest age at entry plus nearest duration at death

Using the code letters and numbers provided, associate with each $E^c_{(x)}$ the most suitable θ_x to obtain $\mathring{m}_x$. Give brief explanatory notes and state as precisely as possible the age description of the lives to which each $\mathring{m}_x$ may be considered to apply.

Dealing with the formulae in the order given

A The ages of $_0P_x$ and $_1P_x$ are x next birthday, and the formula gives an estimate of the mean population during the calendar year of lives between exact age $x-1$ and exact age x.

The numerator that we require is therefore the deaths at age x next birthday (code 3) and the estimate of $\mathring{m}_x$ is the central rate for exact age $x-1$.

B $_1P_{x+1}$ are the survivors of $_0P_x$ (age x next birthday on 1 January). The formula therefore gives us the mean population of lives who were age x next birthday on 1 January. The corresponding deaths are those x next birthday on 1 January (i.e. code 1) and the estimate of $\mathring{m}_x$ is for lives age x next birthday on 1 January or for, say, exact age $x-\frac{1}{2}$.

C The formula is analogous to A and gives an estimate of the mean population during 1978 between exact age $x-\frac{1}{2}$ and exact age $x+\frac{1}{2}$. Therefore the deaths we require are the deaths occurring between these ages, i.e. the deaths at nearest age x (code 5). The resulting $\mathring{m}_x$ is for exact age $x-\frac{1}{2}$.

D This formula corresponds to B except that the lives are nearest age x on 1 January. We therefore require the deaths according to nearest age x on 1 January (code 4) and the resulting $\mathring{m}_x$ is for a body of lives nearest age x, say exact age x subject to investigation.

E This formula is a census formula similar to A and C. The age definition, however, is nearest age at the previous policy anniversary and we require the deaths according to nearest age at policy anniversary previous to date of death (code 2). The resulting m-type rate is for a policy year, although the time interval of the investigation is the calendar year, and the age definition at the beginning of the policy year is nearest age x. Assuming that the average age is close to x, we can take this rate as an estimate of $\mathring{m}_x$ for exact age x.

F This formula corresponds to B and D in giving a value for $\mathring{m}_x$ over a calendar year in respect of a group of lives whose age is fixed at 1 January. In this case the age is nearest age x at previous policy anniversary or, say, exact age $x + \frac{1}{2}$ on 1 January. The deaths are those occurring out of $_0P_x$, i.e. the deaths during 1978 who were nearest age x on policy anniversary in 1977 (code 6).

G $\mathring{l}_x$ is the number of policies on lives who attain exact age during 1978. It can be taken as an estimate of the mean population between exact age $x - \frac{1}{2}$ and $x + \frac{1}{2}$, and hence for an estimate of $\mathring{m}_{x - \frac{1}{2}}$ we require the deaths between these two ages, i.e. the deaths according to nearest age x at death (code 5).

H $\mathring{l}_{(x)}$ is the number of policies on lives who attain the policy anniversary during 1978 on which they were nearest age x. It can be taken as an estimate of the mean population between the midpoint of the policy year at the end of which the lives were nearest age x and the midpoint of the next policy year. We require the corresponding deaths, i.e. the deaths during 1978 who were nearest age x at the policy anniversary nearest to death (code 7).

EXERCISES FOR CHAPTER FOUR

1 The mortality of a group of insured lives is to be investigated. The following list gives some possible age definitions by which the deaths might be grouped.

(a) Age next birthday at entry plus calendar year of death minus calendar year of entry.

(b) Age at the birthday in the calendar year of entry plus calendar year of death minus calendar year of entry.

(c) Age at the birthday in the calendar year of death.

(d) Age at the birthday in the policy year of death.

(e) Age next birthday at entry plus curtate duration at death.

(f) Age at the birthday in the calendar year of entry plus curtate duration at death.

(g) Age next birthday at the policy anniversary falling in the calendar year of death.

(h) Age nearest birthday at 1 January falling in the policy year of death.

(i) Age nearest birthday at the policy anniversary preceding 1 January falling in the calendar year of death.

(j) Age nearest birthday at 1 January in the calendar year of entry plus curtate duration at death.

You are asked:

(1) To state in each case the type of rate-year corresponding to the definition of age.

(2) To determine in each case, the average age $(x+f)$ for which the value of $\mathring{q}_{x+f}$ estimated from data grouped according to age x, as defined above, applies. You should state any assumptions which you make.

2   In each of the following cases, derive suitable exposed to risk formulae for the calculation of q-type mortality rates, stating to what ages the resulting rates relate and any assumptions you make.

Calculate values for $\mathring{q}_x$ for as many ages as possible. In each case the investigation covers the 5 calendar years 1970–4 inclusive.

(a)

Age	In force on 1.1.70	In force on 31.12.74	New entrants	Deaths	Withdrawals
x	b_x	e_x	n_x	θ_x	w_x
40	2650	2500	400	25	480
41	2500	2240	480	28	580
42	2420	2500	440	20	700

$E_{40} = 11{,}300$; b_x, w_x, and θ_x are scheduled according to age x *last* birthday; and e_x and n_x are scheduled according to age x *nearest* birthday.

(b)

x	b_x	e_x	n_x	θ_x	w_x
55	267	259	46	15	46
56	249	256	40	17	38
57	253	245	34	19	40
58	246	253	28	22	32
59	266	228	34	25	30

$E_{55} = 1{,}350$. On average, entry occurs 3 months before a birthday. All items are scheduled according to age x *nearest* birthday.

3   In an aggregate experience which is to be investigated from 1 January 1970 to 31 December 1974, the following information is given on the cards supplied. State what assumptions you would make and the resulting ages under which cases enter and leave the experience. Give the exposed to risk formula and the formula for $\mathring{q}_x$. Schedule the cases, placing in brackets against the numbers inserted the case letters of those included. By way of example, work out the exposed to risk at the different ages and the rate of mortality at age 44, assuming the cases in Table 4.4 to constitute the entire data.

Table 4.4

Case	Age next birthday at date of assurance	Year of entry into assurance	Year and mode of exit
A	42	1971	
B	39	1964	1970 Died
C	38	1962	1970 Withdrew
D	43	1971	1974 Died
E	45	1974	
F	40	1963	1969 Withdrew
G	37	1963	1971 Withdrew
H	44	1972	1973 Withdrew
I	44	1971	1972 Died
J	45	1958	1969 Died
K	38	1964	
L	42	1971	
M	43	1970	
N	43	1968	1970 Withdrew

4 Data set out in Table 4.5 are available for a mortality investigation covering the period 1 July 1970 to 31 December 1975.

Table 4.5

Age x	P_x^1	d_x	P_x^2	n_x	θ_x	w_x	P_x^3
49	—	—	—	600	2	5	—
50	901	17	337	1,000	10	95	228
51	1,122	32	1,842	1,439	30	219	1,892
52	1,533	54	1,600	1,566	42	381	1,926
53	1,929	60	1,932	1,164	58	293	2,140
54	2,082	78	2,362	865	75	152	2,611
55	1,987	83	2,287	983	82	331	2,571

The minimum age at entry is 50.

P_x^1 The number of lives aged x last birthday on 1 July 1970.

d_x The number of deaths in the period 1 July 1970 to 31 December 1972 aged x last birthday at death.

P_x^2 The number of lives aged x nearest birthday on 1 January 1973.

n_x The number of entrants in 1973, 1974 and 1975 aged x nearest birthday on 1 January prior to entry. Most of these entries took place in September of each year.

θ_x The number of deaths in 1973, 1974 and 1975 aged x nearest birthday on 1 January before death.

w_x The number of withdrawals in 1973, 1974 and 1975 aged x last birthday on 1 January before withdrawal.

P_x^3 The number of lives aged x nearest birthday on 31 December 1975.

Explain, giving formulae, how you would calculate $\mathring{q}_x$, using all the available data for the periods:

(a) 1 July 1970 to 31 December 1972.
(b) 1 January 1973 to 31 December 1975.
(c) 1 July 1970 to 31 December 1975.

Use your formulae to calculate $\mathring{q}_{52}$ for each period.

CHAPTER FIVE

MORTALITY RATES BY AGE AND DURATION

Introduction

5.1 In actuarial literature rates according to both age and duration from entry into assurance are usually referred to as 'select' rates. This terminology expresses the fact that, at entry, assured lives are 'select' in the sense that they have, at that time, either undergone a medical examination or they have answered satisfactorily a searching medical questionnaire. The effect of this selection is that, during the first policy year, mortality is much lighter than the average mortality of all assured lives at the same attained age. The mortality advantage diminishes in significance as duration increases, and after a relatively short period (3 to 5 years) the practical effect is negligible. The period for which the duration effect is significant is known as the select period, and if, for example, this period were 5 years, select rates would be obtained for each age at entry and durations 0, 1, 2, 3, 4, these numbers denoting the exact duration at the beginning of the 1st, 2nd, 3rd, 4th and 5th policy years respectively. For durations 5 and over rates according to age only would be required, and they are referred to as the 'ultimate' rates to indicate that these are rates experienced beyond the select period. In practice the actual length of the select period would be determined experimentally, the determining factor being the practical effect of differing select periods on the values of annuities and premiums. The actuary is concerned only with the practical consequences of selection and is not interested in attempting to estimate precisely how long a duration effect actually persists, which would be extremely difficult, as well as valueless in practical terms.

5.2 Other examples of rates in respect of which the duration effect may be important are the following: the mortality rates of annuitants, the mortality rates of pensioners forced to retire through ill-health (duration being measured from the date of retirement), fertility rates (duration being reckoned from the date of marriage), and rates of mortality of patients radically treated for cancer (or other diseases of slow progression), the duration being counted from the date of treatment. Annuitants do not undergo a medical examination, but investigation shows that the duration effect is very significant in the early years, and hence it is concluded (as might be expected) that annuitants exercise a strong degree of self-selection. Ill-health pensioners exhibit what has been sometimes called 'reverse selection', because the mortality during the early years of duration is much heavier than that for ill-health pensioners of the same attained age who retired longer ago and from whom those in the poorest health have been removed by death. Fertility rates vary with both age and duration of marriage. This is the same as saying that age at marriage and duration of marriage are the important factors, and it is in this form that specific fertility rates are usually expressed, especially for use in projection calculations.

5.3   In this chapter we shall confine ourselves to the problem of deriving rates of mortality, experienced by a specified population, according to age and duration from entry to assurance. The same principles apply, however, to the derivation of other types of rates, such as those mentioned above and, indeed, any rates from any type of population if the determining factors are age and duration from some event other than birth. This last exception is made because age itself is duration from birth. The essential problem, therefore, is how to deal with two dimensions of time which have their separate effect upon mortality or some other risk that is being measured.

Exposed to risk formulae

5.4   Since rates are required for age at entry and duration since entry, an obvious procedure would be to classify the population according to age at entry, and then for each age at entry to obtain rates for policy years, i.e. the rate-year is the policy year. Duration would be treated simply as the 'age' of the policy, using exactly the same principles as those used in the previous chapters. For example, consider age at entry nearest age x and suppose that for a specified period of investigation the following data are available for all values of x:

$b_{[x]r}$ the beginners who were nearest age x at entry to assurance and curtate duration r (i.e. exact duration r at the previous policy anniversary) at the beginning of the period;

$n_{[x]}$ new entrants during the period nearest age x at entry;

$w_{[x]r}$ and $\theta_{[x]r}$ withdrawals and deaths during the period, nearest age x at entry and curtate duration r at date of exit;

$e_{[x]r}$ enders nearest age x at entry and curtate duration r at the end of the period.

The values of r range from 0 to an upper value determined only by the data, since at this stage we are not considering the question of a limited period during which duration is important, i.e. a limited select period.

5.5 Let $\mathring{l}_{[x]r}$ denote the lives (or policies) nearest age x at entry who attain exact duration r during the period of investigation.

5.6 Then using familiar arguments

$$\mathring{l}_{[x]r} = \sum_{t=0}^{r-1} b_{[x]t} + n_{[x]} - \sum_{t=0}^{r-1} w_{[x]t} - \sum_{t=0}^{r-1} \theta_{[x]t} - \sum_{t=0}^{r-1} e_{[x]t}$$

5.7 $E_{[x]r}$ will denote the exposed to risk in respect of the $(r+1)$th policy year, i.e. the duration r to $r+1$ for lives nearest age x at entry. This can be obtained by adjusting $\mathring{l}_{[x]r}$ to allow for beginners who entered after duration r but before duration $r+1$, and for exits who left the investigation between durations r and $r+1$. Assuming a uniform distribution of entrants and exits over the policy year

$$E_{[x]r} = \mathring{l}_{[x]r} + \tfrac{1}{2}b_{[x]r} - \tfrac{1}{2}w_{[x]r} - \tfrac{1}{2}e_{[x]r}$$

and

$$E^c_{[x]r} = E_{[x]r} - \tfrac{1}{2}\theta_{[x]r}$$

Differencing

$$E_{[x]r} - E_{[x]r-1} = \tfrac{1}{2}(b_{[x]r-1} + b_{[x]r}) - \tfrac{1}{2}(w_{[x]r-1} + w_{[x]r})$$
$$- \tfrac{1}{2}(e_{[x]r-1} + e_{[x]r}) - \theta_{[x]r-1} \quad (5.1)$$

and the starting point is given by

$$E_{[x]0} = \tfrac{1}{2}b_{[x]0} + n_{[x]} - \tfrac{1}{2}w_{[x]0} - \tfrac{1}{2}e_{[x]0}$$

5.8 In actuarial literature the 0 is usually omitted, only 1, 2, etc., being used in this notation, thus,

$$E_{[x]} = \tfrac{1}{2}b_{[x]} + n_{[x]} - \tfrac{1}{2}w_{[x]} - \tfrac{1}{2}e_{[x]} \quad (5.2)$$

5.9 The rate $\mathring{q}_{[x]r} = \left(\dfrac{\theta_{[x]r}}{E_{[x]r}}\right)$ is strictly the rate for the $(r+1)$th policy year in respect of lives (or policies) nearest age x at entry to assurance.

5.10   The average age at entry is usually assumed to be exactly x (though this should be tested) and the rate is regarded as applying to that exact age at entry.

5.11   Other age definitions can be used. For example, it might be more convenient to tabulate the lives according to age x last birthday at entry so that

$$\mathring{q}_{[x]r} \doteqdot \mathring{q}_{[x+k]r} \, 0 < k < 1$$

k being usually taken at $\frac{1}{2}$, though such an assumption ought to be tested by examination of the data.

Exposed to risk formula for ultimate rates

5.12   Assume that the select period is limited to s years, so that $E_{[x]r}$ is required for $r = 0, 1, 2$ etc. to $s-1$, and $E_{(y)}(y = x+r)$ is required for $r \geq s$. The data would now be obtained in the form:

$n_{[x]}$ according to nearest age at entry for all x;

$\left.\begin{array}{l} b_{[x]r} \\ e_{[x]r} \\ w_{[x]r} \\ \theta_{[x]r} \end{array}\right\}$ for all ages at entry and $r = 0, 1, 2$ etc. to $s-1$, x being nearest age at entry and r curtate duration at entry or exit;

$b_{(y)}, e_{(y)}, w_{(y)}, \theta_{(y)}$ for all $y = x+r, r \geq s$.

Obviously, $E_{[x]r}$, $r = 0, 1$ to $s-1$ can be obtained by means of the formulae of the previous paragraphs and it remains to develop formulae for obtaining $E_{(y)}$.

5.13   The expression for $\mathring{l}_{(y)}$, the number of lives attaining during the period of investigation a policy anniversary on which they were nearest age y, will bring in not only the ultimate items b, n, etc., but the select items also (since y involves some combinations of x and r in which ($r < s$)) and it is necessarily rather long and complicated. It is easier to make use of (5.1) together with the relationships

$$E_{(y)} = E_{[y-s]s} + E_{[y-s-1]s+1} + E_{[y-s-2]s+2} + \cdots \tag{5.3}$$

since $E_{(y)}$ must embrace all durations $\geq s$, the select period, and

$$b_{(y)} = b_{[y-s]s} + b_{[y-s-1]s+1} + b_{[y-s-2]s+2} + \cdots \tag{5.4}$$

together with similar expressions for $e_{(y)}, w_{(y)}$, and $\theta_{(y)}$.

5.14   We may write, from equation (5.1), an expression of the successive terms on the right-hand side of (5.3):

$$E_{[y-s]s} = E_{[y-s]s-1} + \tfrac{1}{2}(b_{[y-s]s-1} + b_{[y-s]s})$$

and similar terms in w, e, θ

$$E_{[y-s-1]s+1} = E_{[y-s-1]s} + \tfrac{1}{2}(b_{[y-s-1]s} + b_{[y-s-1]s+1}) \text{ etc.}$$
$$E_{[y-s-2]s+2} = E_{[y-s-2]s+1} + \tfrac{1}{2}(b_{[y-s-2]s+1} + b_{[y-s-2]s+2}) \text{ etc.}$$

and so on. We then sum both sides vertically, remembering that the relationships (5.3) and (5.4) start from duration s, so that the first term in some columns stands apart. This gives us

$$E_{(y)} = E_{[y-s]s-1} + E_{(y-1)} + \tfrac{1}{2}b_{[y-s]s-1} + \tfrac{1}{2}b_{(y-1)} + \tfrac{1}{2}b_{(y)}$$

and terms in w, e, θ, whence

$$
\begin{aligned}
E_{(y)} - E_{(y-1)} &= \tfrac{1}{2}(b_{(y-1)} + b_{(y)}) - \tfrac{1}{2}(w_{(y-1)} + w_{(y)}) \\
&\quad - \tfrac{1}{2}(e_{(y-1)} + e_{(y)}) - \theta_{(y-1)} + E_{[y-s]s-1} \\
&\quad + \tfrac{1}{2}b_{[y-s]s-1} - \tfrac{1}{2}w_{[y-s]s-1} - \tfrac{1}{2}e_{[y-s]s-1} - \theta_{[y-s]s-1}
\end{aligned}
\tag{5.5}
$$

$$\mathring{q}_{(y)} = \theta_{(y)}/E_{(y)} = \mathring{q}_y$$

5.15 This formula can be obtained by the difference table technique (Table 5.1), but it must be remembered that account must be taken not only of movements from $E_{(y-1)}$ to $E_{(y)}$ but also of movements from $E_{[y-s]s-1}$ to $E_{(y)}$. Lives reaching the end of select rate-year $[y-s]s-1$ to $[y-s]s$ move into the ultimate rate-year (y) to $(y+1)$.

Table 5.1 *Difference table*

Item	$E_{[y-s]s-1}$	$E_{(y-1)}$	$E_{(y)}$	$E_{(y)} - E_{(y-1)}$ $-E_{[y-s]s-1}$
$b_{[y-s]s-1}$	$\tfrac{1}{2}$	–	1	$\tfrac{1}{2}b_{[y-s]s-1}$
$b_{(y-1)}$	–	$\tfrac{1}{2}$	1	$\tfrac{1}{2}b_{(y-1)}$
$b_{(y)}$	–	–	$\tfrac{1}{2}$	$\tfrac{1}{2}b_{(y)}$
$w_{[y-s]s-1}$	$\tfrac{1}{2}$	–	–	$-\tfrac{1}{2}w_{[y-s]s-1}$
$w_{(y-1)}$	–	$\tfrac{1}{2}$	–	$-\tfrac{1}{2}w_{(y-1)}$
$w_{(y)}$	1	–	$\tfrac{1}{2}$	$-\tfrac{1}{2}w_{(y)}$

Note: $w_{(y)}$ will contribute 1 to either $E_{[y-s]s-1}$ or $E_{(y-1)}$, depending on the duration of attainment of nearest age y.

$\theta_{[y-s]s-1}$	1	–	–	$-\theta_{[y-s]s-1}$
$\theta_{(y-1)}$	–	1	–	$-\theta_{(y-1)}$

The entries for e in Table 5.1 will be the same as those for w. The sum of the final column gives the difference formula as before.

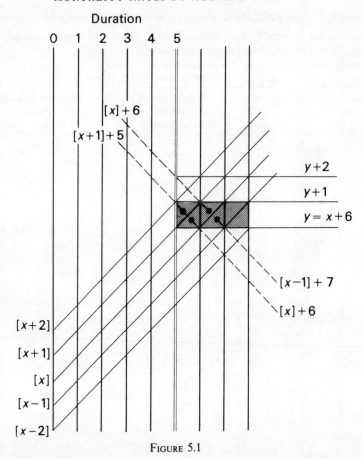

FIGURE 5.1

5.16 It should be stressed that the populations entering at $x-1$, x, $x+1$, etc. are always distinct from each other during the select period, i.e. all the components scheduled at $[x]r$ remain quite distinct from those scheduled at $[x-1]r$ or $[x+1]r$ until the ultimate period when the (y) population recruits from ($y-1$) and $[y-s]s-1$. This can be seen from Figure 5.1.

Example 5.1

5.17 Table 5.2 gives a small section of data tabulated according to nearest age at entry and curtate duration, for durations 0, 1 and 2. For duration 3 and over the data are tabulated according to age (nearest

Table 5.2 *Example of select experience over an investigation period of 5 years*

Nearest age at entry. Curtate duration. There are only two ages at entry 20 and 21 and the select period is 3 years, i.e. $r = 0, 1$ and 2.

		Ten cases	
		Category at entry to period of observation	Category at exit from period of observation
	A	$b_{[20]1}$	$e_{[20]6} \equiv e_{26}$
	B	$n_{[21]}$	$w_{[21]1}$
	C	$n_{[21]2} \quad b_{[21]2}$	$w_{[21]5} \equiv w_{26}$
	D	$b_{[20]7} = b_{27}$	$\theta_{[20]10} \equiv \theta_{30}$
	E	$b_{[21]}$	$e_{[21]5} \equiv e_{26}$
	F	$n_{[20]}$	$e_{[20]2}$
	G	$b_{[20]2}$	$\theta_{[20]5} \equiv \theta_{25}$
	H	$n_{[21]}$	$\theta_{[21]1}$
	I	$b_{[20]6} \equiv b_{26}$	$w_{[20]8} \equiv w_{28}$
	J	$n_{[20]}$	$e_{[20]4} \equiv e_{24}$

Age at entry 20

t	b	n	w	e	θ	$E_{[20]t}$
0	–	FJ	–	–	–	2
1	A	–	–	–	–	$2\frac{1}{2}$
2	G	–	–	F	–	3

Age at entry 21

t	b	n	w	e	θ	$E_{[21]t}$
0	E	BH	–	–	–	$2\frac{1}{2}$
1	–	–	B	–	H	$2\frac{1}{2}$
2	C	–	–	–	–	$1\frac{1}{2}$

Formulae

$$E_{[x]} = \tfrac{1}{2}b_{[x]} + n_{[x]} - \tfrac{1}{2}w_{[x]} - \tfrac{1}{2}e_{[x]}$$

$$E_{[x]r} = E_{[x]r-1} + \tfrac{1}{2}(b_{[x]r-1} + b_{[x]r} - w_{[x]r-1}$$
$$- w_{[x]r} - e_{[x]r-1} - e_{[x]r}) - \theta_{[x]r-1}$$
$$r = 1, 2$$

Ultimate

Age	b	w	e	θ	E	$E_{23} = 3$
24			J		$4\frac{1}{2}$	
25				G	4	
26	I	C	EA		2	
27	D				$1\frac{1}{2}$	
28		I			$1\frac{1}{2}$	
29					1	
30				D	1	

Table 5.2 (*cont.*)

Formulae

$$E_{23} = E_{22}(=0) + E_{[20]2} + \tfrac{1}{2}(b_{22} + b_{23} - w_{22} - w_{23} - e_{22} - e_{23})$$
$$- \theta_{22} + \tfrac{1}{2}(b_{[20]2} - w_{[20]2} - e_{[20]2}) - \theta_{[20]2}$$
$$E_{24} = E_{23} + E_{[21]2} + \tfrac{1}{2}(b_{23} + b_{24} - w_{23} - w_{24} - e_{23} - e_{24})$$
$$- \theta_{23} + \tfrac{1}{2}(b_{[21]2} - w_{[21]2} - e_{[21]2}) - \theta_{[21]2}$$
$$E_{25} = E_{24} + \tfrac{1}{2}(b_{24} + b_{25} - w_{24} - w_{25} - e_{24} - e_{25}) - \theta_{24}$$

and similarly for E_{26} to E_{30}.

Consider E_{24}

No. of lives coming under observation before (24), i.e. ABCDEFGHJ	8
No. of lives leaving observation before (24), i.e. BFH	3
No. attaining (24)	5
Adjustment for J who left during policy year (24)	$-\tfrac{1}{2}$
E_{24} (as in Table 5.3)	$4\tfrac{1}{2}$

Consider E_{26}

No. of lives coming under observation before (26), i.e. ABCDEFGHJ		8
No. of lives leaving observation before (26), i.e. BFGHJ		5
No. attaining (26)		3
Adjustments		
ACE left during policy year (26)	$-1\tfrac{1}{2}$	
I entered during policy year (26)	$+\tfrac{1}{2}$	-1
E_{26} (as in Table 5.3)		2

age at entry plus curtate duration) only. Two ages at entry only, 20 and 21, are illustrated. In practice there would be many more ages at entry but these two serve for illustration since the mechanics would be the same for other ages.

5.18 Table 5.3 shows the contribution to risk time of each case for each duration of age-year. Ages 20 and 21 at entry and durations 0, 1 and 2 are shown in columns 3 to 8, and subsequent columns show the contributions for the policy year at the beginning of which the lives are the nearest age shown at the head of the column.

Census formulae

5.19 Assume, as before, that the deaths $\theta_{[x]r}$, $r = 0, 1, 2$ to $s - 1$ are

Table 5.3 *Contribution to risk time*

	Classification		20			21			23	24	25	26	27	28	29	30
			0	1	2	0	1	2								
A	$b_{[20]1}$	e_{26}		$\frac{1}{2}$	1					1	1	1	$\frac{1}{2}$			
B	$n_{[21]}$	$w_{[21]1}$				1	$\frac{1}{2}$									
C	$b_{[21]2}$	w_{26}						$\frac{1}{2}$		1	1	$\frac{1}{2}$				
D	b_{27}	θ_{30}											$\frac{1}{2}$	1	1	1
E	$b_{[21]}$	e_{26}				$\frac{1}{2}$	1	1		1	1	$\frac{1}{2}$			
F	$n_{[20]}$	$e_{[20]2}$	1	1	$\frac{1}{2}$											
G	$b_{[20]2}$	θ_{25}	$\frac{1}{2}$						1	1	1					
H	$n_{[21]}$	$\theta_{[21]1}$				1	1									
I	b_{26}	w_{28}										$\frac{1}{2}$	1	$\frac{1}{2}$		
J	$n_{[20]}$	e_{24}	1	1	1				1	$\frac{1}{2}$						
Total			2	$2\frac{1}{2}$	3	$2\frac{1}{2}$	$2\frac{1}{2}$	$1\frac{1}{2}$	3	$4\frac{1}{2}$	4	2	$1\frac{1}{2}$	$1\frac{1}{2}$	1	1

available for nearest age at entry x and curtate duration r at death, and $\theta_{(y)}$, $y = x + r$, $r \geq s$, are available for nearest age y at the previous policy anniversary.

5.20 Consider any point of time t in the period of investigation and let $P_{[x]r}(t)$ denote the population at nearest age x at entry and curtate duration r at risk at time t.

If the period of investigation is T years

$$E^c_{[x]r} = \int_0^T P_{[x]r}(t)\,.\,dt$$

$$= \tfrac{1}{2}P_{[x]r}(0) + \sum_{t=1}^{T-1} P_{[x]r}(t) + \tfrac{1}{2}P_{[x]r}(T) \quad (r = 0, 1, \text{to } s-1) \tag{5.6}$$

assuming that censuses are available at times 0, 1, 2, ... T.

For $r \geq s$ and $y = x + s$

$$E^c_{(y)} = \tfrac{1}{2}P_{(y)}(0) + \sum_{t=1}^{T-1} P_{(y)}(t) + \tfrac{1}{2}P_{(y)}(T) \tag{5.7}$$

which is the same as (3.12)

$$\mathring{m}_{[x]r} = \frac{\theta_{[x]r}}{E^c_{[x]r}}, \quad \mathring{m}_{(y)} = \frac{\theta_{(y)}}{E^c_{(y)}} \quad (r = 0, 1, 2, \dots s-1)$$

and these rates would be taken as estimates of rates for exact age x at entry and exact duration r, and age y exactly, respectively.

5.21 A formula sometimes used in practice is one based on a tabulation according to age at death and duration at death. Thus the two time factors are dealt with symmetrically. Suppose, for example, that $\theta_{(y,r)}$ denotes the deaths age y last birthday at date of death and curtate duration r at date of death.

5.22 Denoting by $_tP(y, r)$, a census at time t according to age y last birthday and curtate duration r at time t

$$E^c(y, r) = \tfrac{1}{2}\,_0P(y, r) + \sum_{t=1}^{T-1} {}_tP(y, r) + \tfrac{1}{2}\,_TP(y, r)$$

$$(r = 0, 1, 2 \ldots s-1) \tag{5.8}$$

$$E^c(y) = \tfrac{1}{2}\,_0P(y) + \sum_{t=1}^{T-1} {}_tP(y) + \tfrac{1}{2}\,_TP(y) \quad (r \geq s) \tag{5.9}$$

The second formula is the same as (2.12), i.e. a life-year formula

$$\mathring{m}(y, r) = \frac{\theta(y, r)}{E^c(y, r)} \quad \text{and} \quad \mathring{m}_{(y)} = \frac{\theta(y)}{E^c(y)}$$

5.23 It is necessary to interpret the select rate. The risk time measured by $E^c(y, r)$ is the total risk time in respect of lives while they were simultaneously age y last birthday and duration r curtate and within the period of investigation. The rate $\mathring{m}(y, r)$ applies as did the rate $\mathring{m}_{[x]r}$ to exact duration r, but the age at entry is no longer defined so precisely. The actual age of entry could be from $y-r-1$ to $y-r+1$. However, if the distribution of both age and duration is approximately even, the average entry age is $y-r$.

In other words

$$\mathring{m}(y, r) = \mathring{m}_{[y-r]r}$$

5.24 This type of formula is used in the Continuous Mortality Investigation, conducted by the British Life Offices, nearest age at the census dates being used rather than age last birthday. If y is the nearest age at the census date, then

$$\mathring{m}(y, r) = \mathring{m}_{[y-r-\frac{1}{2}]r}$$

and

$$\mathring{m}(y) = \mathring{m}_{y-\frac{1}{2}}$$

The calendar-year rate interval

5.25 Sometimes records which have to be used for the purposes of a mortality investigation were kept primarily for some quite different purpose, and the data are not in the most suitable form for obtaining accurate mortality rates. Occasionally data are given in a form suitable for a calendar-year method. For example, a card might be available for each life showing the nearest age at entry to assurance and the calendar years of entry, death or withdrawal. The deaths $\theta(x, r)$ can, therefore, be tabulated according to nearest age at entry and duration r where

$$r = \text{calendar year of death} - \text{calendar year of entry}.$$

That is to say, the deaths are given for a calendar year according to nearest age x at entry and duration r at the policy anniversary falling in that calendar year.

5.26   The exposed to risk $E^c(x, r)$ will be the risk time over a rate-year which is the calendar year containing duration r, the lives being nearest age x at entry. The census at the beginning of the calendar year will be $_0P(x, r)$, where x is nearest age at entry and r is the exact duration falling in that calendar year and is equal to the calendar year minus the calendar year of entry. The census at the end of the calendar year will be the survivors of these lives and the corresponding new entrants on the next 1 January, i.e. $_1P(x, r+1)$.

5.27   Thus for a single calendar year C,

$$E^c(x, r) = \tfrac{1}{2}(_0P(x, r) + {}_1P(x, r+1))$$

where $r = C - \text{calendar year of entry}$; and if the experience covered T calendar years,

$$E^c(x, r) = \tfrac{1}{2} \sum_{t=0}^{T-1} (_tP(x, r) + {}_{t+1}P(x, r+1)) \tag{5.10}$$

5.28   The deaths classified to duration r will have exact durations $r-1$ and $r+1$. If policy anniversaries are uniformly distributed over the calendar year, then the deaths, at their dates of occurrence, will be uniformly distributed between exact durations $r-1$ and $r+1$. We can assume that they can be regarded as symmetrically distributed about r at mid-year and effectively as occurring between duration $r-\tfrac{1}{2}$ on 1 January and $r+\tfrac{1}{2}$ on 31 December:

$$\mathring{m}(x, r) = \frac{\theta(x, r)}{E^c(x, r)} = \mathring{m}_{[x]r-\frac{1}{2}}$$

5.29 The formula for the ultimate rates will be

$$E^c(y) \doteqdot \tfrac{1}{2} \sum_{t=0}^{T-1} ({}_tP(y) + {}_{t+1}P(y+1)) \qquad (5.11)$$

where $y = x + r$ and is the nearest age on the policy anniversary following the date of the census, hence

$$\mathring{m}_{y-\frac{1}{2}} \doteqdot \frac{\theta(y)}{E^c(y)}$$

5.30 This method is not very satisfactory because it is not possible to obtain accurate estimates of the rates for the early integral durations. The rate of increase in m with duration is not linear, particularly at the early durations, and therefore the approximation

$$\mathring{m}_{[x]r} \doteqdot \tfrac{1}{2}(\mathring{m}_{[x]r-\frac{1}{2}} + \mathring{m}_{[x]r+\frac{1}{2}})$$

might not be good enough, and more complicated interpolation methods might be required. There is also a special problem when $r = 0$. There is no census ${}_rP(x, 0)$ so that the above formula for $E^c(x, 0)$ requires consideration.

5.31 If the period of investigation is a single calendar year and we use the formula as it stands, putting ${}_0P(x, 0) = 0$, then

$$E^c(x, 0) = \tfrac{1}{2}{}_1P(x, 1).$$

Now ${}_1P(x, 1)$ denotes the survivors of the new entrants during the calendar year, and on the average they will be exposed to risk for $\frac{1}{2}$ year. If, therefore, the withdrawals $w(x, 0)$ out of these new entrants are negligible, then $\frac{1}{2}{}_1P(x, 1)$ will be a reasonable estimate of the risk time contributed by these new entrants. The resulting rate will be an annual rate, but it will be based on risk time heavily weighted by the first half of the policy year. Since the force of mortality is rising rapidly during the first policy year, $\mathring{m}(x, 0)$ will not be a good estimate of $\mathring{m}_{[x]}$ and will in general be much too low. It is doubtful whether anyone would seriously attempt to use $\mathring{m}(x, 0)$ as an estimate of $\mathring{m}_{[x]}$. If we took ${}_1P(x, 1)$ as $E^c(x, 0)$ in conjunction with $\theta(x, 0)$, we should have an estimate of the rate of mortality over the first 6 months of policy duration. If we then took $\mathring{m}_{[x]\frac{1}{2}}$, $\mathring{m}_{[x]1\frac{1}{2}}$, etc. (obtained as above) and interpolated (probably as part of the graduation process) to subdivide mortality into rates for duration $\frac{1}{2}$–1, 1–$1\frac{1}{2}$, $1\frac{1}{2}$–2, etc., we could recombine these 6-monthly rates in pairs to produce rates for exact duration. Whether this particular course is followed or not, it should be stressed that if rates are being obtained in order to construct select life tables for use in calculating assurance premiums, this method of deriving select mortality rates should be avoided, and a method giving rates for integral policy years adopted. If, however, data were already available in calendar year form and the select rates were required for comparative purposes only or in order to determine the approximate length of a practical select period, then it would be both practical and economical to use the calendar-year method.

5.32 We can use the calendar-year interval to derive a difference formula. In the census formula

$$E^c(x, r) \equiv \tfrac{1}{2}[_0P(x, r) + {}_1P(x, r + 1)]$$

the rate year was the calendar year. The lives were nearest age x at entry and exact duration r was attained in the calendar-year rate interval.

5.33 If the deaths and withdrawals $\theta(x, r)$ and $w(x, r)$ are available, tabulated according to nearest age x at entry and duration r falling in the calendar year of death or withdrawal, i.e. r is equal to calendar year of death or withdrawal minus calendar year of entry, then

$$_1P(x, r + 1) = {}_0P(x, r) - \theta(x, r) - w(x, r)$$

for the values of $r > 0$, since there is no census $_0P(x, 0)$.

$$E^c(x, r) = {}_0P(x, r) - \tfrac{1}{2}\theta(x, r) - \tfrac{1}{2}w(x, r).$$

If the period of investigation covers T calendar years, then

$$E^c(x, r) = \sum_{t=0}^{T-1} {}_tP(x, r) - \tfrac{1}{2}\theta(x, r) - \tfrac{1}{2}w(x, r) \tag{5.12}$$

where $\theta(x, r)$ and $w(x, r)$ are now the deaths and withdrawals during the T calendar years.

5.34 We also have the identities

$$_0P(x, r) \equiv b(x, r), \quad {}_TP(x, r) \equiv e(x, r)$$

and

$$\sum_{t=0}^{T-1} {}_tP(x, r) = \mathring{l}(x, r)$$

$$= \sum_{k=1}^{r} b(x, k) + n(x) - \sum_{k=0}^{r-1} w(x, k) - \sum_{k=0}^{r-1} \theta(x, k) - \sum_{k=1}^{r} e(x, k)$$

whence

$$E^c(x, r+1) - E^c(x, r) = b(x, r+1) - \tfrac{1}{2}(w(x, r) + w(x, r+1)) - \tfrac{1}{2}(\theta(x, r)$$
$$+ \theta(x, r+1)) - e(x, r+1) \qquad (5.13)$$

$$\mathring{m}(x, r) = \frac{\theta(x, r)}{E^c(x, r)}$$

and assuming policy anniversaries are distributed uniformly over the calendar year and the average age of lives nearest age x is approximately x, then

$$\mathring{m}(x, r) \doteqdot \mathring{m}_{[x]r - \frac{1}{2}}$$

5.35 The above formula applies for all $r > 0$. The formula for $E^c(x, 1)$ must be obtained before the difference formula can be used.

$$E^c(x, 1) = \mathring{l}(x, 1) - \tfrac{1}{2}w(x, 1) - \tfrac{1}{2}\theta(x, 1)$$
$$= b(x, 1) + n(x) - w(x, 0) - \tfrac{1}{2}w(x, 1) - \theta(x, 0)$$
$$- \tfrac{1}{2}\theta(x, 1) - e(x, 1) \qquad (5.14)$$

5.36 We must also consider $E^c(x, 0)$ again. The problem is essentially that discussed in para. 5.31, although the data are in a slightly different form, and the same considerations (and the same warning) apply.

5.37 The main point to remember is that the difference formula can be used only to obtain $E^c(x, r)$ for $r > 1$ from the commencing value $E^c(x, 1)$. $E^c(x, 0)$ requires a special interpretation and may be of little practical value.

5.38 If the select period is s integral years, then we shall require values of $\mathring{m}(x, r)$ for $r = 1, 2 \ldots s$. Tabulations of $b(x, r)$ etc. will be required for $r = 1, 2 \ldots s$, and of $b(y)$ for $r > s$ where $y = x + r$ and will be the nearest age on the policy anniversary falling in the rate-year (which, it will be remembered, is a calendar year). To obtain the ultimate formula, we can proceed as in paras 5.14–5.15:

$$E^c(y) = E^c(y - s - 1, s + 1) + E^c(y - s - 2, s + 2) + \ldots$$
$$b(y) = b(y - s - 1, s + 1) + b(y - s - 2, s + 2) + \ldots$$

with similar expressions for $e(y)$, $w(y)$ and $\theta(y)$. Applying the difference formula:

$$E^c(y-s-1, s+1) = E^c(y-s-1, s) + b(y-s-1, s+1)$$
$$-\tfrac{1}{2}[w(y-s-1, s) + w(y-s-1, s+1)] \ldots$$

$$E^c(y-s-2, s+2) = E^c(y-s-2, s+1) + b(y-s-2, s+2)$$
$$-\tfrac{1}{2}[w(y-s-2, s+1) + w(y-s-2, s+2)] - \ldots$$

$$\cdots \qquad \cdots \qquad \cdots \qquad \cdots$$

Hence

$$E^c(y) = E^c(y-s-1, s) + E^c(y-1) + b(y) - \tfrac{1}{2}w(y-s-1, s)$$
$$- \tfrac{1}{2}(w(y-1) + w(y)) - \tfrac{1}{2}\theta(y-s-1, s)$$
$$- \tfrac{1}{2}(\theta(y-1) + \theta(y)) - e(y) \qquad (5.15)$$

$$\mathring{m}(y) = \frac{\theta(y)}{E^c(y)} \doteqdot \mathring{m}_{y-\frac{1}{2}}$$

5.39 These formulae can be obtained easily by means of a difference table. Illustrating this with the items b and w, we have Table 5.4.

Table 5.4 *Select formula*

Item	$E^c(x, r)$	$E^c(x, r+1)$	$E^c(x, r+1) - E^c(x, r)$
$b(x, r+1)$	—	1	$b(x, r+1)$
$w(x, r)$	$\tfrac{1}{2}$	—	$-\tfrac{1}{2}w(x, r)$
$w(x, r+1)$	1	$\tfrac{1}{2}$	$-\tfrac{1}{2}w(x, r+1)$

Ultimate formula

Item	$E^c(y-s-1, s)$	$E^c(y-1)$	$E^c(y)$	$E^c(y) - E^c(y-1) - E^c(y-s-1, s)$
$b(y)$	–	–	1	$b(y)$
$w(y-1)$	–	$\tfrac{1}{2}$	–	$-\tfrac{1}{2}w(y-1)$
$w(y)$	–	1	$\tfrac{1}{2}$	$-\tfrac{1}{2}w(y)$
$w(y-s-1, s)$	$\tfrac{1}{2}$	–	–	$-\tfrac{1}{2}w(y-s-1, s)$

5.40 The difference table technique is very simple to use for deriving age rates or for deriving select rates, even when the tabulations are mixed and complicated. In the case of the ultimate exposed to risk generally, the best technique is that which uses the select difference formula.

Period of investigation based on policy anniversary

5.41 Hitherto we have considered periods of investigation consisting of whole calendar years whether the rate interval is a policy year or a calendar year. Sometimes the investigation is arranged to begin on the policy anniversary in year k and end on the policy anniversary in year $k + T$. None of the main principles are affected, but, as in similar circumstances relating to aggregate data, we must be careful about the definition of the symbols used to describe the scheduled data.

5.42 For example, lives starting the period of investigation will be those who, having entered before year k, reach a policy anniversary in year k, $b_{[x]r}$, together with the new entrants of year k, to be included in $n_{[x]}$. On the other hand $e_{[x]r}$ will include only those reaching a policy anniversary in year $k + T$ and will therefore exclude new entrants in year $k + T$. Thus $n_{[x]}$ will include new entrants in years k to $k + T - 1$ only. The withdrawals $w_{[x]r}$ and deaths $\theta_{[x]r}$ will include only those events occurring after a policy anniversary in year k and before a policy anniversary in year $k + T$. Further, $b_{[x]r}$ will be at risk for the whole of the $(r + 1)$th policy year, and $e_{[x]r}$ will not be at risk for any part of that year.

5.43 Formula (5.1) would therefore (and the reader should check this for himself) be amended to:

$$E_{[x]r} - E_{[x]r-1} = b_{[x]r} - \tfrac{1}{2}(w_{[x]r-1} + w_{[x]r}) - e_{[x]r} - \theta_{[x]r-1} \qquad (5.16)$$

and (5.5) will become

$$E_{(y)} - E_{(y-1)} - E_{[y-s]s-1} = b_{(y)} - e_{(y)}$$
$$- \tfrac{1}{2}w_{(y-1)} - \tfrac{1}{2}w_{[y-s]s-1} - \tfrac{1}{2}w_{(y)}$$
$$- \theta_{(y-1)} - \theta_{[y-s]s-1}$$

Example 5.2 *See lesson III pg 8 →*

It is desired to investigate the mortality experience of a body of assured lives between the policy anniversaries in 1971 and 1975. The policy-year rate interval is to be used and selection is to be traced for 3 years after entry into assurance. Describe how you would proceed, stating what exposed to risk formulae you would employ, and indicate how you would deal with the cases in Table 5.5.

How would you modify your procedure, your formulae and your treatment of the specified cases if you were asked to make use of the

Table 5.5

Case	Date of birth	Date of entry into assurance	Date of exit	Mode of exit
A	3.9.1910	1. 6.1971	3. 6.1975	Died
B	28.2.1944	7. 8.1966	5. 7.1972	Surrendered
C	4.8.1944	2. 8.1969	1. 6.1971	Died
D	26.1.1942	29. 1.1968	—	—
E	5.9.1939	3. 4.1969	5. 6.1975	Surrendered
F	13.7.1928	2.11.1972	2. 5.1973	Died
G	15.5.1932	4.11.1962	3. 8.1971	Surrendered
H	5.4.1938	3. 9.1972	5.12.1972	Surrendered
I	1.4.1933	7.10.1975	21.11.1975	Died

experience for the whole of the period between 1 January 1971 and 31 December 1975?

In the first part of the question, observations are limited to the period between the policy anniversary in 1971 or later entry into

Table 5.6

Symbol	Definition	Method of obtaining x (and t)
$n_{[x]}$	New entrants during 1971 to 1974	Age nearest birthday
$b_{[x]t}$	Beginners existing on policy anniversary in 1971 with duration 1 or 2	Age nearest birthday at entry and exact duration
$e_{[x]t}$	Enders existing on policy anniversary in 1975 with duration 1, 2	Age nearest birthday at entry and exact duration
$w_{[x]t}$	Withdrawals between policy anniversaries in 1971 and 1975 with duration 0, 1, 2	Age nearest birthday at entry and nearest duration
$\theta_{[x]t}$	Deaths between policy anniversaries in 1971 and 1975 with duration 0, 1, 2	Age nearest birthday at entry and curtate duration
b_x	Beginners existing on policy anniversary in 1971 with duration 3 or over	Age nearest birthday at entry plus exact duration
e_x	Enders existing on policy anniversary in 1975 with duration 3 or over	Age nearest birthday at entry plus exact duration
w_x	Withdrawals between policy anniversaries in 1971 and 1975 with duration 3 or over	Age nearest birthday at entry plus nearest duration
θ_x	Deaths between policy anniversaries in 1971 and 1975 with duration 3 or over	Age nearest birthday at entry plus curtate duration

assurance and the policy anniversary in 1975 or earlier exit from assurance—with the proviso that deaths shall be exposed throughout the policy year of death in order that the annual rate of mortality may be derived.

The exposed to risk formulae are then:

(1) $E_{[x]} = n_{[x]} - w_{[x]0}$

(2) $E_{[x]1} = E_{[x]} + b_{[x]1} - e_{[x]1} - w_{[x]1} - \theta_{[x]0}$

(3) $E_{[x]2} = E_{[x]1} + b_{[x]2} - e_{[x]2} - w_{[x]2} - \theta_{[x]1}$

(4) $E_x = E_{x-1} + b_x - e_x - w_x - \theta_{x-1} + E_{[x-3]2} - \theta_{[x-3]2}$

and $\mathring{q}_{[x]t} = \dfrac{\theta_{[x]t}}{E_{[x]t}}$ and $\mathring{q}_x = \dfrac{\theta_x}{E_x}$

[handwritten margin note: rate. nearest durn as opposed to curtate durn in 5.43]

These annual rates are derived for 'age nearest birthday' and 'exact duration', but the error in applying rates to exact ages will usually be small. This may, however, require investigation. Table 5.7 gives the treatment of the given cases.

For the second part of the question observations are to extend from 1 January 1971 or later entry into assurance to 31 December 1975 or earlier exit from assurance—deaths still being exposed to the end of the policy year of death. Thus we must estimate the fractional exposures for beginners and enders in respect of the policy year current at 1 January 1971 and 31 December 1975. The recorded

Table 5.7

| Case | Age nearest birthday at entry | Entry | | | | Exit | | | |
| | | Select | | Ultimate | | Select | | Ultimate | |
		Duration	Mode	Age	Mode	Duration	Mode	Age	Mode
A	61	0	n	—	—	—	—	65	e
B	22	—	—	27	b	—	—	28	w
C	—	Not exposed: died before policy anniversary in 1971: no card prepared							
D	26	—	—	29	b	—	—	33	e
E	30	2	b	—	—	—	—	36	e
F	44	0	n	—	—	0	θ	—	—
G	—	Not exposed: surrendered before policy anniversary in 1971: no card prepared							
H	34	0	n	—	—	0	w	—	—
I	—	Not exposed: entrant in 1975: no card prepared							

withdrawals and deaths must now include all such movements within the period of 5 years, irrespective of whether they may occur before the policy anniversary in 1971 or after the policy anniversary in 1975. Cards will be written also for 1975 entrants.

Apart from recording the foregoing additional movements, the changes required are that for beginners and enders the dates of start of, and exit from, observation are now 1 January 1971 and 31 December 1975, and the ages and durations relate to those dates. The durations recorded for beginners and enders may be nearest or curtate. In the former case the assumption is that in respect of the policy years current at 1 January 1971 and 31 December 1975 a fractional exposure exceeding 6 months is treated as 1 year, while a fractional exposure of less than 6 months is ignored. In the latter case an average period of exposure, say one half-year, would be allotted to each case. In this example we have assumed the beginners and enders to be tabulated by nearest duration.

The definition of symbols would require the following modifications:

$n_{[x]}$ New entrants during 1971 to 1975.

$b_{[x]t}$ Beginners existing on 1.1.71.
and b_x Nearest duration t.

$e_{[x]t}$ Enders existing on 31.12.75.
and e_x Nearest duration t.

$w_{[x]t}$ Withdrawals between 1.1.71 and 31.12.75.
and w_x

$\theta_{[x]t}$ Deaths between 1.1.71 and 31.12.75.
and θ_x

The first exposed to risk formula becomes:

$$E_{[x]} = n_{[x]} + b_{[x]0} - e_{[x]0} - w_{[x]0}$$

and the given cases are treated as in Table 5.8.

5.44 The approach of this book to the teaching of exposed to risk measurement springs from the desire of the original authors to break away from earlier methods of teaching, which had tended to treat each tabulation variant as a different method, and to adopt instead a more generalized derivation of exposed to risk formulae that would stress their basic similarity—indeed, in many cases, their identity. The

Table 5.8

| | | Entry | | | | Entry ~~Exit~~ | | | |
| | | Select | | Ultimate | | Select | | Ultimate | |
Case	Age nearest birthday at entry	Duration	Mode	Age	Mode	Duration	Mode	Age	Mode
A	61	0	n	—	—	. —	—	65	θ
B	22	—	—	26	b	—	—	28	w
C	25	1	b	—	—	1	θ	—	—
D	26	—	—	29	b	—	—	34	e
E	30	2	b	—	—	—	—	36	w
F	44	0	n	—	—	0	θ	—	—
G	30	—	—	38	b	—	—	39	w
H	34	0	n	—	—	0	w	—	—
I	43	0	n	—	—	0	θ	—	—

method of derivation has been shown to be uniform. It would be possible to go further and produce a completely generalized mathematical formulation describing all situations; the different situations would simply demand computation of the different parameters, in the formula, appropriate to them.

These computations would be once-for-all. This has, in fact, been accomplished in an elegant paper by G. C. Taylor (1973), and readers who prefer to think mathematically about exposures are referred to this paper. They will find the subject greatly illuminated. It should be borne in mind that in preparing his paper Taylor was confronted by the textbook which preceded this present volume, and which adopted the earlier, less generalized, approach.

REFERENCE

Taylor, G. C. (1973) A generalised approach to exposed-to-risk theory. MacQuarie University, School of Economic and Financial Studies *Research paper* No. 22.

EXERCISES FOR CHAPTER FIVE

1   In an investigation of the mortality of assured lives over a period of 5 years the 'beginners' and 'enders' have been tabulated according to nearest age x at entry into assurance and curtate duration of assurance t at the beginning and end of the period respectively, the new entrants according to nearest age x at entry, and the withdrawals and deaths according to nearest age x at entry into assurance and curtate duration of assurance t at the date of withdrawal and death respectively. These items are denoted by $b_{[x]t}$, $e_{[x]t}$, $n_{[x]}$, $w_{[x]t}$ and $\theta_{[x]t}$ for $t = 0$, 1 and 2; and by b_y, e_y, w_y and θ_y for $t > 2$, where $y = x + t$ and is the nearest age at the previous policy anniversary.

(i)   If $\overset{\circ}{l}_{[x]t}$ denotes the number of lives who were nearest age x at entry into assurance and passed through exact duration t within the period of investigation, express $\overset{\circ}{l}_{[x]t}$ in terms of b, e, n, w and θ.

(ii) Using the expression obtained in (i) derive $E^c_{[x]t}$, the central exposed to risk corresponding to $\theta_{[x]t}$, and similarly derive E^c_y, the central exposed to risk corresponding to θ_y.

(iii) Derive the relationship between $E^c_{[x]t-1}$ and $E^c_{[x]t}$ and that between E^c_{y-1} and E^c_y.

(iv) Use your results in (iii) to calculate $E^c_{[30]2}$ and E^c_{33}, given that $E^c_{[30]1}$ = 300, E^c_{32} = 1,610, and you have the data in Tables 5.9, 5.10 and 5.11.

Table 5.9

[x]	$n_{[x]}$	$b_{[x]t}$			$e_{[x]t}$		
		$t=0$	$t=1$	$t=2$	$t=0$	$t=1$	$t=2$
29	315	35	62	72	81	59	61
30	227	51	49	67	48	53	72
31	261	62	91	45	82	21	56
32	201	47	50	80	73	29	46

Table 5.10

[x]	$w_{[x]t}$			$\theta_{[x]t}$		
	$t=0$	$t=1$	$t=2$	$t=0$	$t=1$	$t=2$
29	13	52	47	–	2	4
30	17	36	53	1	1	–
31	12	29	13	2	3	1
32	5	14	18	2	–	–

Table 5.11

y	b_y	e_y	w_y	θ_y
31	471	627	190	8
32	522	515	151	9
33	391	273	131	4

2   An investigation is being carried out into the mortality experience of a body of assured lives between the policy anniversaries in 1972 and 1977.

The policy year is to be used as the rate interval and selection is to be traced for 2 years after entry into assurance. All the information needed for continuous exposed to risk formulae is available.

(i)   Define all the symbols by which the group data would be classified using age nearest birthday at entry into assurance.
(ii) Obtain the continuous exposed to risk formulae, in initial form, stating any assumptions made.
(iii) The six cases in Table 5.12 were insured for at least part of the period 1 January 1972 to 31 December 1977. State which of the cases would be included in the experience and state by which two symbols defined in (i) each case would be described.

Table 5.12

Case	Date of birth	Date of entry into assurance	Date of exit	Mode of exit
A	3. 8.1901	2. 7.1932	—	—
B	25. 3.1928	3. 5.1948	2. 3.1972	Died
C	5. 7.1933	1. 8.1971	3.10.1972	Surrendered
D	4.10.1933	6.12.1969	29.11.1976	Died
E	15.5.1940	1.10.1977	19.12.1977	Died
F	1.12.1945	2. 7.1972	—	—

3   An investigation into the mortality experience of a large group of assured lives is to be carried out on a select basis by means of the census method. A computer will produce a tabulation of deaths during each calendar year and a tabulation of lives 'in force' on each 1 January, provided the age and duration definitions for these tabulations are clearly specified in advance.

Table 5.13

Symbol	Definition of x	Definition of t
$a\theta_{x,t}$	Nearest age at death	Curtate duration at death
$b\theta_{x,t}$	Nearest age at 1 January before death	Nearest duration at 1 January before death
$c\theta_{x,t}$	Nearest age at 1 January before death	Curtate duration at death
$d\theta_{x,t}$	Nearest age at policy anniversary before death	Calendar year of death minus calendar year of entry

(i) Various possible age and duration definitions for the deaths have been suggested, as in Table 5.13. State the rate year or rate years implied by each of these methods of tabulating the deaths.

(ii) To what ages and durations will the rates derived from each of these methods of tabulating the deaths apply? State any assumptions you make about the distributions of birthdays and policy anniversaries.

(iii) In Table 5.14 $_KP_{x,t}$ represents the number of lives 'in force' on 1 January in the year K at age x and duration t, and the prefixes A, B, C and D denote four suggested age and duration definitions. For each of the four tabulations suggested in (i) of the deaths occurring in the year K derive a formula for the corresponding central exposed to risk in the form $\frac{1}{2}(_K^Z P + _{K+1}^Z P)$, choosing for the prefix Z whichever is most appropriate of A, B, C and D.

Table 5.14

Symbol	Definition of x	Definition of t
$_K^A P_{x,t}$	Nearest age at 1.1.K	Nearest duration at 1.1.K
$_K^B P_{x,t}$	Nearest age at 1.1.K	Curtate duration at 1.1.K
$_K^C P_{x,t}$	Nearest age at policy anniversary in K	Curtate duration at 1.1.K
$_K^D P_{x,t}$	Age next birthday at 1.1.K	K-calendar year of entry

CHAPTER SIX

MULTIPLE DECREMENTS

The multiple decrements table—theory

6.1 Reference has been made in Chapter 1 to the life table, which shows the number of individuals surviving at each integral age out of a specified number of original lives at some commencing age (not always zero) who are subject to a specified set of mortality rates at subsequent ages. In a similar way it is possible to construct a table to show the survivors at each integral age when more than one cause of decrement is operating: for example, death, withdrawal and retirement. In this case three sets of rates are required and such a table is called a multiple decrement table. The life table is an example of a single decrement table.

6.2 The number of survivors at age x in the multiple decrement table will be denoted by $(al)_x$, and the decrements between age x and age $x+1$ from cause α will be denoted by $(ad)_x^\alpha$. Thus in the case of the three decrements death, withdrawal and retirement, the decrements would be denoted by $(ad)_x^d$, $(ad)_x^w$, and $(ad)_x^r$ respectively.

6.3 Table 6.1 is an example of a multiple decrement table. The figure of 10,000 is chosen arbitrarily and

$$(al)_{x+1} = (al)_x - (ad)_x^d - (ad)_x^w - (ad)_x^r$$

6.4 The total number of decrements between age x and age $x+1$ will be denoted by $(ad)_x$, so that

$$(ad)_x = (ad)_x^d + (ad)_x^w + (ad)_x^r$$

Table 6.1

Age x	$(al)_x$	$(ad)_x^d$	$(ad)_x^w$	$(ad)_x^r$
50	10,000	30	80	10
51	9,880	33	69	12
52	9,766	35	54	14
53	9,663	39	39	15
54	9,570			

If the table showed only $(ad)_x$, it would become a single decrement table similar to the life table.

6.5 The figures in Table 6.1 are fictitious. In practice the bulk of retirements take place at a specified normal retirement age such as 60 or later. Those at young ages would be due to disablement.

Probabilities of exit

6.6 According to the multiple decrement table, the probabilities of dying, withdrawing and retiring between age x and age $x + 1$ are

$$\frac{(ad)_x^d}{(al)_x} \quad \frac{(ad)_x^w}{(al)_x} \text{ and } \frac{(ad)_x^r}{(al)_x} \text{ respectively.}$$

They are denoted by $(aq)_x^d$ $(aq)_x^w$ and $(aq)_x^r$. The total probability of exit between age x and age $x + 1$ from any cause is $(aq)_x$ and is equal to $\frac{(ad)_x}{(al)_x}$.

Thus
$$(aq)_x = (aq)_x^d + (aq)_x^w + (aq)_x^r \tag{6.1}$$

6.7 The probability of surviving from age x to $x + 1$ is $(ap)_x = 1 - (aq)_x$. In general $_t(ap)_x$ is the probability of surviving the risk of exit, from any cause, from age x to age $x + t$. The multiple decrement table then can be constructed from values of $(aq)_x^d$ $(aq)_x^w$ and $(aq)_x^r$, calculated from actual data.

Suppose we are given the values in Table 6.2.

Table 6.2

Age	$(aq)_x^d$	$(aq)_x^w$	$(aq)_x^r$
50	0.0030	0.0080	0.0010
51	0.0033	0.0070	0.0012
52	0.0036	0.0055	0.0014
53	0.0040	0.0040	0.0016

6.8 With these data Table 6.2 can start only at age 50, and values can be calculated up to age 54 only. Choosing a radix of 10,000, one can calculate the following multiple decrement table from the relationships

$$(ad)_x^x = (al)_x \cdot (aq)_x^x \text{ etc.}$$

Thus we have Table 6.3. This will be recongnized as the example of para. 6.3.

Table 6.3

x	$(al)_x$	$(ad)_x^d$	$(ad)_x^w$	$(ad)_x^r$
50	10,000	30	80	10
51	9,880	33	69	12
52	9,766	35	54	14
53	9,663	39	39	15
54	9,570			

Forces of decrement

6.9 In order to provide a convenient mathematical basis for theoretical work it is assumed (as for the life table) that $(al)_x$ is a continuous function of x and, in general, differentiable. If we take all causes of decrement together as one, we are concerned only with $(al)_x$ and $(ad)_x$. Table 6.3 is then a single decrement table and all the relationships of the life table may be applied.

6.10 If $(a\mu)_x$ is the force of decrement from all causes at age x, then

$$(a\mu)_x = -\frac{1}{(al)_x} \cdot \frac{d}{dx}(al)_x$$

$$= -\frac{d}{dx}\left[\log_e(al)_x\right]$$

so that

$$\log_e(al)_x = -\int(a\mu)_x dx$$

$$\log_e\left[\frac{(al)_{x+t}}{(al)_x}\right] = -\int_0^t (a\mu)_{x+r} dr$$

hence

$$_t(ap)_x = \exp\left(-\int_0^t (a\mu)_{x+r} dr\right)$$

and

$$(aq)_x = 1 - \exp\left(-\int_0^1 (a\mu)_{x+r} dr\right)$$

6.11 It is now necessary to consider whether the force of decrement from a single cause can be defined.

Let $F(x)$ denote the sum of all the decrements from the youngest age considered to age x, i.e.

$$F(x) = (al)_{x_0} - (al)_x$$

where x_0 is the youngest age.

Denote the sum to age x of the decrements from cause α by $F_\alpha(x)$, so that in the case of a table showing deaths, withdrawals and retirements

$$F(x) = F_d(x) + F_w(x) + F_r(x)$$

If it is assumed that each of these functions is continuous and differentiable, then

$$\frac{d}{dx}F(x) = \frac{d}{dx}F_d(x) + \frac{d}{dx}F_w(x) + \frac{d}{dx}F_r(x)$$

But $$\frac{d}{dx}F(x) = -\frac{d(al)_x}{dx} = (al)_x \cdot (a\mu)_x$$

Hence $$(al)_x(a\mu)_x = \frac{d}{dx}F_d(x) + \frac{d}{dx}F_w(x) + \frac{d}{dx}F_r(x)$$

$$(a\mu)_x = \frac{\frac{d}{dx}F_d(x)}{(al)_x} + \frac{\frac{d}{dx}F_w(x)}{(al)_x} + \frac{\frac{d}{dx}F_r(x)}{(al)_x}$$

so that if we define $(a\mu)_x^\alpha$, the force of decrement from cause α, as

$$\frac{1}{(al)_x} \cdot \frac{d}{dx} \cdot F_\alpha(x)$$

we have $$(a\mu)_x = (a\mu)_x^d + (a\mu)_x^w + (a\mu)_x^r \qquad (6.2)$$

and the force of decrement from all causes operating is equal to the sum of the forces of decrement from the individual causes. It should be noted that this result arises from the definitions used and assumptions made in the foregoing development of the multiple decrement table. The formulation given here is therefore theoretical only and its practical application must be justified.

Central rates of exit

6.12 The following central rates are of importance in the theory of multiple decrement tables.

$$(am)_x = \frac{(ad)_x}{\int_0^1 (al)_{x+r}dr} = \frac{\int_0^1 (al)_{x+r}(a\mu)_{x+r}dr}{\int_0^1 (al)_{x+r}dr} \qquad (6.3)$$

$$(am)_x^\alpha = \frac{(ad)_x^\alpha}{\int_0^1 (al)_{x+r}dr} = \frac{\int_0^1 (al)_{x+r}(a\mu)_{x+r}^\alpha dr}{\int_0^1 (al)_{x+r}dr} \qquad (6.4)$$

These functions are called the central rates of exit from all causes and from cause α respectively. It follows that $(am)_x$ is equal to the sum, over all causes operating, of the central rates from individual causes. For example, in the case of Table 6.2

$$(am)_x = (am)_x^d + (am)_x^w + (am)_x^r$$

It can be seen from the above expressions that the respective m-type functions are weighted means of their related μ-type functions, and weights in each base are the survivors $(al)_{x+r}$ at each instant of time in the interval $0 \le r \le 1$.

Single decrement tables

6.13 The number of decrements from cause α during the infinitesimal interval from $x+r$ to $x+r+dr$ will be

$$(al)_{x+r} \cdot (a\mu)_{x+r}^\alpha dr$$

and hence

$$(ad)_x^\alpha = \int_0^1 (al)_{x+r}(a\mu)_{x+r}^\alpha dr$$

and

$$(aq)_x^\alpha = \int_0^1 {}_r(ap)_x \cdot (a\mu)_{x+r}^\alpha dr$$

6.14 Consider a set of causes of decrement α, β, γ, etc. In order to construct the multiple decrement table, sets of rates of this type $(aq)_x^\alpha$ are required for each cause and over all ages. For mathematical convenience sets of underlying forces of decrement $(a\mu)_x^\alpha$ etc. have been postulated. In principle a single decrement table can be constructed on the basis of one of these causes. In such a table the survivors at each age will be denoted by l_x^α and the rate of decrement by q_x^α. However, $q_x^\alpha \neq (aq)_x^\alpha$, since

$$(aq)_x^\alpha = \int_0^1 {}_r(ap)_x \cdot (a\mu)_{x+r}^\alpha dr$$

whilst $\qquad q_x^\alpha = \int_0^1 {}_r p_x^\alpha \cdot (a\mu)_{x+r}^\alpha dr \qquad$ where $\qquad {}_r p_x^\alpha = \dfrac{l_{x+r}^\alpha}{l_x^\alpha}$

now $\qquad {}_t p_x^\alpha = \exp\left(- \int_0^t (a\mu)_{x+r}^\alpha dr \right)$

hence

$$({}_t p_x^\alpha) \cdot ({}_t p_x^\beta) \cdot ({}_t p_x^\gamma) \dots = \exp\left[- \int_0^t \left((a\mu)_{x+r}^\alpha + (a\mu)_{x+r}^\beta + (a\mu)_{x+r}^\gamma \dots \right) dr \right]$$

$$= {}_t(ap)_x \tag{6.5}$$

In other words, the probability of surviving a period t when all causes of exit are operating is equal to the product of the probabilities of surviving each cause separately.

6.15 This relationship is analogous to the product rule in the mathematical theory of probability. However, it must be remembered that it arises from the definitions of the forces, and does not imply that ${}_t p_x^\alpha$ etc. are a set of independent probabilities, as would be required for the probability product rule.

6.16 We will also have to bear in mind that we have been considering the production of a single decrement table based on one of the forces operating in a multiple decrement table ($(a\mu)^\alpha$ etc.) and we used $(a\mu)^\alpha$ for this single decrement table to emphasize that we were using such a force. This, however, implies that $\mu^\alpha \equiv (a\mu)^\alpha$ where μ^α is the force of decrement in the single decrement table for which unscripted symbols should be strictly employed and will be so employed henceforth. Similarly, if we were to take the separate forces of decrement μ^α etc. of a family of single decrement tables and combine them to produce a parent multiple decrement table, we should have $(a\mu)^\alpha \equiv \mu^\alpha$ etc. The connecting link is that we have constructed the tables by making each force of decrement operating in the multiple table equal to the corresponding force operating in the single tables, and this is a model which it is useful to adopt in practice.

Mathematical relationships between multiple decrement functions and single decrement functions

6.17 It is clear from the expressions for $(aq)_x^\alpha$ and q_x^α given in para. 6.14 that a relationship between them cannot be obtained without making some assumption about the form of $(a\mu)_x^\alpha$ or about some function of $(a\mu)_x^\alpha$. An assumption frequently made in practice is that the decrements in the single decrement table are uniformly distributed over the age interval x to $x+1$. That is

$$l_{x+t}^\alpha = (1-t)l_x^\alpha + t \cdot l_{x+1}^\alpha \qquad 0 \le t \le 1$$

$$= l_x^\alpha - t \cdot d_x^\alpha \qquad \text{and similarly for } \beta, \gamma, \text{ etc.}$$

Dividing by l_x^α we obtain

$$_tp_x^\alpha = 1 - t \cdot q_x^\alpha$$

and we deduce that

$$_tq_x^\alpha = t \cdot q_x^\alpha \qquad 0 \le t \le 1$$

But

$$_tq_x^\alpha = \int_0^t {_rp_x^\alpha} \cdot \mu_{x+r}^\alpha \cdot dr$$

It follows that

$$\int_0^t {_rp_x^\alpha}\mu_{x+r}^\alpha dr = t \cdot q_x^\alpha \qquad 0 \le t \le 1$$

Whence

$$_rp_x^\alpha\mu_{x+r}^\alpha = q_x^\alpha \qquad 0 \le r \le 1$$

Consider now two decrements d and w only.

$$(aq)_x^d = \int_0^1 {_r(ap)_x}(a\mu)_{x+r}^d \cdot dr$$

$$= \int_0^1 {_rp_x^d} \cdot {_rp_x^w} \cdot \mu_{x+r}^d \cdot dr$$

$$= \int_0^1 (1 - rq_x^w)q_x^d \cdot dr \qquad \text{(from above)}$$

$$= q_x^d \int_0^1 (1 - rq_x^w)dr$$

$$= q_x^d \cdot (1 - \tfrac{1}{2} \cdot q_x^w)$$

Similarly $\qquad (aq)_x^w = q_x^w \cdot (1 - \tfrac{1}{2}q_x^d) \qquad$ (6.6)

6.18 It is worth noting that this result is consistent with para. 6.14, since

$$
\begin{aligned}
(ap)_x &= 1 - (aq)_x^d - (aq)_x^w \\
&= 1 - q_x^d(1 - \tfrac{1}{2}q_x^w) - q_x^w(1 - \tfrac{1}{2}q_x^d) \\
&= 1 - q_x^d - q_x^w + q_x^d \cdot q_x^w \\
&= (1 - q_x^d)(1 - q_x^w) \\
&= p_x^d \cdot p_x^w.
\end{aligned}
$$

6.19 By a similar procedure it can be shown that if there are three causes of decrement, say α, β and γ, and the same assumption is made, then

$$(aq)_x^\alpha = q_x^\alpha(1 - \tfrac{1}{2}q_x^\beta - \tfrac{1}{2}q_x^\gamma + \tfrac{1}{3}q_x^\beta \cdot q_x^\gamma) \tag{6.7}$$

with similar expressions for $(aq)_x^\beta$ and $(aq)_x^\gamma$.

6.20 It should be carefully borne in mind that the relationships between $(aq)_x^\alpha$, $(aq)_x$ and q_x^α given in the preceding paragraphs depend on two assumptions: (1) that all decrements in the single decrement tables are uniformly distributed over any interval of time considered, and (2) that the relationship between the rates of decrement remains invariant over this same interval of time. The rate $(aq)_x^\alpha$ is frequently referred to as the dependent rate from cause α, while q_x^α is known as the independent rate. This terminology should not be confused with that used in association with the theory of probability. For these rates the word 'dependent' is used because the rate is a function of (i.e. dependent upon) all the forces of decrement operating, whereas the word 'independent' implies that the rate itself is a function of one force only while contributing to the 'dependent' rate. It is very important to remember this when the models are to be used for practical purposes.

6.21 Formulae for $(aq)_x^d$ and $(aq)_x^w$ in terms of q_x^d and q_x^w are given in para. 6.17. The inverse problem of determining q_x^d and q_x^w from $(aq)_x^d$ and $(aq)_x^w$ is slightly more difficult. The obvious approach is to eliminate q_x^d and q_x^w from the formulae for $(aq)_x^d$ and $(aq)_x^w$ and solve the resulting quadratic equation for q_x^d and q_x^w. The rates involved are often quite small, and it is usually simpler to employ an iterative method based on the equations

$$q_x^d = \frac{(aq)_x^d}{(1 - \tfrac{1}{2}q_x^w)} \tag{6.8}$$

$$q_x^w = \frac{(aq)_x^w}{(1 - \frac{1}{2}q_x^d)} \tag{6.9}$$

The dependent rates $(aq)_x^d$ and $(aq)_x^w$ are used as initial values for q_x^d and q_x^w. Convergence is extremely rapid.

6.22 It should be emphasized, however, that multiple decrement techniques are not really necessary to obtain independent rates of mortality. The methods of Chapters 2–5 can always be used. The techniques of para. 6.21 are, however, sometimes needed in multiple decrement table manipulation.

Further remarks on central rates

6.23 In para. 1.33 we defined L_x as $\int_0^1 l_{x+r} . dr$. Using the Euler-Maclaurin expansion, we can write

$$\int_0^1 l_{x+r} dr = l_x + \frac{1}{2}(l_{x+1} - l_x) - \frac{1}{12}(l'_{x+1} - l'_x) + \dots$$

therefore

$$L_x \doteqdot l_x - \frac{1}{2}d_x - \frac{1}{12}l''_x$$

Dividing through by d_x

$$\frac{1}{m_x} \doteqdot \frac{1}{q_x} - \frac{1}{2} - \frac{\Delta^2 l_x}{12 d_x}$$

$$= \frac{1}{q_x}\left[1 - \frac{\Delta^2 l_x}{12 l_x}\right] - \frac{1}{2}$$

or

$$q_x \doteqdot \frac{2m_x}{2 + m_x}\left(1 - \frac{\Delta^2 l_x}{12 l_x}\right)$$

Similarly

$$q_x^\alpha \doteqdot \frac{2m_x^\alpha}{2 + m_x^\alpha}\left[1 - \frac{\Delta^2 l_x^\alpha}{12 l_x^\alpha}\right] \tag{6.10}$$

and

$$(aq)_x = \frac{2(am)_x}{2 + (am)_x}\left[1 - \frac{\Delta^2(al)_x}{12(al)_x}\right]$$

also

$$(am)_x^\alpha = \frac{\int_0^1 {}_r(ap)_x(a\mu)_{x+r}^\alpha dr}{\int_0^1 {}_r(ap)_x dr}$$

$$= \frac{(aq)_x^\alpha}{\int_0^1 {}_r(ap)_x dr}$$

Hence

$$\frac{(aq)_x^\alpha}{(am)_x^\alpha} = \int_0^1 {}_r(ap)_x dr = \frac{(aq)_x}{(am)_x}$$

and

$$(aq)_x^\alpha = \frac{(am)_x^\alpha}{(am)_x} \cdot (aq)_x$$

$$\doteqdot \frac{2(am)_x^\alpha}{2+(am)_x}\left[1 - \frac{\Delta^2(al)_x}{12(al)_x}\right] \tag{6.11}$$

6.24 If l_x^α etc. are linear in x over the interval x to $x+1$, we obtain the exact relationships

$$q_x^\alpha = \frac{2m_x^\alpha}{2+m_x^\alpha} \quad q_x^\beta = \frac{2m_x^\beta}{2+m_x^\beta} \text{ etc.} \tag{6.12}$$

but only the approximate relationships

$$(aq)_x^\alpha = \frac{2(am)_x^\alpha}{2+(am)_x} \quad (aq)_x^\beta = \frac{2(am)_x^\beta}{2+(am)_x} \text{ etc.} \tag{6.13}$$

and

$$(aq)_x = \frac{2(am)_x}{2+(am)_x} \tag{6.14}$$

6.25 These are approximate because it may be shown by (6.5) that if the l_x^α are linear, then $(al)_x$ will be a polynomial of the nth degree where n is the number of forces operating.

6.26 If, however, $(al)_x$ is linear in x, then relationships (6.13) and (6.14) are exact, and (6.12) is approximate, except when some of the l_x^α etc. are linear also.

6.27 In practice (6.12), (6.13) and (6.14) are generally adopted. The error found is usually small in actuarial practice.

6.28 Another approximate formula sometimes used in practice, when two forces only are operating, can be obtained from (6.6)

$$(aq)_x^\alpha = q_x^\alpha(1 - \tfrac{1}{2}q_x^\beta) \doteqdot \frac{m_x^\alpha}{1+\tfrac{1}{2}m_x^\alpha}\left[1 - \frac{m_x^\beta}{2+m_x^\beta}\right]$$

$$= \frac{m_x^\alpha}{(1+\tfrac{1}{2}m_x^\alpha)(1+\tfrac{1}{2}m_x^\beta)} \tag{6.15}$$

If three forces are operating, (6.7) can be used to give

$$(aq)_x^\alpha = \frac{m_x^\alpha}{(1+\tfrac{1}{2}m_x^\alpha)(1+\tfrac{1}{2}m_x^\beta)(1+\tfrac{1}{2}m_x^\gamma)} \tag{6.16}$$

term of $\tfrac{1}{2}\cdots$ ignored

6.29 In the theoretical development given above it has been assumed that the forces operate continuously. This is a reasonable assumption for death, but it is not always reasonable to make the assumption for such causes as withdrawal or retirement. It is conceivable that such decrements can occur at fixed ages (e.g. retirements) and therefore it is necessary to enquire whether the theory can be adapted to fit such circumstances of discontinuity.

6.30 Consider two types of decrement from causes α and β and let α operate continuously and β at age $x + k$ only. $0 \leq k < 1$. At all ages $x + r$, $r \neq k$, $(a\mu)^\beta_{x+r} = 0$.

Define

$$(aq)^\beta_x = \frac{(ad)^\beta_x}{(al)_x} \qquad q^\beta_x = \frac{(ad^\beta_x)}{(al)_{x+k}}$$

so that

$$(aq)^\beta_x = {}_kp^\alpha_x \cdot q^\beta_x$$

since

$$_k(ap)^\alpha_x = {}_kp^\alpha_x$$

Also

$$(aq)^\alpha_x = \int_0^1 {}_rp^\alpha_x(a\mu)^\alpha_{x+r}dr - q^\beta_x \int_k^1 {}_rp^\alpha_x \cdot (a\mu)^\alpha_{x+r}dr$$

$$= q^\alpha_x \left[1 - q^\beta_x \cdot \frac{\int_k^1 {}_rp^\alpha_x \cdot (a\mu)^\alpha_{x+r}dr}{\int_0^1 {}_rp^\alpha_x \cdot (a\mu)^\alpha_{x+r}dr} \right]$$

6.31 In order to put this expression into a practical form we must postulate the form of ${}_rp^\alpha_x \cdot (a\mu)^\alpha_{x+r}$ over the interval $0 \leq r < 1$. A simple solution would be to assume that decrements in the single decrement α table are uniform over the year of life (para. 6.17), in which case

$$_rp^\alpha_x(a\mu)^\alpha_{x+r} = q^\alpha_x \quad 0 \leq r < 1.$$

Hence

$$(aq)^\alpha_x = q^\alpha_x \left[1 - q^\beta_x \frac{(1-k) \cdot q^\alpha_x}{q^\alpha_x} \right]$$

$$= q^\alpha_x [1 - q^\beta_x(1-k)]$$

and similarly

$$(aq)^\beta_x = q^\beta_x(1 - k \cdot q^\alpha_x)$$

6.32 It should be noted that these relationships agree with para. 6.14, since

$$1 - (aq)^\alpha_x - (aq)^\beta_x = (1 - q^\alpha_x)(1 - q^\beta_x)$$

6.33   Let us now consider some special values of k.

(a) $k = 0$, i.e. β decrements occur just after the attainment of age x

$$(aq)_x^x = q_x^x[1 - q_x^\beta]$$

$$(aq)_x^\beta = q_x^\beta$$

(b) $k = \frac{1}{2}$, or β decrements occur in the middle of age interval

$$(aq)_x^x = q_x^x[1 - \tfrac{1}{2}q_x^\beta]$$

$$(aq)_x^\beta = q_x^\beta[1 - \tfrac{1}{2}q_x^x]$$

This agrees with (6.6), which was obtained when both forces were assumed to operate continuously (and on the average decrements occur at the midpoint of the interval).

(c) k infinitesimally less than 1, or β decrements occur just before the attainment of age $x + 1$

$$(aq)_x^x = q_x^x$$

$$(aq)_x^\beta = q_x^\beta(1 - q_x^x).$$

6.34   It is clear that the theory is easily adapted to the assumption of discontinuous forces. In practice the specific conditions of the particular experience must be considered before deciding what adaptation is necessary. The relationships given in this chapter should not be accepted blindly but only if the assumptions on which the model is based are broadly justified in the real situation to which they are to be applied.

The interpretation of the multiple decrement table and its family of single decrement tables

6.35   The multiple decrement table is an indispensable tool of the actuary; it can be regarded as a model depicting a commonly encountered real situation. The table is, however, based on a set of forces, and a force is a mathematical concept involving a differential coefficient, so that it cannot be measured directly. Only rates over finite intervals can be measured. The model generates these rates; they are logically entailed by the set of forces and other postulates. Conversely, if numerical values are given to a set of rates based on measurement of an actual population, then, by means of the relationships set out in the previous paragraphs, the model can be constructed.

6.36 Populations consist of individuals. They do not vary in number continuously, but by discrete amounts. The assumption of continuity is convenient and it is not necessary to indulge in a metaphysical enquiry as to whether forces really exist. It is sufficient that from them we can infer rates which do exist in that they can be measured in the real world. The reader will appreciate the convenience of postulating μ_x from his study of life contingencies, but he will also know that it is possible to go very far in the development of this subject with q_x as the basic concept. It is true that when the multiple decrement table is used in connection with the finances of a pension fund, there is less use for forces than in the subject of life contingencies. However, it would be difficult to develop a satisfactory theory about the relationship between the multiple decrement table and its family of single decrement tables without postulating forces for one or more of the causes of decrement.

Homogeneity

6.37 Numerical values of $(aq)_x^z$, q_x^z and hence $(a\mu)_x^z$ are obtained from measurement on actual populations. However, almost any population can be sub-divided according to some factor other than age which influences the cause of decrement under consideration. For example, consider a mixed population of males and females. One can measure mortality rates according to age from this population. It is known, however, that if the population is sub-divided into males and females, the mortality rate for males at age x will differ significantly from that for females of the same age x. Similarly, differences will be found if the male population is sub-divided according to marital status, or according to occupation; in fact one can go on until one is almost forced to the conclusion that each individual should be considered in isolation and group measurement is impossible. Certainly in respect of mortality any population is in practice very heterogeneous. A mortality investigation always raises the question of sub-division. The amount of sub-division must depend on the purpose the investigation is to serve. Thus, if a population is mixed and rates are obtained from such a population, these rates can be used only in connection with similarly mixed populations. We have already stressed this principle of specificity in Chapter 2, but it is worth repeating it.

6.38 An exception to this rule may have to be made in practice where no exactly relevant prior experience exists. For example, an actuary concerned with the setting up of a new pension fund may be justified in making use of the rates of decrement derived from some other fund until sufficient data have accumulated to provide reliable rates based on the experience of the new fund itself.

6.39 Investigations are frequently made to find out as much as possible about a cause of decrement—for example, mortality from a particular disease, especially a disease which follows a long chronic course, such as diabetes, or a disability such as that which follows a stroke or a myocardial infarction. Multifactorial enquiries of this kind make great demands of sub-division on the data. The limitation is smallness of numbers. Actuaries do, in practice, co-operate with medical examiners in order to assess appropriate extra rates of premium for so called 'impaired' lives. Further reference is made in para. 7 of Chapter 10 to the need for care in the classification of impairments in order to ensure homogeneity of mortality risk within the groups which are to be studied. There are not usually any special exposed to risk measurement problems, since impairment groups (e.g. diabetics, coronary thromboses, strokes) are followed up by hospital clinics from the date of first coming under their care—in most cases this is close to the onset of the impairment—and records are kept of this date and of the dates of follow-up attendance at clinic together with an assessment of the disease condition. There are two problems: tracing deaths as soon as they occur and recording the failure of patients to maintain their attendance at the clinic. The latter must be treated as exits from observation as at their last recorded attendance, since their subsequent experience is unknown. This is a source of bias in the results of the investigation because those patients who fail to maintain attendances are, more often than not, those who feel very well and consider that they need no further surveillance. These problems depend for their solution upon the efficiency of the hospital medical records department.

6.40 Impairment studies are usually concerned with only a single decrement, namely death, as the mortality rates are compared with those of unimpaired lives. Occasionally problems of multiple decrement do arise. For example, a heart valve transplant patient can leave the 'first transplant' group either by death or by the malfunction of the transplant and the need to renew it (in the latter event he passes into a 'first renewal' group). Exposure records would need to be kept both for patients (within their transplant groups) and transplants.

Selective decrements

6.41 In the previous paragraphs we have considered the possibility of sub-division of the data before the rates are measured, in order to render the rates more highly specific. In this section we consider 'sub-division' that cannot be avoided, namely the sub-division brought about by the operation of some of the causes of decrement. Let us consider decremental data from a life office. The decrements consist of deaths, surrenders, lapses and maturities. For convenience, let us group the surrenders, lapses and maturities and call them withdrawals. Thus withdrawal sub-divides the original population into those who remain with the life office and those who withdraw. Death itself is a sub-division, though of course we are interested only in the remainder who are alive. There is, however, the question of 'interaction' between the two causes of decrement. Is the mortality after withdrawal the same as the mortality of those who remain active policy-holders with the life office?

6.42 This question does not appear to have been statistically investigated. One would not expect a life in very bad health to surrender his policy if he could possibly avoid doing so, and hence one would expect the mortality of withdrawals to be lighter than that of those who do not withdraw. If this is the case, it is said that withdrawal is selective, or in other words, that withdrawals are not a random sample of the population under investigation with respect to mortality. A more obvious example is ill-health retirement. It would be expected and it has been frequently shown that those who retire from employment on grounds of ill-health experience much heavier mortality than the average of the staff at the same age, particularly during the early years after retirement.

6.43 So far we have been concerned with assumptions made in deriving independent rates from dependent rates. However, even if sets of dependent rates are obtained and a multiple decrement table is constructed, then if some of the forces of decrement are selective, care must be exercised in its interpretation or in using it to calculate the decrements to be expected in the future from an entrant population of policy-holders. Suppose, for example, that there are two decrements, death and withdrawal, then the rate $(aq)_x^d$ will depend on the rates of withdrawal to age x. These rates of withdrawal are not those derived from recent experience, but those experienced by the earlier generations to which the lives aged x belonged. These earlier withdrawal rates may have been very different in their degree of selectivity from those recently operating. In using a multiple decrement table an actuary must bear this point in mind. In practice he will have to take account of other factors affecting the future population—for example, the secular trend in mortality, a change of administrative policy, or a change in economic conditions, affecting withdrawal rates or retirement rates. These changes may be thought to be much more important than errors arising from the treatment of selection.

6.44 In any case these rates and the calculations based upon them are only means to an end. The fundamental task is that of financial planning to ensure that emergent liabilities can be met as they fall due. It is of course essential to estimate these liabilities as accurately as circumstances permit but the actuary will make a judgement about the likely degree of accuracy (taking account among other things of the considerations we have been discussing) and will provide some cover for this. There are various ways of doing this but their discussion is outside the scope of this textbook.

6.45 An interesting problem arises when one of the single decrement tables is used. An imporant example is the life table as used by the life-assurance companies. The mortality rates are measured from data in which several other forces of decrement are in fact operating. On the other hand, the life table when calculated is a model which shows how a group of lives would survive under the influence of rates of mortality (as obtained from the data) and assuming no other forces of decrement operate. We cannot say that $_rp_x$ taken from the life table is the probability that an assured life age x will survive to age $x + r$. The reason for this has got nothing to do with the secular trend in mortality. A statement that the likelihood of survival is measured by $_rp_x$ would still be open to question even if there were no secular trend. First, the life must be chosen at random from a group of policy-holders similar in all relevant characteristics to the group of policy-holders constituting the data from which the life table was derived. Second, the possibility of the life withdrawing must be considered. In general nothing is known about mortality after withdrawal, and if it is different from that of the life table, it is not possible to say that $_rp_x$ is the probability of a life actually surviving to age $x + r$ (whether or not still a life-assurance policy-holder). It is only if the withdrawals are not selective that it is reasonable to accept the statement. (It should be noted that we have spoken here of using only mortality in the premium calculation. A premium calculation could make allowance for withdrawal but in practice it does not.)

6.46 Is it then reasonable for a life office to use such a table to calculate premiums? Yes, it is. A premium calculation is concerned with the risk of death while surviving as a policy-holder, i.e. among a population from which withdrawals at earlier ages have been removed. If the withdrawal experience is not different from that inherent in the data from which the life table was calculated, the life office will be using a mortality table which is progressively selective to the correct extent.

6.47 Consider now a pension fund into which the employee pays a contribution and the employer also pays a contribution in respect of each employee. Suppose that on withdrawal or death before pension age the employee receives only the return of his own contributions with interest while the employer's accumulated contribution falls into the fund. In this example the employer's contribution in respect of those who withdraw or die goes towards the provision of pension to those who retire in the normal way. In order to value a proper contribution it is necessary to use a multiple decrement table allowing for deaths, withdrawals and retirement. A single decrement life table or withdrawal table would be difficult to interpret and would have no application.

6.48 Finally, let us turn to an example that might be confused with the situation we have just described. Ill-health retirement is necessarily selective in that the unhealthy lives which are subject to heavier mortality than the average tend to retire prematurely in this way. Retirement may, however, also have a beneficial effect in the sense that the mortality of those who retire in this way is probably lighter than it would have been if these lives had remained in active service. Hence the estimated mortality rates of prematurely retired lives would be a compound of two opposing factors—the selection of ill-health and the beneficial effect of discontinuing employment—and it would be difficult to disentangle them.

6.49 The normal statistical procedure would be to design a longitudinal study of the mortality of cohorts of ill-health pensioners retired under different conditions, some being retired at an earlier stage of disability than others. What we are stressing is that the multiple decrement table is an essential piece of equipment in the financial planning of pension funds and similar institutions, but it does not answer every decrement question, and there may often be a need for special study.

Retirement rates

6.50   The provisions for retirement on pension vary considerably from one pension fund to another, but there is often an option available to members to retire on pension at any time between a minimum and a maximum age, e.g. from 60 to 65. Current practice in framing rules now often provides for a fixed normal pension age with provision for early or late retirement. Possibly late retirement will be more common in the years to come in view of the growing proportion of the aged to the total population, though in periods of very high unemployment this factor may be counter-balanced by pressure for workers to retire early and make more jobs available. In computing retirement rates at individual ages a concentration of retirements at particular age-points may need special treatment. It will be likely, for example, that a definite proportion of those reaching, say, age 60 will retire on or near their 60th birthdays; then there may be a steady flow of retirements with possibly minor concentrations at the 61st to 64th birthdays, with the remainder retiring on their 65th birthday. In such circumstances the exposed to risk must take account of the practical features. The number retiring at age 60 in the investigation period would be related to the total number reaching age 60 in the period to produce a 'point-rate' at age 60. A similar process would be used for retirements at age 65. For intermediate retirements the usual yearly type of rates would probably be appropriate. In practice it would often be sufficient to compute rates for the retirements between ages 60 and $60\frac{1}{2}$, between $60\frac{1}{2}$ and $61\frac{1}{2}$, and so on up to $64\frac{1}{2}$ to 65.

Incapacity retirements

6.51   Many pension funds provide for a pension benefit to start on retirement as a result of an accident or a breakdown in health causing 'total permanent' incapacity to continue working. Accordingly, an investigation into the rates of incapacity retirement is often required as well as the mortality and withdrawal investigations. The principles are the same as for the other decrements.

6.52   If the membership is large enough, it may be worth while to investigate the mortality of the incapacity pensioners separately. This would be done in select form, showing the rates according to age at retirement and duration since retirement. Investigations of this kind have shown rates of mortality which are very heavy immediately after retirement, falling fairly rapidly over the ensuing 5 years or so and then merging into an ultimate table of rates somewhat higher than normal mortality rates for the same age. Provision may be made for the pension to cease on recovery of health, but these cases are usually too few to make an investigation of the incidence of recovery worth while.

6.53 Similar problems arise in connexion with what is called 'permanent disability' insurance. The actuarial principles employed consider the rates of becoming disabled and the rates of mortality and recovery among the disabled. The more liberal the office is in judging disability claims, the greater becomes the premium that is necessary for the risk, the greater the need to pursue the possibilities of recovery and the more nearly the insurance approaches to a sickness insurance of the kind granted by friendly societies. The stage in the range between a full sickness insurance and a strict total permanent disablement income insurance at which it is wise to pass from the sickness technique to the technique of rates of occurrence and rates of recovery will depend upon the financial considerations that arise.

Example 6.1

In order to examine the experience of a large pension fund the data in Table 6.4 have been supplied.

Table 6.4

Age x	b_x	e_x	θ_x	r_x	E_x	q'_x
55	33	18	9	12	431	0·028
56	24	42	5	19		
57	51	36	17	10		
58	32	45	13	22		
59	39	26	10	16		
60	–	–	–	307		

The terms b_x and e_x are the numbers of lives aged x last birthday at the beginning and end respectively of the period of observation. θ_x and r_x are the deaths and retirements respectively at age x during the period of observation, x being the age last birthday at the date of death or retirement. Retirement is compulsory on the 60th birthday.

The term q_x^r is the probability of retirement over the exact year of age x to $x+1$ on the assumption that retirement is the only decrement, and E_x is the required exposed to risk.

Complete the last two columns of the table, showing clearly how your figures have been calculated and how you would check the figures in the E_x column.

From the definitions in the question, and in particular the definition of retirement as being at age x last birthday at the date of retirement, it is clear that the rate-year should be chosen as the life-year (x to $x+1$). On the assumptions that (a) the average ages of beginners and enders are $x+\frac{1}{2}$, (b) the average age at death is $x+\frac{1}{2}$, b_x contribute on average $\frac{1}{2}$ year each to E_x and similar considerations apply to θ_x and e_x. The difference formula for the exposed to risk, allowing a full year of exposure in the year of retirement, therefore becomes

$$E_x = E_{x-1} + \tfrac{1}{2}(b_x + b_{x-1}) - \tfrac{1}{2}(\theta_x + \theta_{x-1}) - r_{x-1} - \tfrac{1}{2}(e_x + e_{x-1})$$

and $q_x^r = \dfrac{r_x}{E_x}$

Consequently Table 6.4 can be completed as shown in Table 6.5.

A first check on the E column (which is calculated by a continuous process) is that E_{60} equals the number of retirements r_{60}. This must be correct, since compulsory retirement occurs at exact age 60, so that the rate of retirement, q_{60}^r, must be equal to 1. A second check is obtained by summing the difference formula for the range $x = 56$ to 60 inclusive. Whence

$$E_{60} = E_{55} + \tfrac{1}{2}(b_{55} - e_{55} - \theta_{55}) + \sum_{56}^{59}(b_x - e_x - \theta_x) - \sum_{55}^{59} r_x$$

$$= 431 + 3 + (146 - 149 - 45) - 79$$

$$= 307.$$

Table 6.5

x	E_x	q_x^r
55	431·0	0·028
56	410·5	0·046
57	379·0	0·026
58	355·0	0·062
59	321·5	0·050
60	307·0	1·000

Example 6.2

A company maintains a contributory pension fund for the benefit of its female staff. Employees become members of the fund at age 21 or on completion of 6 months' service, whichever is later. The following benefits are available:

(a) a marriage benefit, payable on marriage during service after at least 5 years' membership of the fund, of an amount equal to the member's contributions paid up to that date;

(b) a return of the member's contributions on death or on leaving service before retirement for any reason;

(c) a pension on attaining age 60 or on retirement due to ill-health not earlier than age 55.

A member who wishes to continue in service after marriage has the option of withdrawing her own contributions as well as taking the marriage benefit and ceasing to be a member of the fund or of taking only the marriage benefit and remaining a member of the fund. A member entitled to the marriage benefit may receive the benefit once only. Information relating to all female staff employed during the period of investigation is available in the form of punched cards, which show the calendar years of birth, entry into the fund, marriage while entitled to the marriage benefit, and exit from the fund and the cause of exit.

You have been asked to prepare a service table with a radix of 10,000 lives at age 21, based on the experience of the active members of the fund during the calendar years 1974–8.

1   State the headings of the columns of the service table.
2   Derive the appropriate exposed to risk formulae, defining carefully all symbols used and ages required.

1   The service table to age 60 would be as Table 6.6. In Table 6.6 $(al)_x$, $(ad)_x$ and $(aw)_x$ represent, as usual, those attaining age x and those dying or leaving service between ages x and $x+1$; $(am)_x$ represents those marrying while entitled to the marriage benefit and withdrawing from the fund; and $(ar)_x$ those retiring between the same ages. It is not necessary to use separate symbols for ill-health and age retirements in view of the retirement rules $((aq)_x^r$ runs to $x = 59$ and must refer to ill-health; all $(al)_{60}$ retire so that $(aq)_{60}^r$ does not need to be calculated). The symbol M_x represents the

Table 6.6

Age x	$(al)_x$	$(ad)_x$	$(aw)_x$	$(am)_x$	$(ar)_x$	M_x
21	10,000				–	
22						–
.						
.						
.						
55						
56						
.						
.						
.						
60		–	–	–		

proportion of $(al)_x$ who will marry between ages x and $x + 1$, being entitled to the marriage benefit, and remain in the fund. It is akin to a sickness rate, being non-decremental, and it might in practice be more convenient to use a central rate.

2   For the main part of the table where data are available only in calendar-year form, define the following items:

$b_{(x)}$ = number of employees on 1 January 1974 aged x next birthday at that date.

$e_{(x)}$ = number of employees on 31 December 1978 aged x next birthday at that date.

$n_{(x)}$ = number of new employees between 1 January 1974 and 31 December 1978 attaining age x in the calendar year of entry.

$\left.\begin{array}{l} w_{(x)} \\ \theta_{(x)} \\ m_{(x)} \\ r_{(x)} \end{array}\right\}$ are defined similarly to $n_{(x)}$ in the four categories of exits recorded in the service table

$N_{(x)}$ = number of employees in the period marrying and remaining in the fund attaining age x in the calendar year of marriage

If we assume that entry is uniformly spread over the calendar year of entry, and define $E_{(x)}$ as the exposure during the calendar year of attaining age x, all exits being exposed for the full calendar year,

$$E_{(x)} = E_{(x-1)} + \tfrac{1}{2}(n_{(x)} + n_{(x-1)}) + b_{(x)} - e_{(x)}$$
$$- w_{(x-1)} - \theta_{(x-1)} - m_{(x-1)} - r_{(x-1)}$$

For $x = 21$, $E_{(21)} = \tfrac{1}{2}n_{(21)}$ for consistency. Dependent rates are then obtained as follows:

$$(aq)_x^d = \theta_{(x)}/E_{(x)} \text{ etc.,} \quad \text{and} \quad M_{(x)} = N_{(x)}/E_{(x)}$$

Assuming an average spread of birthdays, the resulting rates would apply to age $x - \tfrac{1}{2}$ from $x = 22$ to 60. Rates would be interpolated for exact ages and extrapolated for age 21.

It is worth noting that the marriage benefit could be dealt with differently. All withdrawals, whether on account of marriage or not, could be lumped together. The benefit taken into account on withdrawal would then be the normal withdrawal benefit of the member's contributions. The whole marriage benefit and not merely that of those remaining in the fund could then be valued as a claim rate, as is done in the case of sickness benefit. Thus for each age we would require a claim rate equal to the total marriage benefit paid within that age divided by the appropriate exposed to risk. The advantage of the method used above is that in calculating a contribution the actuary may wish to scale down $(aq)_x^w$, leaving $(aq)_x^m$, say, unchanged.

Practical considerations

6.54 Hitherto in this chapter we have dealt with the measurement of exposed to risk in a largely theoretical manner. However, in actuarial practice the need to calculate a multiple decrement table as a working model for financial purposes arises frequently and often in situations where theoretical refinement has to give way to practical constraints, e.g. limitation of amounts of data or difficulties presented by the form in which the data are recorded. It is necessary for the sake of completeness (even at the risk of some repetition) to review the problems that may arise in the real life application of multiple decrement theory.

6.55 It will probably be helpful to carry out this review by reference to a practical example. We shall suppose that in a certain city there is an employer of labour who runs a pension fund for the benefit of such employees as are eligible to join and that he wishes to meet the cost of the benefits of the fund by means of contributions which are expressed as a percentage of the payroll in respect of those employees who are members of the fund and have not yet become recipients of any benefit.

6.56 In this example there is a specific population in which we are interested, namely those employees in respect of whom contributions are payable. The population is increased by new entrants and depleted by deaths, withdrawals from service and retirements. We shall assume that the benefit on death is a pension to a surviving spouse if any; that on withdrawal a 'frozen' pension is granted to the former member, with a contingent pension payable to a spouse in the event that the holder of a frozen pension dies while it is frozen or after the frozen pension has become payable at the normal pension age; that on retirement a pension is granted to the retired member, with a contingent pension payable to a surviving spouse in the event that the pensioner dies. There are, in all, four distinct groups of persons—current employees who are members, holders of frozen pensions, pensioners and spouse pensioners. Employee members are increased by new entrants and depleted by deaths, withdrawals and retirements; 'frozen' pensioners are increased by withdrawals and depleted by deaths or retirements; pensioners are increased by retirements of employees and of 'frozen' pensioners, and depleted by deaths; and spouse pensioners are increased by deaths in the employee, 'frozen' pensioner or retirement pensioner classes, and depleted by deaths.

6.57 Failure to observe which is the correct population to analyse is a major cause of failure to construct a satisfactory multiple decrement table. In the present problem the purpose of such a table is to enable the employer to calculate rates of contribution related to the payroll of *employees* who are *members*, not of all employees. The employer might very well decide to pay contributions related to the total salary and pension payroll in respect of members of the fund, in which case the population for that purpose is the total of employed members, retired members and pensioner spouses. This total would not necessarily be the population to be investigated for any other purpose, however.

6.58 If the investigator is able to control the manner in which the data are tabulated, he is able to specify the rate-year in advance and require the data to be tabulated to conform to this specification. If the data are received already tabulated, possibly for a different original purpose, then the investigator must adapt to this situation. Furthermore age is the principal time measure for mortality and retirement rates, while duration of employment is the principal time measure for withdrawal rates and for calculating amounts of benefit, and so the investigator must decide whether or not to make a select investigation. In practice the data are usually too scanty to support a select investigation, with both age and duration traced separately, and so some form of compromise is necessary. A typical compromise is to determine duration-specific withdrawal rates for broad age bands such as 10-year groups; another compromise is to determine age-specific withdrawal rates for individual ages and for average duration for each age.

6.59 It is usually desirable on practical grounds to confine the investigation to produce age-specific rates and to deal with duration in a fairly broad way, but whatever decision is taken, it is essential to define the rate-year for calculating the exposed to risk. The in force data may be collected and tabulated according to age (next birthday, last birthday or nearest birthday) at the beginning of a calendar year, at the fund anniversary or at the beginning and end of the investigation period. Entrants and exits may be classified according to age (next birthday, last birthday or nearest birthday) at exit, at the fund anniversary preceding or nearest to entrance or exit, at the age at joining the fund plus duration in the fund where duration may be in complete years since joining or calendar year of exit minus calendar year of joining. There are many variations, and different modes of entry or exit may be tabulated in different ways, so compromise will be needed again.

6.60 The usual rule for determining the rate-year is to take cognizance of the manner in which the deaths are tabulated, but in this fund death may not be the most important decrement. Indeed it may very well be of minor importance. In fact, whatever the decrement, the rate-year for that decrement is the year for which the data unit concerned was definitely a member at the beginning of the year and definitely not a member at the end. The distribution of exits over the rate-year is not relevant to the fixing of the rate-year, and so it need not be taken into account for that purpose. As an example of determining the rate-year, let it be supposed that deaths are classified by age last birthday at death, withdrawals by age last birthday at entry plus calendar year of exit minus calendar year of joining, and retirements according to age last birthday at entry plus number of complete years of membership, assuming that entry to the scheme takes place only on a scheme anniversary. This is a mixed bag. Deaths are in life-year form because it is certain that a death tabulated at age x was alive at exact age x and not alive at exact age $(x + 1)$, but it is not known whether the death occurred before or after the beginning of the calendar year or before or after the fund anniversary. It is known in which calendar year the withdrawals occurred, but not whether they occurred before or after the birthday or the fund anniversary, so withdrawals are in calendar-year form. Retirements are in fund-year form because it is known that the persons were employed members at the previous fund anniversary but not at the following fund anniversary, whereas it is not known which calendar year they occurred in nor whether or not they occurred before the birthday. In the case of retirements it may be known or suspected that the majority took place exactly on the birthday, but that does not give them life-year status if they are not tabulated in life-year form.

6.61   With such a mixed bag there are two ways of dealing with the calculation of decrement rates. The first is to calculate the exposed to risk for each decrement according to its own rate-year, and obtain independent rates after estimating the exposure contributed by the other decrements. The second is to select the rate-year of the most important decrement and estimate the exposure contributed by the other decrements. Then, for the most important decrement, the rate is obtained by dividing the number of decrements by the exposed to risk, but for the other decrements the numbers have to be redistributed to conform with the chosen rate-year before they can be used in the numerator. If retirements have to be redistributed, then the investigator must use any knowledge he has of the fact that at some ages retirements occur mainly on the birthday.

6.62   In the preceding example let it be supposed that the rate-year is to be the life-year throughout. Then the investigator should define:

b_x = the number existing at the beginning of the investigation aged x last birthday.

e_x = the number existing at the end of the investigation aged x last birthday.

n_x = the number of new entrants aged x last birthday.

w_x = the number of withdrawals aged x last birthday ~~at the start of~~ the calendar year of withdrawal. *on the anniversary / entry in*

r_x = the number of retirements aged x last birthday at the start of the fund year of retirement.

d_x = the number of deaths at age x last birthday.

E_x = the exposed to risk of exit from any cause between exact ages x and $x+1$.

6.63 The exposed to risk formula is built up from these definitions by means of the following statements:

1 The b_x who existed at the beginning contribute $\frac{1}{2}$ year to E_x and 1 year to E_{x+1}, and the e_x who existed at the end contribute 1 year to E_{x-1} and $\frac{1}{2}$ year to E_x.

2 The n_x new entrants contribute $\frac{1}{2}$ year to E_x and 1 year to E_{x+1}.

3 The w_x withdrawals are aged x last birthday on the anniversary of entry in the calendar year of withdrawal. If it is assumed that entries and exits are uniformly distributed over both the calendar year and the year of life, then the average birthday falls at the end of the calendar year, and this is the beginning of a rate-year; the average exit therefore occurs half-way through a rate-year. The range of exact ages is very wide (from $x-1$ to $x+2$) but the average age is $x+\frac{1}{2}$, so the withdrawals contribute 1 year to E_x and nil to E_{x+1} because they are exposed up to the end of the rate-year in which the exit occurs. If a central rate were being calculated, then the exposure contributed by this group would be 1 year to E^c_{x-1} and $\frac{1}{2}$ year to E^c_x.

4 The r_x retirements are aged x last birthday at the beginning of the fund year of retirement, and if retirements are assumed to take place uniformly over the fund year, and birthdays are also uniformly distributed over the fund year, then $\frac{1}{2}r_x$ will take place before the $x+1$th birthday and $\frac{1}{2}r_x$ will take place after the $x+1$th birthday. The retirements classified as x therefore contribute 1 year to E_x, $\frac{1}{2}$ year to E_{x+1} and nil to E_{x+2}. When retirements take place exactly on a birthday, as at age 60, a 'point-rate' should preferably be calculated, and these retirements should be eliminated from the exposed to risk for other decrements, including retirements taking place after the birthday. If a central exposed to risk were required, then the $\frac{1}{2}r_x$ who retire before the $x+1$th birthday would retire on the average at age $x+\frac{3}{4}$, and the $\frac{1}{2}r_x$ who retire after the $x+1$th birthday would retire on the average at age $x+1\frac{1}{4}$, so that retirements would contribute 1 year to E^c_{x-1}, 7/8 year to E^c_x, 1/8 year to E^c_{x+1} and nil to E^c_{x+2}.

5   The d_x deaths contribute a whole year to the exposed to risk at age
x and nothing to age $x+1$.

The exposed to risk formula follows from these differences.

6.64   In many cases pension-fund data are supplied with exact dates
of birth, joining and exit, and so the devices described above are not
needed. In these cases the rate-year is chosen and the cases are
tabulated accordingly. The only complication is when a central
exposed to risk is being calculated from data where retirements at
some ages occur at exact ages, in which case the exposure in the year of
age at exit is nil if the rate-year is the life-year.

6.65   The pension-fund situation has been discussed here in some
detail. Other situations must be dealt with by analogy, not by direct
copying or by repeating the foregoing processes automatically.

6.66   In many practical situations the data are insufficient to
generate decrement rates which are capable of being graduated and
used without help from other sources, and so an attempt may have to
be made to find a pre-existing set of rates to fit the experience. The
standard rates are applied to the exposed to risk and expected
decrements are calculated for comparison with the actual decrements.
When a set of standard rates is brought together for this purpose, they
must be combined into a mutually compatible set of dependent rates,
which means, in turn, that if they have been extracted from other
multiple decrement tables, they must be converted to independent
rates before further use. It is not correct to take dependent death rates
from one table and withdrawal rates from another and use them as
dependent rates in a third table. It is also incorrect to attempt to
construct a table by means of death rates which are age-specific and
withdrawal rates which are duration-specific. The correct procedure
in such cases is, as mentioned earlier, to consider whether a select type
of table can be constructed and, if not, to settle for an age-specific
table for use with a table of average durations at exit for each age
attained, or for a duration-specific table with average attained ages for
each duration.

6.67   The multiple decrement table for a pension fund is called a
service table, and it is constructed by starting with a radix, the number
in existence at the lowest age, which is multiplied by the dependent
probability of each form of exit for that age to obtain the number of
each type of decrement; the resultant numbers are subtracted from

the radix to give the number of survivors to the second age, and so on until the latest retirement age is reached, when the decrements in the final year should remove all the survivors. The table is not incremented for new entrants. Where entitlement to benefit depends upon marital status, a marriage and mortality table might be constructed from the data, but it is usually more convenient to prepare a subsidiary table of proportions married at each attained age.

6.68 A marriage and mortality table is one which begins with a radix for unmarried men that is a fairly large number, and a corresponding radix of zero for married men. The unmarried men are decremented by marriage or death, while the married men are incremented by marriage and decremented by death. If necessary, withdrawal rates may be used in the table, and the withdrawal rates might depend upon marital status. The marriage and mortality table is of limited use because it does not facilitate direct calculation of the probability that an unmarried man aged x will die at age y as a married man, except when x is the lowest age in the table; nor does it facilitate the calculation of the probability that a married man aged x will die at age y as a married man. Probabilities like these must be calculated by other means, using the marriage and mortality rates.

6.69 Homogeneity of data is always an important consideration. It may be that the persons who comprise the data are not homogeneous in relation to rates of mortality, withdrawal and retirement because of differences of sex, marital status, education or job-type, and so it may be necessary to divide the data into sub-groups which are thought likely to be homogeneous. Obviously a married person can generate a spouse pension, whereas an unmarried person cannot; an employee can generate a contribution but a pensioner cannot. Women suffer lighter mortality than men and are subject to different pressures which cause them to leave their employment. Failure to deal with the question of homogeneity might lead to failure to produce a satisfactory multiple decrement table.

6.70 Finally, it is worthy of note that, especially in general insurance applications, time is not always considered directly, but may be considered indirectly in relation to something else, such as growth and decay. An example is the depletion of a fleet of buses when buses are scrapped after a number of miles rather than at a specified age. This example is really based upon time, but the time scale may not be linear. In the present note the time scale is linear and is used directly.

EXERCISES FOR CHAPTER SIX

1   A large engineering firm began on 1 January 1966 to manufacture
aeroplanes, and a certain section of the staff, as from that date, were
permanently engaged in aviation tests, causing an additional mortality
hazard. You are required to construct for this section of the staff a special
service table, like Table 6.7, based on the experience of the whole staff for
the years 1970–75 in respect of normal mortality, withdrawal and
retirement, and on estimates which have been made of 'annual rates of
death by aviation'.

Table 6.7

Age	Living	Deaths (normal and aviation)	Withdrawals and retirements

Full particulars as to dates of birth, entry and exit, and also as to cause of
exit, are available for all employees in the service of the firm at any time
during 1970–75. Explain in detail how you would proceed. No reference
need be made to graduation.

2   Table 6.8 is an extract from a service table which has been in use for a
number of years for a certain pension fund.

Table 6.8

Age	Number living at age x l_x	Number of deaths at age x last birthday d_x	Number of withdrawals (including retirements) at age x last birthday w_x
25	100,000	176	3996
26	95,828	174	3351
27	92,303	173	2766
..	......	...	....
..	......	...	....

It is felt that the withdrawal rates assumed in Table 6.8 are no longer
realistic, and it is proposed to construct a new service table, using the same
mortality assumptions as in the old table but new withdrawal assumptions.
The new withdrawal basis is to be determined from an investigation of the
company's turnover of staff during the 3 years ending on 31 December
1976. An extract from the data of this investigation is given in Table 6.9.

Table 6.9

Age x	Number of staff aged x last birthday on 1.1.1974	Number of staff aged x last birthday on 31.12.1796 *1976*	Number of staff withdrawing during the investigation aged x last birthday at withdrawal
25	269	262	96
26	272	285	88
27	251	270	71
..	...	...	..
..	...	...	..

Construct the new service table for ages 25 and 26, using the information provided and stating all assumptions made. You may ignore graduation and should use a radix of 100,000 at age 25.

3   It is desired to construct a table that will indicate the prospects of survival of patients with a particular form of heart disease who have been given valve replacements. A replacement valve which fails may be renewed by a further operation (called a 'repair'). It is important that the survivors should be classified according to whether or not they have had a 'repair'. It may be assumed that all original operations take place at the same age and that the only important time scale is duration from the original operation. Show the column headings of the table you propose to construct. What data would you call for and how would you derive the values in your table?

4   Tables 6.10 and 6.11 relate to the experience of a large fund for bachelors and married men over the period 1 January 1965 to 1 January 1971. New members join the fund on their 25th birthday, and over the period there were 8,019 entrants, of whom 1,357 were already married.

Table 6.10   *Bachelors*

Age	Existing at 1.1.65	Deaths	Marriages	Withdrawals	Existing at 1.1.71
25	348	39	259	193	872
26	759	36	238	174	731
27	2093	41	259	190	347
28	1356	48	293	215	562
.	.	.	.	.	.
.	.	.	.	.	.
.	.	.	.	.	.

The numbers existing at 1 January 1965 and 1 January 1971 are tabulated according to age at entry plus duration where duration equals

1964 or 1970 less year of entry; deaths, marriages and withdrawals are tabulated at age last birthday. Construct a combined marriage and mortality table.

Table 6.11   *Married men*

Age	Existing at 1.1.65	Deaths	Withdrawals	Existing at 1.1.71
25	383	8	16	103
26	236	10	22	270
27	240	12	27	102
28	184	14	31	406
.	.	.	.	.
.	.	.	.	.
.	.	.	.	.

CHAPTER SEVEN

SICKNESS RATES

7.1   The concept of a sickness rate is more complicated and much less definite than that of a mortality rate. The complications and vagueness are not, however, associated with the denominator of the rate. The principles for estimating exposure to risk are exactly the same for sickness as for mortality rates, although, as we shall see later, there are one or two technical points which are specific to sickness rates. It is with the idea of sickness itself as it affects the numerator of the rate that the main complications and special problems arise. There is nothing vague about the state of death. During a given period a person either dies or survives; there is no intermediate condition. Sickness, on the other hand, is a relative state. There are degrees of sickness, although there is not any obvious scale of measurement. At a given time it would be possible to identify individuals who would be generally regarded as completely healthy (i.e. not sick) and others who are obviously sick. But there will always be an intermediate group who might be regarded as sick or not according to the type of person observing and the stringency of the criteria adopted by the observer. An experienced medical practitioner will see signs of disease which are not apparent to an untrained observer, and may not be apparent to the person under observation unless they interfere with his normal activity or cause discomfort. A medical practitioner might well vary his view as to the exact extent of abnormality which constitutes sickness according to whether he is free to use his own criteria or is, for example, advising on a claim for disability, and is compelled to concentrate upon restriction of activity.

7.2   This reference to extent of abnormality strikes at the heart of the problem of defining sickness; for in considering what is ill-health we are confronted with a wide range of variability between one individual and another in every structure and function in the human body. There is no unique pattern of structure or of behaviour to which all living members conform, but a whole distribution of bodily structures and functions which are equally 'healthy' in the sense that there is no observable impediment to existence.

7.3 Suppose we were to examine a group of young men generally considered to be in 'good health', and took measures, for example, of blood pressure. We should find that the values of resting diastolic pressure (in mm of mercury) are distributed approximately normally, with a mean value of, say, 70 and a range from 40 to 100. Although there is a central tendency around which most values would be clustered, there would also be many values much greater or much less than the mean without any apparent correlation with lack of well-being or activity. What then is abnormal? What is the significance of abnormality in relation to sickness? Medicine approaches the problem by considering not just one variable but a number of variables, and looking for particular patterns of abnormal test results which appear to occur frequently and become established as disease entities (i.e. sets of symptoms which can be medically recognized and labelled as distinct 'diseases') with or without physiological or anatomical explanation. A person may be shown, for example, to have liver dysfunction without necessarily feeling any discomfort. On the other hand, there may be no medical explanation of this kind for the fact that a person 'complains' of a headache.

7.4 It is perfectly valid to identify those who complain of ailments as sick, even though it is medically unsatisfactory, so long as we keep the criterion used (i.e. personal declaration) constantly in mind. Other criteria might be used. We might count those who at any one time are under treatment by their general practitioner as sick, but we would then have to define what we mean by 'under treatment'. This could embrace those who have begun a series of consultations and have not been discharged. There would, however, be the difficulty that many patients discharge themselves, without formally notifying the practitioner, by the simple process of failing to attend the next scheduled consultation. We could take only first attendances but this would include those attending for some trivial reason, e.g. vaccination certificate. Another criterion might be absence from normal employment by virtue of sickness. We still have to accommodate vagueness. What of those who have no normal employment at the time of starting an episode of sickness, either because they have never worked or are suffering a period of unemployment? Then there is the problem of distinguishing between sickness which can be medically validated and absenteeism masquerading as sickness. What 'sickness' means depends upon the criteria used to identify it, and the criteria must be related to the use to which the measure of sickness is to be put.

7.5 In World War II it was desired not so much to measure the true incidence of disease in medical terms as to assess the state of public morale. The Government wanted to know literally what the public complained of. For this reason the regular Sickness Survey carried out by the then Government Social Survey was based on house-to-house interviews of a representative sample of the households in the country in which interviewees were asked questions about illnesses they had suffered in the 2 months preceding the interview. If, on the other hand, a quite different purpose were to be served—for example, an assessment of the work-load on hospital out-patient departments, the measure of sickness would need to be restricted to those conditions for which an attendance at an out-patient department was necessary.

7.6 The purpose of collecting actuarial statistics of sickness is to administer sickness insurance: to estimate the emergent liabilities and the factors (changes in benefits, etc.) that may influence them in order that they may be adequately provided for. The criterion for identifying sickness is therefore the establishment of a claim for sickness benefit from public or private insurance. A claim to sick-pay is usually supported by a medical certificate and is sometimes checked by a special investigation. Whatever methods are employed for checking the validity of the claim, the records from which statistics are derived will be of claims admitted rather than of sickness as such. Since one insurance organization may be more or less stringent in testing its claims than another, and may have different rules for entitlement to benefit than another, the claim statistics of the one may be quite unsuitable for use in connexion with the financial affairs of the other. It has to be borne in mind too that even when allowance is made for factors known to influence claim rates, such as sex, age, area of residence, or occupation, there is still the same variability in claim experience between individuals as for sickness generally, a feature we have already discussed at the beginning of this chapter.

7.7 Another complication of sickness measurement is that it is not an event taking place once for all at an instant of time. It is a state continuing over a period of time terminated by death or recovery. It may also recur, not necessarily in the same medical form but in the same financial form—another sickness insurance claim. To put it another way, a sickness claim does not, like death, remove a person from the exposed to risk.

7.8 Bearing in mind the definition of sickness referred to above, we can consider different forms of measurement.

7.9 We could consider the proportion of persons in a given group who fall sick in a given period of time (e.g. a year). If we treated individuals falling sick more than once during the period as separate casualties on each occasion, i.e. if we treated spells of sickness as individual events, we should have what the medical statisticians call an 'inception rate'. This would exclude persons already sick at the beginning of the period and include persons still sick at the end of the period, i.e. becoming sick during or before the beginning of the period and not recovered or dying before the end of the period. This would be a frequency rate analogous to the mortality rate, but it would not be useful for our present (insurance) purpose, because it makes no reference to the length of the spells of sickness; for the cost of sickness, which is the basis of the claim, is dependent on the duration of the spell.

7.10 We could also consider a different proportion—the proportion sick (i.e. actually in benefit) at a point of time. This too contains no reference in itself to the durational element of claims, but we can use it more easily to derive the 'sickness rate' used by actuaries and referred to by medical statisticians as a 'duration rate', i.e. the average amount of sickness (measured in a defined unit of time, commonly a week) per person (strictly per unit of risk time) during a defined interval of age (usually 1 year but sometimes 5 years).

7.11 Suppose we take a census, on every working day of a year, of those successfully claiming sick-pay for the day. Let $_tP$ represent the total number (sick or not) in the group under observation on day t and $_tS$ represent the number sick on day t; then the proportion sick on day t, say $f(t)$, would be the ratio $_tS/_tP$. If it is assumed that there are no new entrants or leavers during the year and that $_tP$ is affected only by deaths, we may define the sickness rate for the calendar year as either $\sum_t {_tS}/_0P = \mathring{s}$ or in the 'central' form as $\sum_t {_tS}/(\sum_t {_tP}/N) = \mathring{z}$, where N is the number of working days in the year.

7.12 Clearly $\sum_t {_tS}$ is the total number of working days lost during the year through sickness or the total number of days' sick-pay successfully claimed for the year; $_0P$ is the number of persons starting the year of observation and analogous to the exposed to risk for the q-type of mortality rate; $\sum_t {_tP}/N$ is the average total number in the group during the year (counting working days only) and analogous to the exposed to risk for the m-type mortality rate; $\mathring{s}$ is the average number of days of sickness per person starting the year; and $\mathring{z}$ is the average number of days of sickness per year of exposure. To convert $\mathring{s}$ and $\mathring{z}$ from days into weeks we should divide by the relevant length of the working week, taken either as 5, as is usually appropriate, or conventionally, if any part of Saturday is worked, as 6.

7.13 If the group is a large one in which there have been a number of deaths spread fairly uniformly over the year, the expression $_0P - \dfrac{\sum_t {_tP}}{N}$ would be approximately equal to half the deaths for the year. Hence we may write

[handwritten margin note: If only 2 days $_0p = 10$, $_tp = 5$ $_0p - \dfrac{z}{N} = 10 - \dfrac{15}{2} = 2\frac{1}{2}$]

$$\tfrac{1}{2}\mathring{q} \doteqdot (1 - \tfrac{1}{2}\mathring{p}) \doteqdot \left(1 - \frac{\sum_t {_tP}}{_0P \cdot N}\right)$$

and since

$$\mathring{s} = \mathring{z} \cdot \sum_t {_tP}/(_0P \cdot N)$$

$$\mathring{s} \doteqdot \tfrac{1}{2}\mathring{p} \cdot \mathring{z}$$

Generalization of the sickness rate

7.14 If we generalize $_tP$ and $f(t)$ by assuming that they each vary continuously throughout the year, the sickness rate $\mathring{z}$, expressed in terms of a year as the unit of time, is then

$$\frac{\displaystyle\int_0^1 f(t) \cdot {_tP}\, dt}{\displaystyle\int_0^1 {_tP}\, dt}$$

and this may be compared with the definition of the theoretical central sickness rate at age x usually given in life and other contingencies textbooks as follows:

$$z_x = \frac{52.18 \displaystyle\int_0^1 f_{x+t} l_{x+t}\, dt}{\displaystyle\int_0^1 l_{x+t}\, dt}$$

where l_{x+t} is the life-table function and the factor 52.18, representing the average number of weeks in a year, changes the measurement of the sickness from years to weeks. (The textbook by Neill uses $\bar{z}$ instead of f.)

The total sickness in a year

7.15 The general expression $\int_0^1 f(t) \cdot {}_t P\, dt$ represents the total sickness in years during the year, and it may be compared with

$$\sum_t {}_t S = \sum_t f(t) \cdot {}_t P$$

which represents the actual total sickness in the year expressed in working days. It may thus be seen that for the sickness rate the daily censuses are assumed to take place only to build up the figure for the total sickness in the year. The denominator of the central rate, i.e. the central exposed to risk, can be obtained in the usual way by deducting half the number of deaths in the year from the number starting the year. If, therefore, the total sickness can be obtained in a simpler way, the daily censuses can be dispensed with. In fact, such a simpler approach has long been in use by actuaries for friendly society and other sickness insurance statistics. This approach is to record in respect of each individual the number of weeks and odd days of sickness in the year and to compute the total of such weeks and days for the group, taking care to convert every 6 days (or 5 in the case of a 5-day week) into a week.

7.16 We have defined $\mathring{s}$, the average days of sickness per person starting the year, as $\sum_t {}_t S / {}_0 P$. We can, without altering its value, introduce a constant F in the numerator and denominator of this expression, viz.

$$\mathring{s} = F \cdot \left[\sum_t {}_t S / (F \cdot {}_0 P) \right]$$

If we can define F as the proportion falling sick during the year, then $F \cdot {}_0 P$ is the number of persons who are sick during the year, and the expression in brackets is clearly the average period of sickness for those who are sick during the year. We have, therefore, component factors of $\mathring{s}$: (1) the proportion sick, and (2) the average period of their sickness. In practical actuarial work it is sometimes helpful to consider these two component factors of $\mathring{s}$ separately. The second factor of $\mathring{s}$, i.e. the average period of sickness for all those who are sick during the year, itself comprises two factors: (a) the average number of spells of sickness per person falling sick, and (b) the average duration per spell. If there is no linking up of spells of sickness for the same individual, the sickness rate may factorize in the form $F.(a) \times (b)$ instead of in the form $F \times (a).(b)$ as given above. The advantage of this form of analysis is that, if the average duration per spell can be assumed to be unaffected, the effects of changes in the frequency of spells can be investigated.

The frequency distribution of duration of sickness

7.17 When compiling the statistics of total sickness, one must usually refer to the duration of sickness of each individual. As we are concerned only with sickness in the investigation year, the duration of sickness of any individuals who were sick at the beginning of the year would be computed on the assumption that their sickness began then; similarly, the sickness of those still sick at the end of the investigation year would be assumed to terminate at the year-end. If the information is on cards, a convenient way of doing the work would be to sort the cards according to the number of days' sickness suffered by the individual and then to tabulate the number of individuals for each number of days' sickness. A simple computation would then provide the total sickness. Where a more direct method of obtaining the total sickness is available (e.g. from punched cards or computer records), the tabulation of the frequency distribution of durations of sickness would not be necessary for this purpose, but it would still be well worth doing for the insight that it provides into the incidence of sickness as between sickness of short, medium and long duration. It has the further advantage that it enables an estimate of the standard deviation of the sickness rate to be made for the purpose of judging the significance of variations in the rates from time to time and between different groups. It has to be borne in mind that this is the frequency distribution not of all spells of sickness but only of those spells or parts of spells occurring in the rate-year; but, by the same token, it is a measure of the variability of sickness included in the sickness rate.

7.18 Suppose that a sample experience has been recorded and tabulated in a frequency table of duration of sickness (Table 7.1).

7.19 Let x_j be a random variable representing the duration of

Table 7.1

Duration in days	Frequency
0	n_0
1	n_1
2	n_2
3	n_3
.	.
.	.
.	.
i	n_i
Total	$_0P$

sickness of a jth person. The distribution of x_j is given approximately by

$$
\begin{array}{ccccc}
x & 0 & 1 & 2 & 3 \quad \ldots \\
P(x_j = x) & n_0/_0P & n_1/_0P & n_2/_0P & n_3/_0P
\end{array} \quad (7.1)
$$

7.20 If we start with N persons, then

$\mathring{s} = \dfrac{1}{N}(x_1 + x_2 \ldots + x_N)$, where $\mathring{s}$ is a random variable representing the average duration of sickness.

7.21 From (7.1), $E(x_j) = \Sigma i . n_i/_0P$ for $j = 1,2,3 \ldots N$

$$\text{var}\,(x_j) = \Sigma i^2 . n_i/_0P - (\Sigma i . n_i/_0P)^2$$

and $\text{var}\,(\mathring{s}) = \text{var}\,(x_j) . /N$

$$= \frac{\Sigma i n_i}{N . _0P}\left[\frac{\Sigma i^2 . n_i}{\Sigma i . n_i} - \frac{\Sigma i . n_i}{_0P}\right]$$

7.22 If y_k is a random variable representing the duration of sickness of a kth person *who becomes sick*, then the distribution of y_k is given by

$$
\begin{array}{cccc}
y & 1 & 2 & 3 \\
P(y_k = y) & n_1/(_0P - n_0) & n_2/_0P - n_0) & n_3/(_0P - n_0)
\end{array}
$$

7.23 Now $\text{var}\,(x_1 + \ldots + x_N) = N^2 \text{var}\,(\mathring{s})$

$$= N . \frac{\Sigma i . n_i}{_0P}\left[\frac{\Sigma i^2 . n_i}{\Sigma i . n_i} - \frac{\Sigma i . n_i}{_0P}\right]$$

$$= N \cdot E(x_j) \cdot \left[\frac{\Sigma \cdot i^2 \cdot n_i / (_0 P - n_0)}{\Sigma i \cdot n_i / (_0 P - n_0)} - \frac{(_0 P - n_0)}{_0 P} \cdot \frac{\Sigma i \cdot n_i}{(_0 P - n_0)} \right]$$

$$= E(x_1 + x_2 \ldots x_n) \cdot \left[\frac{E(y_k^2)}{E(y_k)} - F \cdot E(y_k) \right]$$

where F is the proportion who are sick at some time during the sample experience (this is not the same concept as $f(t)$ of para. 7.11, which is the proportion of an observed population who are sick not at any time but on a particular day). So, variance of total sickness = (mean of total sickness) $\times [m_2/m_1 - F \cdot m_1]$, where m_1 and m_2 are the first and second moments about zero of the sickness durations of all those who become sick (i.e. of y_k).

7.24   Since $m_2 > m_1$, we might further approximate, provided that F is not too large, by omitting the second term within the brackets, viz.

$$\sigma_S^2 \doteqdot \text{total sickness } (m_2/m_1)$$

7.25   Since the moments m_1 and m_2 could be estimated sufficiently closely from a random sample of claims (possibly at quinary or denary age-intervals when sickness rates are analysed by age) to provide an approximation to the value of m_2/m_1 at successive ages, it will be seen that an approximate significance measure is obtainable from the claims alone without computing the exposed to risk.

7.26   G. F. Hardy in 1888 devised the approximate formula $2\sqrt{S}$ for the mean deviation of the sickness (s being the total sickness). Assuming that the mean deviation is 0.8 of the standard deviation, the corresponding approximation to the variance is

$$2\sqrt{S} = 0.8\,\sigma_S^2$$
$$\therefore \sigma_S^2 = \left(\frac{0.8}{2}\right)^2 S$$

$$\sigma_S^2 \doteqdot 6 \cdot 25 S$$

$$\text{Mean deviation} = \Sigma \left| x_i - \bar{x} \right| \frac{f_i}{n}$$

where S and σ are expressed in 6-day weeks. σ^2 in days is, of course, $6^2 \times (\sigma^2$ in weeks), and S in days is $6 \times (S$ in weeks), so that Hardy's formula in days becomes

$$\sigma_S^2 = 37 \cdot 5 S$$

7.27   Thus Hardy's formula takes $37 \cdot 5$ as an approximation for

$$(m_2/m_1 - F \cdot m_1)$$

The accuracy of this approximation depends on the shape of the sickness distribution. Evidently the distribution is highly skew, with a long tail towards the longer periods of sickness. For the diminishing exponential distribution ($n_i \alpha e^{-im_1}$) we have $m_2 \doteqdot 2m_1^2$, while for the diminishing triangular distribution ($n_i \alpha 3m_1 - i$) we have

$$m_2 \doteqdot 3m_1^2/2$$

7.28 In the Manchester Unity experience the value of F for 'all sickness' of the A.H.J. Group was 0·213 at age 25, 0·216 at age 35, 0·241 at age 45, 0·297 at age 55 and 0·434 at age 65, with rapidly growing proportions at the older ages. Thus, if we exclude the older ages, the value of σ_S^2/S for the Manchester Unity A.H.J. experience was probably in the neighbourhood of $1·25m_1$. The values of m_1 were 24, 29, 41, 65 and 113 days for ages 25, 35, 45, 55 and 65 respectively, giving values for σ_S^2/S of 30·0, 36·3, 51·3, 86·3, and 141·3, Hardy's approximation of 37·5 is, therefore, only broadly applicable and then only at younger ages. It could not be applied at older ages or to the partial sickness statistics for the individual pay periods, i.e. first 3 months, second 3 months, etc., in which the rate of sickness benefit varies (see below).

7.29 L. E. Coward (1949) has investigated the distribution of sickness and has expressed the variance of sickness in terms of the moments of sickness rates and the number of lives, and has done this separately for the different periods of sickness. To a first approximation, the variance of sickness is twice the first moment of the sickness rates. He also investigated the theoretical relationship between S and σ_S^2. The ratio $\sigma_S/\sqrt{S}$ (where sickness is expressed in weeks), which Hardy found empirically to be 2·5, should, on the basis of the Manchester Unity (Whole Society) rates (all periods), vary from 2·84 at age 20 to 4·64 at age 40 and 5·44 at age 70. For 'first 3 months' sickness the ratio would be expected to show a remarkable constancy, varying only a little from 2·30 at age 20 to 2·69 at age 70. Other empirical investigations have (like Hardy) given lower values than the theoretical values of Coward, and this is thought to be due to positive correlation between sickness at adjacent ages, which would tend to reduce variance.

Periods of reduced sick-pay and the off-period

7.30 In sickness insurance, particularly as conducted by friendly societies, it is usual to provide, in respect of each sickness attack, for the rate of benefit to be reduced after a fixed duration of sickness and to be further reduced after further fixed durations of sickness. For example, there might be a reduction to half-pay after 3 months and to quarter-pay after 6 months. In applying the rules governing these reductions it is usual to link up all claims not separated by a minimum off-period (commonly taken as a year) and to treat a succession of linked-up claims as a single continuous period of sickness. Sickness attacks separated by more than the off-period are treated as distinct attacks for the purpose of determining the rate of benefit.

7.31 The system of reduction of the rate of sick-pay makes it essential to separate the total sickness and the sickness rates into the various 'periods of sickness' if the statistics are to be used for financial estimates. If all the members were 'off the funds' at the beginning of the investigation year and there was no occurrence of attacks of sickness subsequently requiring to be linked up with a previous attack before the beginning of the investigation year, statistics in the form of the frequency distribution of durations of sickness discussed above would provide all that was needed for sub-division of the sickness according to rate of sick-pay. This simple situation never exists. For each individual it is necessary in practice to obtain two measures of sickness duration, i.e. the duration of sickness in the investigation year (i) and the linked-up duration (j) which determines the rate of sick pay at the commencement of the sickness in the investigation year. As an alternative to recording j we might record $l(= i+j)$, the linked-up duration at the end of the sickness in the investigation year, and for some purposes this might be a preferable course, i and l both then being durations at the termination of the sickness. A bivariate frequency distribution according to i and j or i and l would clearly enable the total sickness to be divided up either in the ranges of linked-up durations corresponding to the rates of sick-pay or according to shorter range for use in a variety of problems. The classic Manchester Unity Experience of 1893–7 provided, for each age x, five convenient sickness-duration ranges, viz. first 3 months, second 3 months, second 6 months, second 12 months and after 2 years. It should be borne in mind that sickness 'after 12 months' and 'after 2 years' arises not only from the linking up, for rate-of-pay purposes, of sickness that occurred in the years immediately preceding the investigation year but also from unbroken long-term sickness continuing from a previous year. G. F. Hardy subsequently devised an approximate technique for splitting up the rates at each age into individual weeks, a process that could have been easily carried out from the data if the bivariate frequency distribution had been recorded for each age.

7.32 In day to day actuarial work when the sickness experience of a society is investigated for the purpose only of the financial administration of the particular society, the simple procedure of recording separately the number of weeks and days of sickness which rank for full pay, reduced pay, further reduced pay and so on would be used. Writing S_1, S_2, S_3, etc., for the total sickness eligible for full pay, reduced pay, further reduced pay, etc., and $\mathring{s}_1$, $\mathring{s}_2$, $\mathring{s}_3$, etc., for the corresponding rates, we then have the following additive relation:

$$\mathring{s} = S/_0P = S_1/_0P + S_2/_0P + S_3/_0P + \text{etc.,}$$
$$= \mathring{s}_1 + \mathring{s}_2 + \mathring{s}_3 + \text{etc.}$$

i.e. the sum of the partial rates equals the all-sickness rate.

7.33 The expression in 7.21 for the variance of $\mathring{s}$ applies also to each of the partial sickness rates, provided that we interpret n_i as the number of members successfully claiming for i days' sickness at the relevant rate of pay.

Influence of reduction of sick-pay on sickness rates

7.34 Where absence from work entails a reduction in income, the amount of the reduction must have some influence upon the desire to return to work (though is not the only influence), and, therefore, upon the duration of sickness claim. The force of this influence depends upon the efficiency of the administration of claims as well as upon the economic pressure upon the individual. It is important therefore to bear in mind that sickness as expressed in insurance claims is to some extent controllable by administrative means. For this reason it is dangerous to assume without investigation that sickness statistics obtained from one organization are suitable for use in connexion with another organization, whose arrangements may be significantly different in their impact upon the decision to go 'sick' or to remain 'sick'.

Sickness rates analysed by age

7.35 So far we have discussed the compilation of sickness rates for a group of persons over a calendar year. Total sickness rates show a marked tendency to rise with age in much the same way as mortality rates, although the partial rates (for different periods of sickness) may vary in age trend. Sub-division of the group by age is, therefore, usually necessary if a full understanding of the experience is to be gained. The problem of allocating the exposed to risk to individual ages is the same as for mortality rates. The allocation of the sickness to individual ages also follows the same principles as for deaths. The sickness for a given age should normally be that relating to the lives included in the exposed to risk at that age, so that if the ages for the exposed to risk are defined as at the beginning of the calendar year, the sickness should be allocated by reference to the age at the beginning of the calendar year. The principle of correspondence applies, but if the latitude with regard to approximate correspondence as is possible in a mortality experience were exercised, a complication would arise in the allocation of the sickness to the individual ages. For example, if the exposed to risk are according to nearest age on 1 January and the sickness is to be allocated according to age last birthday at the date of the sickness, in many cases the sickness in the calendar year would have to be divided between two adjacent ages. It might be, for example, that some first-period sickness and part of some of the second-period sickness would be allocated to age x and the rest of the second-period sickness to age $x + 1$. For this reason it is usual to preserve a strict correspondence between the sickness and the exposed to risk.

7.36 It would, of course, be possible to make a life-year investigation or a membership-year investigation, but as sickness investigations are, in practice, almost invariably on a calendar-year basis, we shall not pursue these possibilities.

7.37 The process of combining two or more years of experience follows the same lines as for a mortality investigation, the exposed to risk being combined in exactly the same way and the sickness at each age being combined in the same way as the deaths. Continuous exposed to risk formulae equally apply to a sickness investigation. The equivalence of continuous exposed to risk and census formulae also holds.

New entrants and withdrawals

7.38 A feature sometimes found in the rules of a friendly society is the provision that no sick pay will be allowed for sickness in the first n months of membership. This period, which may be 6 months, is usually called the 'waiting period'. The obvious course to take would be to defer the inclusion of new entrants in the exposed to risk until n months after the date of entry. In practice, however, the new entrants are often recorded according to their actual years of entry and ages at entry, and, accordingly, appropriate adjustments have to be made in estimating the exposed to risk. Apart from this point the fractional exposure to be allowed for new entrants is estimated as for a mortality investigation.

7.39 A rule providing for complete cessation of benefit on reaching a fixed advanced age such as 65 or 70 or on retirement is commonly applied by friendly societies. These cases are appropriately dealt with as withdrawals by providing for the fractional exposure in the year of cessation as for the withdrawals in a mortality investigation. Members may, however, cease paying contributions before reaching the maximum age. The rules may provide for the defaulting members to continue in full benefit for a fixed period (e.g. 6 months) and then go out of benefit for a period (e.g. another 6 months) before being finally struck off the membership roll. A member who puts himself back into benefit by paying up his arrears of contribution would be treated as having been continuously in benefit. Any attempt to allow for the hiatus in eligibility for benefit would be fraught with difficulty and would not usually be justified by the effect on the results. Some kind of health test—at least a declaration of good health—would usually be required to prevent defaulting members from getting back into benefit while sick merely by paying up the arrears. Adjustments are, however, usually made for members actually struck off the roll. The easiest course would be to antedate the date of withdrawal to correspond with the date of going out of benefit, but in practice these withdrawals are often recorded in the year in which, and at the age at which, they are struck off the roll, and appropriate adjustments have to be made in estimating the exposed to risk similar to those required in respect of the waiting period for the new entrants.

7.40 When an investigation is being made of the sickness experience of a large friendly order in which the rules or practices differ among the lodges, some reasonable practical rule must be adopted for dealing consistently with the new entrants and withdrawals. It was this variation between the lodges that created the need for the special treatment accorded to new entrants and withdrawals in the Manchester Unity Experience of 1893–7. An example of the kind of adjustment made is given below.

An illustration of a sickness investigation

7.41 Let us suppose that an investigation is to be conducted into the sickness experience in the 5 years 1973–7 of a society granting sickness benefits in the form of full pay for the first 6 months, half-pay for the next 6 months and quarter-pay thereafter, subject to a 1-year off-period, a 6-months' waiting period and a 3-months' out-of-benefit period before expulsion. The data would be collected on cards, which would normally be completed by the officials of the society. A suitable form of card is illustrated in Figure 7.1. These cards would normally be arranged to facilitate the preparation of punched cards as input for a computer (see para. 7.49). The details are omitted from Figure 7.1 for simplicity.

am info. required on cards

Sickness Claims					
		Period			
Year	Age	1st *week day* W D	2nd W D	3rd W D	
1973					
1974					
1975					
1976					
1977					
Total					

No.....................Name..

Occupation .... Sex.......................

Date of birth...

Date of entry.. Age.......................

Date of exit.. Age.......................

Cause of exit...

Other information ....

....

FIGURE 7.1

7.42 In filling in the particulars of the sickness, reference may be made to the rate of benefit actually paid in order to allocate the sickness to the correct periods. The amount paid at each rate could be recorded instead of the number of weeks and days, and the total amounts at each age for each rate of pay could then be converted into weeks by dividing by the appropriate rate of pay. If only the dates of the sickness were recorded in the society's records, it would be necessary to refer all claims for sickness in the first year of the investigation back to the sickness in the preceding year or two in order to secure a proper allocation of sickness to appropriate periods, having regard to the provision for linking up separate periods of sickness under the off-period rule. Sometimes this linkage would be ignored except for members actually claiming at the start of the period of the investigation.

7.43   The form in which to enter the age would depend on the information available. Often the date of birth would not be known. The year of birth might be available, in which case the age last birthday on 1 January could be used for all members. Alternatively, the only information might be the age next birthday at entry, in which case the age on 1 January would be taken as age next birthday at entry plus the curtate duration. Let us assume that age last birthday on 1 January of each year is available for all members and that new entrants and withdrawals have been recorded according to their actual dates of joining and withdrawing and not according to the dates of coming into and going out of benefit. (In the latter circumstances, of course, the details on the cards would take a somewhat different form from that indicated in the specimen card shown in Figure 7.1.)

7.44   We now define

b_x as the beginners at age x last birthday on 1 January 1973;

e_x as enders at age x last birthday on 1 January 1978;

n_x, w_x, θ_x as the new entrants, withdrawals and deaths during the period of the investigation whose age last birthday on 1 January of the calendar year of entry, withdrawal or death was x (it is assumed that all withdrawals are expulsions);

S_x^m as the total number of weeks of sickness claim within the period 'after m weeks' in any calendar year during the period of the investigation in which the age of the life on 1 January was x last birthday. For 'all-sickness', i.e. $m = 0$, the symbol is written as S_x.

7.45   We have now to decide on the appropriate adjustments for the new entrants and withdrawals. A simple course for the new entrants would be to exclude them entirely from exposure at the age corresponding to the calendar year of entry, and to give them a full year's exposure at the age corresponding to the year following the year of entry. The justification for this course would lie in the balancing of a deficit of exposure in the calendar year of entry with an excess of exposure in the following year. The entrants in the first half of a calendar year t may be regarded as exposed, on the average, for a quarter of a year in the year of entry, i.e. $\frac{1}{4}(\frac{1}{2} \cdot {}_t n_x)$ on the usual uniformity assumptions; the entrants in the second half are not exposed at all; while the entrants in the second half of the previous year should be exposed in the year following their year of entry for only three-quarters of the year on the average, i.e. $\frac{3}{4}(\frac{1}{2} \cdot {}_{t-1} n_{x-1})$. To make proper allowances we would need to know the number of new entrants in the half-year next before the start of the period of investigation which are included in b_x. To avoid these complications the simple course that would usually be adopted in practice, where there is a 6-months' waiting period, would be to give ${}_{t-1} n_{x-1}$ a full year's exposure at age x in year t and not to expose ${}_t n_x$ at all at age x in year t. It would be assumed that the excess of exposure of ${}_{t-1} n_{x-1}$ is balanced by the deficit of exposure of ${}_t n_x$.

7.46 Similar arguments apply to the withdrawals. Those occurring in the last 9 months of a calendar year would, on the average, be exposed for 3/8 of the year, while those in the first 3 months of the year would not be exposed at all in that year and on the average would have been exposed in the previous year for only 7/8 of that year. To make allowances on these lines we should need to know the withdrawals in the first 3 months after the end of the investigation period which would have been included in e_x. For the exposed to risk at age x in year t we ought therefore to deduct $(\frac{1}{4} + \frac{3}{4}(1 - 3/8)) \, {}_t w_x = \frac{23}{32} \, {}_t w_x$ and also $(\frac{1}{4} \times 1/8)_{t+1} w_{x+1}$. The practical course, however, would be to deduct $\frac{24}{32} \, {}_t w_x = \frac{3}{4} \, {}_t w_x$.

7.47 The continuous exposed to risk formulae (x = age last birthday) would then be as follows:

$$E_x = E_{x-1} + b_x - e_x - \theta_{x-1} + n_{x-1} - \tfrac{3}{4} w_x - \tfrac{1}{4} w_{x-1}$$

$$E_x^c = E_x - \tfrac{1}{2} \theta_x$$

$$\mathring{s}_x^m = S_x^m / E_x$$

$$\mathring{z}_x^m = S_x^m / E_x^c$$

These rates are for age x last birthday (not x exact), since the ages are all defined as ages last birthday on 1 January, the beginning of the rate interval. The same formula would apply if the ages were all defined as age x nearest birthday on 1 January, and the rates would then be for nearest ages.

Permanent health insurance—the analyses of the C.M.I.

7.48 In 1970 the Life Offices' Association and the Associated Scottish Life Offices invited the Continuous Mortality Investigation Bureau (see para. 18.22) to undertake an investigation into the sickness rates experienced under Permanent Health Insurance Policies, and the C.M.I. began making analyses of this experience from 1972. Permanent Health Insurance contracts are issued as ordinary policies on individual lives, or under group policies arranged with the employer of the lives insured. Benefits may be in the form of income during qualifying disability, lump sums on permanent disablement, and waiver of premiums under life policies during disablement. Premiums may be level or varying annual premiums. For group business the recurring single premium system ('current cost') may be used.

7.49 The data are collected either on eighty-column punched cards or, by arrangement with the C.M.I. Bureau, on magnetic tapes with fields to match. For individual business the following information is collected:

In force cards

1   Type of record, i.e. individual.
2   Contributor's office number.
3   Record year, i.e. calendar year to end of which record refers.
4   Location (U.K., Republic of Ireland, etc.).
5   Age definition (may be month and year of birth, age nearest birthday at end of calendar year of record, or age next birthday at same date).
6   Sex
7   Occupational rating (yes or no).
8   Period of deferment.

9   Year when policy first went on books.
10   Month and year of birth or office year of birth. The instruction reads 'contributors will have the option of showing the month of birth and the last two digits of the year of birth or of showing the office year of birth, which allows the calculation of the age next birthday or the nearest age (at end of year of record). If possible offices are requested to adopt the former method since it is more accurate'.
11   Ceasing year, i.e. calendar year in which cover will cease.
12   Period of benefit payment: weekly, monthly, yearly, etc.
13   Rate of benefit (gross of reinsurance).
14   Type of benefit (level, increasing, decreasing, etc.).
15   Medical evidence (medical, non-medical, non-selection limit applies).
16   Type of premium.
17   Underwriting impairment (if any).
18   Policy number.

Claim cards
1   Type of record (i.e. individual).
2   Items 2–17 above.
3   Date of falling sick.
4   Date payments began (a new card is prepared each time a claim is resumed after an interruption or change in degree of disability).
5   Mode of commencement of present benefit (continuation from previous record year, new claim, new claim following interruption of sickness in the deferred period, etc.).
6   Percentage of full rate paid under present claim.
7   Date of cessation of benefit under present claim *or* claim in force at end of record year.
8   Mode of cessation.
9   Cause of disability (coded to List C of International Statistical Classification of Diseases [W.H.O., 1968]).
10   Policy number.
7.50   The data are analysed into the following sickness periods:

Over   1 week but not over   4 weeks.
Over   4 weeks but not over   13 weeks.
Over 13 weeks but not over   26 weeks.
Over 26 weeks but not over   52 weeks.

Over 52 weeks but not over 104 weeks.

Over 104 weeks.

Note

7.51 The exposed to risk are calculated from tabulations by age nearest birthday of the business in force on 1 January and 31 December of the year of investigation. The exposed to risk for each experience group is calculated by following the experience of the group from age x at the beginning of the calendar year of investigation to age $(x+1)$ at the end of that calendar year. By this method an insured continuously disabled throughout the year of investigation does not have his claim apportioned to two experience groups, as would be the case if the census method were used. A central exposed to risk is calculated, giving a full year for those included at the beginning *and* at the end of the year and half a year for those included only at the beginning of the year; the tabulated rates are central rates. It should be noted (see para. 3.1.3. of C.M.I. *Reports*, No. 2) that new entrants require special treatment, since a new entrant in year y could not claim in the 104/all period until year $y+2$. A new entrant is included in the exposed to risk for a particular period of sickness only to the extent that it is possible for a claim to become payable in that period.

7.52 The claims are classified according to age nearest birthday at the beginning of the calendar year in which they occur and to periods of sickness passed through; sickness which terminates before the end of the deferred period is not recorded in the claims data.

Other factors affecting sickness rates

7.53 We have been discussing the need to allow for the variation of sickness with age. Age is not the only factor to be considered, however. Men and women differ considerably in their sickness experience. At each age women, especially married women, have heavier claims than men. For longer-term sickness married women experience lighter rates than single women, though still heavier than for men. Social and economic conditions too are as important (perhaps even more important) in relation to sickness as they are in relation to mortality.

Standard tables

7.54 The only sickness investigation for which full details have been published and which has formed the basis of an extensive set of standard tables is the Manchester Unity investigation of 1893–7. The Manchester Unity standard tables, with or without adjustment, are still in use today for friendly society work. However, the C.M.I. (paras 7.48–7.53) are in process of building up a substantial body of tables for Permanent Health Insurance and these will eventually become a standard source of reference.

7.55 The Manchester Unity of Oddfellows comprises a large number of lodges spread throughout the United Kingdom, each lodge having a large element of autonomy in its administration, its rules and its finance. One of the main objects of the investigation of 1893–7 was to provide a large volume of sickness and mortality data which could be used to form the basis of a number of standard tables from which to choose the most suitable for the valuation and other purposes of particular lodges. We have already mentioned the need to adopt consistent procedures for dealing with the differing waiting periods and withdrawal rules. These assumptions were different as between mortality and sickness. A uniform off-period of 12 months was used to link up sickness, and sickness rates for the uniform periods mentioned in 7.31 were computed despite the variation in the rules governing rates of pay in the different lodges.

7.56 The mortality and sickness data were divided between three major geographical areas of residence, and each of these groups was sub-divided into rural and urban areas according to density of population. These sub-groups were further sub-divided according to eight broad occupational groups. After a careful analysis and study of the results it was decided to construct separate mortality tables from the data of each of the geographical areas, taking the rural and urban data separately and together. For the sickness tables the occupations were grouped into three broad groups. It is the table of sickness rates for one of these groups (the A.H.J. table) that is still largely in use, though, of course, in conjunction with more modern mortality tables.

7.57 The reader should not conclude from the groupings of the data for the construction of standard tables that it was thought that the only environmental factor affecting mortality was geographical area of residence and that occupation was the only important factor for sickness rates. The decisions were convenient for the practical purposes in view and took account of the fact that individual lodges tended to be dominated by a particular occupation, which was often fairly widespread in the district in which the lodge operated. It was, therefore, not unreasonable to use tables for a particular lodge based on the sickness of the dominant occupation and the mortality of the district.

Durational effects on sickness rates

7.58   While it is not usual for a friendly society to require a new entrant to submit to medical examination, it is usual to exclude persons who are already sick, and to endeavour to exclude impaired lives by such means as requiring applicants to sign a declaration of good health. As a consequence some element of 'selection', e.g. age for age, lighter sickness for recent entrants than for longer established members, should be exhibited by the all-sickness rates. The use of a waiting period seems, therefore, to be unnecessary, but while it serves as a further safeguard against the admission of poor lives, it also reduces the significance of 'selection' due to the initial health requirements. In fact, in friendly society work no account is usually taken of this kind of selection. There is, indeed, a much more significant durational (or generation) effect which is also usually ignored in the statistical treatment of data commonly sufficient for the financial administration of friendly societies. This effect is manifest as differential year to year changes in the rates of sickness in the separate pay periods. A new entrant cannot possibly claim in the first year in the pay period 'after 12 months' nor in the second year in the pay period 'after 2 years'. For a group of new entrants a number of years must elapse before, as a group, they contribute to the later-period rates applicable to members of the same age who have been in the society for a longer period. The early-period rates of recent entrants could be abnormally high and could raise the average early-period rates without any increase being seen at later periods until sufficient time had elapsed. In the Manchester Unity investigation members of different durations at the same attained age were grouped together, and 'average' partial rates were computed despite the disturbance due to the practice of admitting new entrants up to quite advanced ages such as 40 or 45. In connexion with 'transfer values' under National Health Insurance, as it was operated before the National Insurance Act 1946 abolished the Approved Society system, this inherent 'selection' was regarded as an important factor. A member transferring from one Approved Society to another was necessarily a non-claiming member. Accordingly, for the purpose of computing the transfer value to be passed from the one society to the other, a set of adjustments to the sickness rates on which the National Health Insurance finances were based was devised.

Problems arising out of special rules affecting sickness benefits

7.59 Among the many friendly societies in existence there are all kinds of variations in the rules affecting sickness benefits, quite apart from the variations in the length of the waiting period and of the off-period. Sometimes the rules are designed to restrict payments due to long attacks of sickness, the function of the society being regarded as that of providing benefits for short-term sickness rather than for permanent disability. Sometimes the rules are designed merely to keep the claims within the scope of a modest rate of contribution. Any investigation into the experience of a society with the view to providing a financial basis for the operations of the society must necessarily be concerned with successful claims to benefit rather than with sickness as such. A member who, although sick, is not entitled under the rules to benefit would be treated in the investigation as 'not sick'. We remind ourselves that actuaries are concerned with claim rates rather than with duration of sickness.

7.60 Sometimes the effect of the rules is to render unsuitable the usual assumptions regarding the uniform distribution of sickness over calendar years or years of age; special treatment for withdrawals might then be required. As an example, we may mention an actual case where members were entitled to not more than 8 weeks' sick-pay in any one calendar year. Clearly the usual treatment of withdrawals would be unsatisfactory, because a member might tend to leave early in a calendar year after drawing all or most of his current maximum sick-pay for 8 weeks. The possibility of such a tendency would have to be statistically investigated and the actual adjustment would depend on the result of this investigation.

7.61 A fairly common type of limitation of benefit is for continuous sickness benefit to be restricted to, say, 6 months at a time. After receiving sick-pay for 6 months the member would be ineligible for a period fixed by the rules, e.g. for a year. He would then become eligible again for benefit. The year of ineligibility should not be confused with the off-period, which might also operate if there were more than one rate of pay. A member who is permanently disabled would receive benefit in a recurring cycle. The cycle might, for example, be full-pay for 6 months, half-pay for 6 months, no pay for a year, full-pay for 6 months and so on.

7.62 The principles applying to the computation of sickness claim rates are not affected by such rules, since the rates are necessarily based on allowable claims, but difficulties may arise when it is desired to compare the rates with those of some other society or with a standard table, or to modify the rates of a standard table as a basis for valuation.

Example 7.1

An investigation into the mortality and sickness experience of a Friendly Society is being carried out in respect of the calendar years 1973–8. The data have been listed in Table 7.2.

Table 7.2

Age x	b_x	n_x	θ_x	w_x	e_x	No. of weeks' sickness at age x
16	30	130	1	20	0	15
17	87	581	2	35	83	70
18	200	803	3	70	173	150
...	...	...	...	...	...	...

The functions used are defined in Table 7.3.

Table 7.3

Function	Definition	Age assumption
b_x	Existing on 1 January 1973	1972 minus valuation year of birth
n_x	Entrants 1973–8	Calendar year of entry minus valuation year of birth
θ_x	Deaths 1973–8	Calendar year of death minus valuation year of birth
w_x	Withdrawals 1973–8	Calendar year of withdrawal minus valuation year of birth
e_x	Existing on 31 December 1978	1978 minus valuation year of birth
Sickness	–	Calendar year of sickness minus valuation year of birth

The valuation year of birth is the calendar year of entry minus the age next birthday at entry.

There is a 6 months' waiting period for the sickness benefit.

Obtain exposed to risk formulae for calculating rates of mortality and central rates of sickness and apply your sickness formula to obtain the central sickness rate at age 17.

Substituting the exact definition of 'valuation year of birth' in the definitions of the functions we have the following:

b_x	Existing on 1 January 1973	$x = 1972 -$ calendar year of entry + age n.b.d. at entry	= Age x n.b.d. on entry anniversary in 1972 *not 1973*
n_x	Entrants 1973–8		Age x n.b.d. at entry
θ_x	deaths 1973–8	$x =$ calendar year of death − calendar year of entry + age n.b.d. at entry	= Age x n.b.d. on entry anniversary in calendar year of death
w_x	Withdrawals 1973–8	As for deaths	
e_x	Existing on 31 December 1978	$x = 1978 -$ calendar year of entry + age n.b.d. at entry	= Age x n.b.d. on entry anniversary in 1978
	Sickness		Age x n.b.d. on entry anniversary in calendar year of sickness

Clearly, then, the appropriate rate interval is the calendar year, and E_x will be defined as the risk time contributed during the calendar year in which the lives were aged x n.b.d. on the entry anniversary.

E_x^θ for mortality will be in 'initial' form.
E_x^s for sickness will be in 'central' form.

Mortality
b_x each life will contribute nil to E_x^θ and a full year to E_{x+1}^θ.

e_x each life will contribute a full year to E_x^θ and nil to E_{x+1}^θ.

n_x assuming a uniform distribution over the calendar year, the average contribution to E_x^θ will be $\frac{1}{2}n_x$ and n_x to E_{x+1}^θ.

n_{x+1} average contribution will be nil to E_x^θ and $\frac{1}{2}n_{x+1}$ to E_{x+1}^θ.

θ_x each life contributes a full year to E_x^θ and nil to E_{x+1}^θ.

w_x assuming a uniform distribution, the average contribution to E_x^θ will be $\frac{1}{2}w_x$ and nil to E_{x+1}^θ.

w_{x+1} average contributions will be w_{x+1} to E_x^θ and $\frac{1}{2}w_{x+1}$ to E_{x+1}^θ.

Hence

$$E_{x+1}^\theta = E_x^\theta + b_x - e_x + \tfrac{1}{2}(n_x + n_{x+1}) - \tfrac{1}{2}(w_x + w_{x+1}) - \theta_x$$

$$\mathring{q}_{x+1} = \frac{\theta_{x+1}}{E_{x+1}^\theta}$$

This rate will be in respect of the calendar year in which the lives were age $(x+1)$ n.b.d. on entry anniversary. If it is assumed that exact age x is attained on the average on 1 January, then $\mathring{q}_{x+1}$ can be taken as an approximation to $\mathring{q}_{x[\text{exact}]}$.

Sickness

We must modify the formula in the case of n and θ.

In the case of n_x it will not be good enough to assume that they will all come on risk at the end of the calendar year, as this will lead to a negative E_{16}, although there is some sickness for this age. It should also be noted that the number of new entrants at each age is large relative to the other statistics.

Let us assume a uniform distribution of entrants over the calendar year so that the average risk time for sickness contributed to E_x in the case of n_x is $1/8\, n_x$.

The formula for sickness will then be

$$E_{x+1}^s = E_x^s + b_x - e_x + 1/8\, n_{x-1} + \tfrac{3}{4}n_x + 1/8\, n_{x+1}$$
$$- \tfrac{1}{2}(w_x + w_{x+1}) - \tfrac{1}{2}(\theta_x + \theta_{x+1})$$

or

$$E_{\hat{x}}^s = \sum_{x+1}^{x} b_y - \sum^{x} e_y + \sum^{x-1} n_y + 7/8\, n_x + 1/8\, n_{x+1}$$
$$- \sum^{x} w_y - \tfrac{1}{2}w_{x+1} - \sum^{x} \theta_y - \tfrac{1}{2}\theta_{x+1}$$

The question asks for the sickness rate for age 17 (Table 7.4). The answer depends on the interpretation that is put on age 17. If it is

[margin notes]

since θ_{16} contr. $\frac{3}{4}$ n_{16} to E_{16} whereas w_{16} contributes something

o Denotes entrants in 1st half of year

$\frac{1}{4}$ enter in 1st half. Av. exposure = $\frac{1}{4}$ after 6 mths

∴ $\frac{1}{8}n_x$

	E_x	E_{x+1}
n_{x-1}^0	1	1
$\tfrac{1}{2}n_{x-1}$	$\tfrac{3}{4}$	1
$\tfrac{1}{2}n_x^0$	0	1
$\tfrac{1}{2}n_x^0$	$\tfrac{1}{4}$	1
$\tfrac{1}{2}n_{x+1}^0$	0	$\tfrac{1}{4}$
$\tfrac{1}{2}n_{x+1}$	0	0

Table 7.4

Age x	b_x	e_x	$1/8(n_{x-1}+6n_x+n_{x+1})$	$\frac{1}{2}(w_x+w_{x+1})$	$\frac{1}{2}(\theta_x+\theta_{x+1})$	E_x^s
15			16·2	10	0·5	
16	30	0	170·1	27·5	1·5	5·7
17	87	83	552·3	52·5	2·5	176·8
18	200	173				678·1

interpreted as the rate for the calendar year during which the lives were age 17 n.b.d. on the entry anniversary, then the rate is $\dfrac{70}{176\cdot8}$. If, on the other hand, the rate for the age interval exact age x to exact $x+1$ is required, then the best approximation is $\dfrac{150}{678\cdot1}$.

National insurance statistics

7.63 Readers should be aware of the statistics of sickness based on national insurance records and published annually by the Department of Health and Social Security, partly because these statistics form the basis of the Government Actuary's estimates of future national insurance expenditure on sickness claims and partly because they provide reliable background information of the trend of the level of sickness claims in the general population, and of the differentials between various groups in the population. The annual volume is entitled *Digest of Statistics analysing Certificates of Incapacity*, and the tables are based on an analysis of the certified incapacity for work of a 2·5 per cent sample of claimants. The main aggregates analysed are spells of incapacity beginning in the statistical period to which the volume relates, spells terminating in the period, days of incapacity in the period and claimants incapacitated on the last day of the period. The population at risk for sickness and injury are shown in the tables and represent the men and women who, if incapacitated, would be entitled to claim sickness or injury benefit or the award of credits; these populations are estimated by the Government Actuary on the basis of samples of national insurance records and are analysed by age, area, industry or occupation, as appropriate to particular tables. Tables indicating trends in incapacity over a period of years show rates standardized for age. A description of the method of sampling, and all necessary explanations of the definitions of terms used in the tables, are carefully set out in an introductory text. Days of sickness benefit and spells of sickness benefit are analysed both in total and separately for different groups of medical causes, and the main differentials examined are sex, age, area, occupation and industry. The injury benefit experience is similarly analysed.

7.64 It is sometimes argued that the analysis of sickness claims by medical cause is of little value, because the certificates given by medical practitioners are written in the knowledge that they will be read by their patients and the statements of cause are deliberately vague. It is true that the statements of cause are likely to be descriptions of symptoms rather than of the abnormality or disease producing these symptoms, and terms likely to cause undue distress (e.g. cancer) would clearly be avoided. Nevertheless for a broad range of diseases the statements do not have to be inhibited, and for many other causes, despite their vague description, a useful interpretation can be made by those who are experienced in the handling of these statistics. Moreover the errors and biases are reasonably stable from year to year, so that trends can be observed with greater accuracy than absolute levels of disease. On these grounds it may be claimed that these analyses of sickness claims by medical cause do make a considerable contribution to the limited information available in this country about the pattern of disease incidence in the general population. At the time of writing the latest published annual National Insurance sickness and injury statistics relate to 1976.

REFERENCES

Continuous Mortality Investigation *Reports*, No. 2 (1976). Institute of Actuaries and the Faculty of Actuaries.

Coward, L. E. (1949). The Distribution of Sickness. *J. Inst. Act.*, **75**, 12.

World Health Organisation (1968). *International Statistical Classification of Diseases and Injuries*, 8th Revision, W.H.O., Geneva.

EXERCISES FOR CHAPTER SEVEN

1. A friendly society grants sickness benefit at full pay during the first 6 months of sickness and at reduced pay for the remainder of sickness. The 'off-period' is 1 year and no sickness benefit is payable during the first 3 months of membership. Show how, from the experience of the society during a period of consecutive calendar years, you would construct an ungraduated table of the function 'Proportion of members sick in a year', tabulated according to 'First 6 months of sickness', 'Remainder of sickness' and 'All-sickness'.

It has been stated that this function may be used to test whether differences between rates of sickness at a specified age in two or more experiences are due to differences in the average duration of attack. Comment on this statement.

2   A large centralized friendly society provides sickness benefits for its members and a funeral benefit up to age 65. The weekly rate of benefit payable during sickness reduces after 6 months of continuous sickness, and sickness is treated as continuous unless there is an interval of at least 12 months between claims for benefit. All benefits cease on withdrawal from the society. A small life annuity is provided for members attaining age 65.

Data have been tabulated in the following form:

(a) number of members on 31 December in each year according to age last birthday on that date;

(b) number of members dying or withdrawing in each calendar year according to age last birthday at death or withdrawal respectively.

(c) number of weeks of sickness benefit at each rate paid in each calendar year according to the age on the birthday falling in that calendar year.

In order that the benefits payable before age 65 may be valued, the following, based on the experience of 5 calendar years, are required:

(i) a service table with radix 10,000 at age 21;

(ii) sickness rates for ages 21 to 64 inclusive.

Show how these may be prepared, defining carefully all symbols and giving the column headings of any working sheets required. Ignore graduation.

3   (i) A friendly society operating in a certain town has been providing sickness benefits to its members for many years. The main benefit table provides, in return for a regular contribution, full sickness benefit each week for the first 6 months of sickness, reducing thereafter to one-half of the full weekly rate. This reduced rate of benefit is, however, payable only so long as a member's total contributions, since joining, exceed the total sickness benefit paid to the member.

There is an off-period of a year between successive claims in determining the rate of benefit (if any) to which a member is entitled, and a new member is not eligible for benefit for the first 6 months after joining the society.

You are asked to investigate the sickness experience for the year 1978, and, to this end, a card is available for each member showing, *inter alia*,

(a)   Date of birth

(b)   Date of exit and whether by death or withdrawal

(c)   Total sickness benefit received in each calendar year, sub-divided according to the rate of benefit.

State what other information you would require and, using it, obtain expressions for the central rates of sickness, defining carefully the symbols you use.

(ii) A similar society with identical rules was set up in a neighbouring town about 10 years ago. Rates of sickness for this new society have been calculated for the year 1978.

At each age the first 6 months' sickness rate of members of the new society is rather higher than that of the old, but the 'after six months' sickness rate is materially lower. Suggest possible reasons for these differences.

CHAPTER EIGHT

MARRIAGE AND FERTILITY
RATES

Marriage rates

8.1 As for all other vital rates, marriages must be related to the population at risk, viz. first marriages of females to the spinster population, and remarriages to the numbers of widowed and divorced. The likelihood of marriage varies very much with the age of the prospective bride (or bridegroom).

8.2 It is usual, therefore, to calculate age specific marriage rates as, for example in Table 8.1.

Table 8.1 *Annual marriage rates per 1,000 bachelors, widowers and divorced men, spinsters, widows and divorced women, by age—England and Wales 1974*

Age	Bachelors	Widowers and divorced men	Spinsters	Widows and divorced women
16–19	22·9	–	81.0	–
20–24	143·3	456·4	209·1	490·1
25–29	154·2	387·8	164·5	314·1
30–34	84·5	313·2	83·5	211·9
35–39	43·7 ⎫	219·1	42·8 ⎫	121.3
40–44	23·9 ⎬		22·3 ⎬	
45–49	16·2 ⎫	124·1	15·0 ⎫	46·5
50–54	10·7 ⎬		10·3 ⎬	
55 and over	4·2	26·3	2·2	4·2

8.3 It will be noticed that the rates peak at different ages for bachelors and spinsters. Husbands tend to be older at marriage than their wives by 2 or 3 years. The average difference increased before 1950, owing to the then excess of spinsters (see para. 8.5), but has narrowed in recent years, as can be seen from the figures for England and Wales in Table 8.2. It will be noticed from Table 8.2 that there was a sharp fall in the age difference in 1966–70. This was because the average age at marriage of spinsters had fallen as low as it could without implying more teenage girl marriages than was the social norm, while there was still scope for the average age of bridegrooms to fall further.

Table 8.2 *England and Wales—average ages at marriage for bachelors and spinsters*

Year of marriage	Bachelors (marrying spinsters)	Spinsters (marrying bachelors)	Difference
1936–40	27·26	24·84	2·42
1941–45	26·34	23·81	2·53
1946–50	26·54	23·83	2·71
1951–55	25·93	23·28	2·65
1956–60	25·34	22·69	2·65
1961–65	24·80	22·17	2·63
1966–70	24·08	21·84	2·24
1974	24·10	21·90	2·20

8.4 The likelihood of marriage also depends on the relative supply of bachelors and spinsters at their respective marriageable ages. As an illustration, we may look at changes in England and Wales in recent times. In the early 1930s, as a result of a constant stream of emigration of men from this country and the heavy losses of men in World War I, there were in England and Wales more spinsters than was necessary to meet the bachelor demand.

Table 8.3 shows the numbers of bachelors and spinsters at the 1931 census of England and Wales, in quinary age groups, and the marriage rates at those ages. It will be borne in mind that, at that time, the average age difference between bachelor bridegroom and spinster bride was about $2\frac{1}{2}$ years, so that to test the supply of bachelors or spinsters as a guide to marriage prospects in 1931, one should, for example, compare numbers of bachelors at age 25–9 with the mean of the numbers of spinsters aged 20–4 and 25–9. It will be seen that in 1931 the number of bachelors aged 25–9 was considerably less than half the number of spinsters aged 20–9. The average marriage rate of spinsters of that age group (at about 110 per 1,000) was lower than that of bachelors aged 25–9 (about 160 per 1,000). The rates in

Table 8.3 England and Wales—bachelors' and spinsters' marriage rates

Age	Census 1931 (000s)		Marriage rates (per 1,000) 1931		Census 1971 (000s)		Marriage Rates (per 1,000) 1971	
	Bachelors	Spinsters	Bachelors	Spinsters	Bachelors	Spinsters	Bachelors	Spinsters
15–19	1,704	1,694	3·3	17·0	1,661	1,477	26·0*	93·5*
20–24	1,463	1,332	72·5	106·5	1,186	737	169·5	250·0
25–29	767	702	140·8	96·9	415	210	169·9	168·3
30–34	312	403	52·3 }	22·3 }	202	111	85·7	76·1
35–39	176	313 }			156	97	43·8	38·4
40–44	139	260	18·0 }	8·2 }	158	109	24·2	21·8
45–49	130	229 }			154	124	15·5	14·8
50–54	120	202 }			123	124	10·4	10·6
55 and over	291	567	5·7	2·2	398	891	4·4	2·6
Total	5,102	5,702	56·2	51·8	4,453	3,880	82·7	97·6

* These rates are for the age group 16–19.

brackets have been interpolated on the basis of more detailed rates available for 1931–5.

8.5   After the economic depression of the 1930s the flow of emigrants was reversed, and has only recently been resumed. The war losses of 1939–45 were much lower than those of the period 1914–18. Furthermore the progressive reduction of foetal mortality has resulted in a higher male/female ratio at birth. The reduction of mortality at younger ages too has narrowed the mortality differential between the two sexes and postponed the age-group by which the excess of males at birth is countered by excess male mortality, from 5–9 in 1911 to 40–4 in 1971. All in all, as can be seen from Table 8.2, the spinster excess of former years at the marriageable ages has largely disappeared. For example, we can compare 1,186,000 bachelors at age 20–4 in 1971 with one-half of the 2,214,000 spinsters aged 15–24.

Economic and social factors affecting marriage rates

8.6   An atmosphere of economic security encourages high marriage rates. The conditions of full employment in England and Wales in the early 1950s operated in two ways. First, employers had to compete for labour and had to offer, at the outset, rates of pay much nearer to full adult rates than were formerly regarded as appropriate. Secondly, because jobs were not so eagerly sought after, spinsters no longer had to make way on marriage for unmarried women. It became possible and indeed became regarded as desirable for women to follow a career without having it cut short by marriage; or to put it the other way round, to be able to contemplate marriage against a background of joint earnings and a high level of living from the outset. Marriage need not, as was formerly the case, be deferred until savings had been acquired to furnish a home and provide protection against any risk of economic troubles in the early years of marriage. There was no longer any economic obstacle to early marriage. Another important factor to be mentioned is the general emancipation of women, which has progressed at a faster rate from that time. Marriage is no longer regarded as the only 'safe' career for a girl; she now has the choice of a wide variety of careers. Socially, as well as economically, girls can regard marriage as incidental to their fuller lives.

8.7   As a result of all these factors, in Britain, as in many other countries, the period since World War II has been characterized by high marriage rates and earlier marriage ages. This change is evident from Table 8.3. The 1971 rates are higher and peak at earlier ages than those for 1931. The figures in Table 8.2 also show a progressive reduction in average age at marriage from 1950 until 1970.

8.8 One way of summarizing a set of marriage rates is to produce a table showing, out of a given generation of female births, the proportion still alive and (a) unmarried or (b) married, at any particular age. Such a table is derived from a combination of marriage rates and mortality rates and is called a 'net nuptiality table'. The term 'net' indicates that mortality has been taken into account as well as nuptiality. If marriages only were considered, it would be a gross nuptiality table, but this type of table is rarely used. Table 8.4 shows an extract from a net nuptiality table. It will be recognized as a double decrement table for spinsters, the decrements being death and marriage.

Table 8.4 *Extract from a net nuptiality table*

x	No. of spinsters living at exact age x	Central rates of death dm_x	Central rates of first marriage mm_x	Probability of death or marriage $\dfrac{2(dm_x + mm_x)}{2 + (dm_x + mm_x)}$	deaths x to $x+1$	marriages x to $x+1$
0	10,000					
15	9,661*	0·00052	–	0·00052	5	–
16	9,656	0·00058	0·00657	0·00712	6	63
17	9,587	0·00064	0·02599	0·02628	6	246

* By ordinary life table processes (as in the line for age 15). For age 17 we have total decrement $= 9,587 \times 0·02628 = 252$, of which deaths = mean population × central death rate = $[9,587 - \frac{1}{2}(252)] \times 0·00064 = 6$, and marriages = $252 - 6 = 246$.

8.9 The probabilities of marriage on which the nuptiality tables for a given year are based refer to the experiences of different generations within a single calendar year. One effect of this is to make them of limited value as a guide to long-term prospects. For this purpose it would be bettter to compare the experiences of different generations at the same ages but in different calendar periods, rather than different generations at different ages in the same calendar period.

Total married women of reproductive age

8.10 The effect of high marriage rates in raising the proportion of the population which is married is an important influence on the fertility of the community, since this depends on the number of married women in the population.

8.11 The proportion married increases with advancing age, at first rapidly and then more slowly, and then begins to decline as new marriages are increasingly offset by widowhood. In Britain the proportion married has increased within each age-group throughout the current century.

8.12 The proportion married in the 15–49 age-group represents the fraction of the reproductive years which fall within married life. In England and Wales, for example, there was a slight increase in this fraction from 50·2 to 52·9 per cent between 1911 and 1931, followed by a more rapid rise to 56·6 per cent in 1938 and to 70·9 per cent in 1971. These increases are partly due to the ageing of the 15–49 age-group since 1911, which has increased the relative number at the older ages within the age-group, i.e. the ages at which the proportion married is greater.

Other fertility effects

8.13 Apart from adding to the flow of births generally by increasing the stock of married women, the rise in marriage rates had from 1955 an accelerating effect on the flow of births in so far as the rise in marriage incidence was concentrated at young ages and helped, together with faster family building within marriage, to lower the average age at parenthood. This meant, shortly, borrowing births from the future to augment temporarily the normal flow. It was estimated that of the rise in annual births between 1955 and 1960 in England and Wales about one-quarter was due to earlier marriage and a higher proportion marrying, and about three-quarters to shortening of the average interval between marriage and first birth and between subsequent births. There was no substantial rise in average family size. Table 8.5 shows the dramatic rise in the annual numbers of births in England and Wales from 1955 and, in contrast, the relatively small increase in average family size. The so-called 'baby boom' was not a significant increase in fertility; it was not a 'boom' at all but a change in the timing (i.e. advancement) of births that would have occurred later but for the factors mentioned above. It was recognized by demographers that as soon as the new timing had established itself, the borrowing from the future had to end; and it did so in 1965.

8.14 Any permanent effect upon fertility arising from earlier marriage and shorter birth spacing was reduced by the growing tendency (common to most communities where family limitation is

Table 8.5   *England and Wales—live births, 1955-74*

Year	Annual numbers of live births (000s)	Period	Average number of children born to women married in the period*
		1945–49	2·2
		1950–54	2·3
1955	668		
1956	700		
1957	723	1955–59	2·4
1958	741		
1959	749		
1960	785		
1961	811		
1962	839	1960–64	2·3
1963	854		
1964	876		
1965	863		
1966	850		
1967	832	1965–69	2·2
1968	819		
1969	798		
1970	784		
1971	783		
1972	725	1970–74	2·1
1973	676		
1974	640		

*There is an element of projection in the rates for marriages from 1955 which can still possibly produce further children. The final rates may turn out to be lower than the projected rates.

practised) for family building to be completed relatively early in married life and not to be proportionally extended by any increase in the length of married life falling within the reproductive age period. In a developing country, without widespread family-planning services, fertility would probably rise with an extension of married life within the reproductive age period.

Employment of married women

8.15 The changes in marriage rates are connected with the employment of married women. The rise in marriage rates was encouraged by the extensive employment of married women; this extensive employment became essential when labour was in short supply in the 1950s, and it has persisted with the growth of the feminist movement even though the original stimulus—a surfeit of jobs—has been replaced by high unemployment—a surfeit of workers. There has been established, in Britain, a pattern of early marriage and child-bearing with, as soon as is practicable, a return of the women to the adopted vocational career—provided that the job is not less interesting than staying at home, though the compulsion of extra earnings may override this consideration.

Summary

8.16 Marital condition is an important factor in relation to mortality and employment but obviously from a demographic point of view the level and future course of marriage rates are most important in relation to their influence on fertility. Indeed it is impossible to separate fertility rates from the age and marriage duration structure of the population of married women supporting these rates. Fertility rates must always be considered against the marriage experience permitting them. In general, higher marriage rates, especially at younger ages, tend to higher fertility simply because more married women are exposed to the risk of conception for longer, though the widespread acceptance of contraception for family limitation has reduced the force of this factor of extended exposure. When we come to discuss fertility measurement, it will be seen that the number of married women at a particular age enters into the calculation of reproduction and replacement rates.

Fertility rates

8.17 Fertility measures the rate at which a population adds to itself by births and is normally assessed by relating the number of births to the size of some section of the population, such as the number of married couples or the numbers of women of child-bearing age, i.e. an appropriate yardstick of potential fertility. The number of births, though determined by attitudes toward family size, is limited by the number of women exposed to the risk of pregnancy; and, in the consideration of fertility measures, the choice of the population at risk is important.

Fertility variation

8.18 Since some 93 per cent of all births in England and Wales are within marriage, the extent to which people marry at any time exercises a powerful influence on the subsequent flow of births. The number of couples who marry will depend upon the available numbers and the relative age distributions of men and women within the marriageable age period, and these will depend upon antecedent births (and the marriage experience producing them); thus future fertility depends upon past fertility. Though there are, thus, these quantitative restraints on the variation of fertility, there is also an important element of variation due to changes in attitude. More widespread knowledge of contraceptive methods and the introduction of more efficient methods have, in this country as in many other developed countries, resulted in an approach to a state of fertility control, i.e. a state of closeness of achievement to intention. The gap between attained family size and desired family size is very small. Fertility is now therefore much more sensitive to social and economic changes affecting attitudes to family size. In addition, throughout western society and elsewhere (The People's Republic of China, for example) profound social changes have been taking place affecting the family as an institution, and both marriage and fertility as the process of family building. These changes may be summarized briefly (and probably with some degree of over-simplification) by saying that while, more than ever, young people are taking positive and responsible decisions about living together, marriage and having children, they nevertheless refuse to accept that these three events are inextricably bound together as they were before World War II. Feminism has played a part in this change but it is by no means the only factor. As to the size of family desired in this country, there has been, antedating these social changes and beginning in the latter part of the nineteenth century, an almost continuous decline in family size from an average of 5·8 children for marriages of 1870–9 to 2·4 for marriages of 1920–4 and 2·2 for marriages of 1965–9.

8.19 This decline in family size can be explained in part by the beginning of the now familiar and all too frequent cycles of over-production, followed by depression, retrenchment and unemployment, which led to much poverty. However, it is explained mainly by the enactment of the Shaftesbury legislation prohibiting the employment of young children, and the Elementary Education Act of 1870, which made attendance at primary school compulsory from the age of 5 to 13. Almost overnight young children ceased to be economic assets to their parents and became economic liabilities. A further dramatic change took place at the turn of the century as a

consequence of a sharp decline in infant mortality. This was brought
about by the 1875 Public Health Act and by specialised maternity and
child welfare centres. The first health visitors' training courses began
in 1892. At the beginning of the century a number of towns had milk
depots for the provision of clean cows' milk for poor mothers unable
to breastfeed their infants. These and similar agencies formed the
foundation of the maternity and child welfare service as we know it
today. In addition to this concentration on the health of mothers and
babies, social conditions were generally improving. As a result, infant
mortality (deaths under 1 year of age per 1,000 live births), which had
been above 150 throughout the latter half of the nineteenth century,
fell from 156 in the period 1896–1900 to 90 for the period 1916–20 and
55 for 1936–40. There was a new confidence about the survival of
infants. It was no longer necessary, as it had been in Victorian times,
to think in terms of producing seven children in order to retain five.
All these influences taken together, but especially the economic
influences, brought about a profound change of attitude to family
size: a swift progression to a smaller norm. For the poorer
circumstanced, to whom knowledge of and the means to exercise
contraception has remained less accessible, the norm has remained
higher than for the better circumstanced, but in all levels of society
smaller families have become the order of the day. The former wide
range of family has given way to a greater degree of uniformity; there
are relatively fewer childless families or one-child families and fewer
families of four or more children. There is a relative concentration of
families of two or three children.

8.20 It is not to be overlooked that the greater part of this steady
reduction of family size was achieved at a time when modern easy and
highly effective methods of contraception were not yet available; the
main method was coitus interruptus. The change of attitude in favour
of smaller families was clearly a very determined one, and it is not
likely to be reversed without positive motivation.

8.21 What would be likely to reverse it? Young people of today have
concerns about long-term economic growth, its feasibility and, if
feasible, its effects; about conflicts; about world population pressure;
about pollution, especially atomic energy pollution. Unless and until
these anxieties are relieved, attitudes towards child-bearing are
unlikely to change.

Factors affecting fertility variation

8.22 The number of children produced by a group of women in a given year will depend upon their ages, whether they are married, how long they have been married, and how many children they have already borne. It will depend also upon the economic resources, housing conditions and the educational facilities available. It may also depend upon where they live, e.g. whether in an urban or a rural environment. It will, as we have remarked in para. 8.21, depend on the couples' view of the quality of life into which they are bringing children. This latter factor is general, apparently affecting all levels of society. In the following sections we shall be more concerned with factors which produce fertility differentials in society, and with measures that illustrate their effects.

Birth rate

8.23 The crude birth rate (simply referred to as the 'birth rate') is calculated by relating total live births in a year to the total population of all ages, and expressing it as a rate per 1,000. The total population is not the proper population at risk so far as births to women are concerned, since it contains males, and also females outside the child-bearing ages. The crude birth rate is satisfactory only when the true exposed to risk is a fixed proportion of the total population, i.e. when it is used for the same community in a short series of years, or in comparing the birth rates of communities whose populations are known to be nearly, if not quite, equal in their age and sex composition and in marital condition. If, however, the number of women, especially of married women, of child-bearing age changes in the one community studied or differs in the two populations compared, the crude birth rate will vary from this cause apart from true fertility variations. However, though misleading as a measure of fertility, the crude birth rate does measure the gross rate of increase of the population by births.

Fertility rate

8.24 The general fertility rate is obtained by expressing the live births as a rate per 1,000 of women of child-bearing age, taken as either 15–49 or 15–44, more usually the latter. The difficulty is that although this rate is properly related to the population at risk, it requires estimates of the female population by age and marital status

central exposed to risk : see revision test 1, Q3 (1)

in inter-censal years, and for small local areas this may lead to more error than would be entailed in using crude birth rates for comparison. It is possible to introduce some correction to birth rates for differences in population age structure. One can calculate an area comparability factor, which represents the ratio of an 'expected' birth rate—obtained by applying standard (usually national) fertility rates by age to the local population structure—to the actual rate recorded in the standard population. If this factor is above (below) unity it indicates that the local rate must be correspondingly reduced (increased) to allow for departure from standard population structure. If local birth rates in inter-censal years are multiplied by the appropriate census-based factors, the rates thus adjusted are comparable. This is the method used by the Registrar General for England and Wales.

Legitimacy

8.25 Where possible it is appropriate to sub-divide the general fertility rate into two components, (1) the ratio of legitimate births to married women 15–44, and (2) the ratio of illegitimate births to unmarried women 15–44. This secures a better relationship between births and exposed to risk, but even so it is not a precise method. If a marriage takes place during pregnancy, the birth is registered as legitimate, and this tends to reduce the true illegitimate fertility and to increase the legitimate component. If a married man dies before his child is born, the birth is legitimate and appears in the numerator of (1), while the mother as a widow appears in the denominator of (2). Broadly, however, an accurate picture is obtained.

8.26 Illegitimacy is commonly expressed by calculating illegitimate births as a percentage of total live births. Though satisfactory when applied to short-term comparisons, this method may be misleading over a long term. If, for example, the legitimate birth rate were declining and the illegitimate birth rate were constant, the percentage illegitimacy would show an increase. The percentage illegitimacy may fluctuate considerably when war conditions disturb normal relationships.

Multiple births

8.27 Owing to the occurrence of twins, triplets and higher orders of multiple deliveries, a distinction has to be drawn between the number of mothers confined in a particular period usually referred to as the number of maternities, and the total resultant births, live and still. (Strictly a maternity is defined as a pregnancy which has terminated in the birth of one or more live or still-born children.) In England and Wales in 1965 the ratio of live and still births to maternities was 1·0114. In 1975 the ratio was 1·0101, the decrease since 1965 being mainly due to a reduction in still-births.

Variation of fertility with age of mother and duration of marriage

8.28 We may calculate age- and marriage-duration-specific fertility rates by classifying both maternities in the period and the average married female population in the period according to age of mother and duration of marriage, and dividing the number of maternities for a particular age of mother and marriage duration by the appropriate number of women at risk. In general these fertility rates decline with advancing age of mother and with lengthening duration of marriage. At each duration the rates decline with increasing age of mother, and at each age of mother, after rising to a maximum in the second year of marriage (except in those under age 20 where pre-marital conceptions are relatively more numerous), they decline with lengthening duration of marriage.

8.29 These two factors of age and marriage duration are of considerable importance in assessing fertility prospects for a particular population. It should be noted that sometimes the classification is by age at marriage and marriage duration, the addition of the two giving attained age.

Other indices of fertility

8.30 The birth rate in a particular year is merely a short-term measure of the flow of births and gives no guidance to the long-term effects of contemporary variations in fertility. The important fact to be ascertained is whether or not the current level of fertility, if maintained, is such that in the long run the population will change in size and age structure. From this question there emerges the concept of population maintenance or replacement.

8.31 It might be thought that the natural increase was itself an adequate measure of population maintenance. The natural increase, however, though a correct arithmetical expression of the balance of births over total deaths, indicates only the population changes (aside from migration) in one year, and not the trend. In any one year the total deaths depend upon the present age structure of the population,

Table 8.6

Year	Births (000s)	Deaths (000s)	Natural increase (000s)
1961	811	552	+259
1966	850	564	+286
1971	783	567	+216
1973	676	587	+ 89
1976	584	599	− 15

which, though affected by past fertility, is not sensitive to current changes in fertility. If past fluctuations in fertility and mortality have been such that a bulge in the curve of age distribution is working its way up through age groups, there will come a time when a large increase in the population at advanced ages will produce a sharp rise in the annual deaths. Thus it may be that, even though fertility at that time may be rising, the natural increase will be more affected by the change in the number of deaths than by changes in the flow of births. For example, in England and Wales annual deaths are increasing as a consequence of the passage upward through the age structure of the larger pre-1910 generations, and the natural increase, already depleted by the decline in annual births, has been further depleted and even converted to a negative quantity on this account. The figures in Table 8.6 are illustrative. The two components of the natural increase are quite unrelated to each other, and their coincidental balance or imbalance, though important, cannot be expected to give an indication of the long-term growth of the population.

8.32 The concept of replacement demands measurement of effects over a period of time, and requires that attention be focused upon generations and the births they produce rather than upon the annual flow of births in the country over a short period of time.

Replacement *Consider pop as stationary*

8.33 Suppose we consider the simplest measure of population maintenance. Assume that the current annual number of births continues indefinitely and calculate (using life-table factors based on current mortality rates) the size of population that would ultimately result when stationary conditions had been attained. In England and Wales in 1971–5 the average number of live births was 685,000 and the deaths averaged 583,000. A population recruited from this supply of births and exposed to current mortality would number 49.7 millions. (We multiply the male and female births by the life-table factor T_0/l_0 for males and females respectively. Note that $T_0/l_0 = \mathring{e}_0$.) The actual average population in the same period was 49.1 millions. Thus the number of births in 1971–5, though 17 per cent greater than the number of deaths in the period, was only 1·2 per cent more than that (677,000) required to maintain the population.

8.34 It has, however, to be borne in mind that a large proportion of the population are not in the child-producing age-group and, therefore, the current births can hardly be related to them. If the important proportion within the child-bearing age-group is temporarily unduly high, the births will be high in relation to the total population, and the percentage maintenance of the current population of all ages will be misleadingly raised. We shall have no warning that, when the temporary inflation of the child-bearing age-group passes, the flow of births may not suffice to maintain the population. We might, therefore, consider whether or not parents are maintaining the population of parents, calculated in exactly the same way as before except for the restriction of age.

8.35 Suppose we take the child-producing age-group as 15–44. The 1971–5 births (685,000 average per annum) would maintain a stationary population containing 19.89 million persons (both sexes combined) aged 15–44. The actual population in England and Wales in this age group numbered 19·18 million in 1971–5 (average). The extent of 'parental maintenance' as a percentage of 19·18 millions was 104. It would have required 659,000 births a year for parental replacement compared with 677,000 required on the total population basis used above. Thus, owing to the 1971–5 age structure of the population (with a low proportion in the parental age-group), the number of births required to produce parental replacement would be less than sufficient to support the total population of all ages, though the difference is not great.

Gross reproduction rate

8.36 Although we have taken account of the child-bearing population as distinct from the total population, we have not sub-divided this population according to age in order to take account of differential fertility at different ages within the group. It is necessary to do this in order to obtain a clearer picture of possible variations, such as may arise from unusual features of the age structure of the

Table 8.7 *England and Wales—fertility* 1971

Age	Female population (000s)	Total live births (females only)	Mean fertility rate
15–19	1,618	39,729	0·02455
20–24	1,855	138,877	0·07487
25–29	1,579	119,726	0·07582
30–34	1,411	53,173	0·03768
35–39	1,376	22,145	0·01609
40–44	1,468	5,763	0·00393
Total	9,307	379,413	0·23294

population even within the child-bearing group. The first step is to calculate the fertility rate, at each age, of parents, i.e. the ratio of the female births born to mothers of a particular age to the number of mothers living at that age (or the corresponding rate for fathers in terms of male births).

8.37 With age-fertility rates available we may now consider whether, if these rates are maintained, the mothers (or fathers) will produce sufficient girl infants (or boy infants) during the reproductive part of their lives* to replace themselves before they pass out of the parental age-group. If mortality is ignored we add together the age-fertility rates (for births of a particular sex) to yield the expected number of girls (or boys) produced by women (or men) in their reproductive lives. This is known as the gross reproduction rate, and a value of unity might be held to indicate 'replacement' (though we shall see later that this is not valid).

8.38 The calculation proceeds as in Table 8.7 (for women).

8.39 It may be assumed that the mean fertility rate can be applied at individual years of age, so that the sum of the age rates over the period 15–19 will be five times the mean rate (since there are five individual years of age). Thus the total fertility (i.e. total expected female births

*For women this is assumed to be from age 15 to 44. The fertility rate for women at ages 45–9 is negligible and it would add less than 0·2 per cent to the gross reproduction rate in Table 8.7. For men, the limitation to age 44 is not automatically appropriate and the age period would be extended until the added fertility ceased to be of any significance. In 1975 in England and Wales the paternity rates per 1,000 (live births only) were 5·4 at 45–9, 1·6 at 50–4, and 0·6 at 55–9. The total of 5 year age rates above age 49 was only 0·3 per cent of the total of all rates, so that a limitation to age 49 would be justifiable.

to a woman passing through the age group 15–44) = 5×0.23294 or
1.165. (Note that the total fertility rate is, for female births,
379,413/9,307,000 or 0·0408, and that applying this at all ages would
give a crude index of 0.0408×30 or 1.224. This is a higher figure than
five times the sum of the age-specific rates because of the young age
structure of the female population.)

8.40   The gross reproduction rate may be expressed symbolically by
the formula

$$\sum_{x=0}^{x=w} {}^{s}i_x$$

where ${}^{s}i_x$ = fertility rate at age x, specific for sex, i.e. female births to
females or male births to males, and w is the upper limit of
reproductive age.

Net reproduction rate

8.41   The gross reproduction rate fails to take account of the
mortality of infants before they themselves become the same age as
that of the parents they are supposed to replace, and of mortality
among parents before the end of the child-bearing period. In order to
make allowance for the mortality of infants we need to apply, to the
estimated births in each age-group, survival factors up to the present
age of the parent. The formula becomes

$$\sum_{0}^{w} {}_{x}p_0 \cdot {}^{s}i_x$$

where ${}_{x}p_0$ is the chance of survival from birth to age x according to the

Table 8.8   *England and Wales, 1971—survival factors*

Age-group (1)	Fertility rate (female births) (2)	Survival factor (3)	$(2) \times (3)$ (4)
15–19	0·02455	0·9647	0·02368
20–24	0·07487	0·9609	0·07194
25–29	0·07582	0·9559	0·07248
30–34	0·03768	0·9500	0·03580
35–39	0·01609	0·9425	0·01516
40–44	0·00393	0·9321	0·00366
Total			0·22272

Female net reproduction rate = 5×0.2227 or 1.114

currently applicable life table for the appropriate sex. The calculation proceeds as in Table 8.8.

8.42 It is important to bear in mind that for replacement to be attained a generation of women (or of men) must produce a replacement for every member of the generation. Thus the surviving adults of a generation must on average produce rather more than one replacement each, to allow for the fact that some children will fail to survive to adult life. Similarly a cohort of married couples must produce on average more than two children, since they must count on a double loss, namely, from death and from failure to marry. These generations or cohorts may replace themselves at any time during the 30 years or so of female reproductive life. It does not matter very much in which years they produce their children, and any one year is a small fraction of the total 30 years. Furthermore the total birth experience of a single calendar year consists of the aggregate of the experiences of a number of generations or alternatively of a number of marriage cohorts (i.e. women married in the same year). If each generation or cohort concerned has but few children in that year for such reasons as economic depression, danger from war, or wartime separation, nothing could be more ridiculous than to hypothecate that some future generation will, at each age, have the same low rates as those of the many generations concerned in the fertility of the particular year in question. The average addition to a family in a single year is thus a small part of the whole average family, and calendar-year reproduction rates (in any shape or form) are very imperfect measures of replacement. They are, in fact, nothing more than standardized calendar-year birth rates on a scale which approaches unity at a replacement level. The value for a single year has no more significance than any other birth rate, and only a persistent trend substantially above (below) unity might be an indication of a growing (declining) population.

The period total fertility rate

8.43 A rate similar to that of Table 8.7 but including male as well as female births is often calculated. It can be represented as the total births produced by a woman during her reproductive lifetime if she experiences, throughout that period, the age-fertility rates of the particular year. It is, however, likely to be misleading to the public, who may think it represents the current prospects for average family size. This is not so. It is a mixture of fertility rates of many generations.

It is a secular and not a generation rate. For this reason it is called the period total fertility rate. If the younger couples are postponing births, the rate will be depressed, though their ultimate family size may, after this postponement, turn out to be much greater. The period total fertility rate has, in short, all the weaknesses of the reproduction rates discussed in paras 8.36–8.43.

Other factors

8.44 The net reproduction rate makes allowance only for abnormal age distribution and mortality. Other factors need to be considered. A sudden rise in the marriage rate would produce temporary increases in age–fertility rates in subsequent years. For this reason reproduction rates are sometimes marriage-standardized, though this raises the problem of choice of marriage basis, and the index is no longer automatic. It must be reiterated that family building suffers temporary fluctuations too—for example, when war or economic crises cause postponement of births which are later made up by equally temporary high fertility. As we have remarked, this last type of variation may only be a change in the timing of births within the individual families without affecting the ultimate size of the families when completed. Fertility rates in such a period would not reflect the current trend of size of family in the population.

Cohort or generation analysis

8.45 Sharp changes in duration–fertility rates may arise from changes in the timing of family building within married life without necessarily implying any change in the ultimate size of family. It is not therefore surprising that the average size of family of completed fertility (number of live born children produced by a married woman by the end of her reproductive period of life) has been found to exhibit much more stability than do the specific fertility rates from year to year. As the estimation of completed family size of married couples (as a means of estimating replacement prospects) is in fact the primary object of fertility studies, modern demography has turned its attention to this measure.

8.46 Statistically this means following through a group of persons born in a particular year (a generation) or married in a particular year (usually called a marriage cohort) throughout their lifetimes and recording the number of children they produce.

8.47 Considering first the marriage cohort, we can see that the women who contribute to the fertility rate for marriage duration 0 – in 1961, will contribute to the fertility rate for marriage duration 1 – in 1962, 2 – in 1963 and so on. The cumulation of these rates for all durations will produce the ultimate or completed family size of women married within the same period. In this example, however, the period will overlap calendar years as the births at duration 0 – in 1961 will include those of women married in 1960 as well as those married early in 1961. It is usually desirable to follow a group of women married in a particular calendar year. For this reason it is necessary to tabulate the births not only by marriage duration but also by calendar year of marriage. The tabulation is also carried out separately for different age-groups at marriage, as the marriage age has an important effect on the family size—women married for the first time at age 45, for example, will already be at the end of their reproductive life and will have no opportunity to produce a large family. The cohort is then specified by age at marriage and (usually) calendar year of marriage.

Generation replacement rates

8.48   For considering the extent to which the population is replacing itself the marriage cohort experience is not very satisfactory, mainly because it is necessary to make some allowance for the number of female offspring who do not marry and are therefore not going to contribute to the replacement of the cohort (apart from the general allowance for illegitimate fertility). Their numbers can hardly be assessed from the marriage experience of the year in question, for we are concerned with making some allowance for those only then born who will reach the end of their reproductive period without being married. For this purpose the marriage experience of a single, and current, year may be a misleading guide: for example, economic conditions may later produce some temporary postponement of marriages or a general reduction in marriage prospects. Nevertheless we can only use recent nuptiality, based on a period of years, to assess the proportion of female births who will marry and survive the reproductive age period as in the example of Table 8.9.

8.49   The calculation is not entirely satisfactory, because it mixes generations with differing marriage and mortality prospects. It seems preferable, therefore, to abandon year of marriage as the reference point in favour of year of birth, i.e. to calculate a replacement rate applicable to a single generation—those born in a particular calendar

Table 8.9 *England and Wales—marriages of* 1960

Age at marriage	No. of spinster marriages (000s)	Projected ultimate family size*	Combined chance of surviving and of marrying between ages 15 and 45†
Under 20	81·7	3·40	
20–24	163·7	2·63	
25–29	36·4	2·26	
30–34	12·3	1·64	
35–39	6·1	0·81	
40–44	3·2	0·27	
	303·4	Mean 2·691	0·9082

Replacement Index (assuming female births 0·4854 of all births):

Legitimate (2·691 × 0·9082 × 0·4854)	1·186
Illegitimate (add 5·4 per cent)	0·064
	1·250

*By simple extrapolation of family size (live-born children) as shown for successive years of marriage duration year by year in Table QQ of the Registrar General's *Statistical Review*, Part II.

†According to a joint mortality and nuptiality table (with allowance for risk of marriage being broken before age 45). Strictly this factor should be varied according to the period of time over which the family is produced to allow for generation changes in mortality and marriage rates, but this has been ignored for simplicity.

year. For this purpose we follow the generation throughout childhood, marriage and reproductive life, subjecting to it the mortality, nuptiality and fertility actually recorded for that generation if it has reached the end of reproductive life, or projected for it, if not.

8.50 The stages in the computation are as follows:

1 Construct combined mortality and nuptiality table which shows at age x the number of women surviving to that age from 100,000 births (or some other convenient starting number, or radix), and among these the distribution by marital status. The table would also show the number of spinster marriages, widowhoods, divorces, remarriages and deaths, based on the rates of decrement assumed

in the table. The married women of age x are divided according to the duration of their current marriage.

2   At each age and marriage duration the specific legitimate fertility rate appropriate to the age and duration and to the class of married woman (once married or remarried) is applied to estimate the number of live births for that interval. At each age illegitimate fertility rates are applied to the unmarried woman. The addition of these births when divided by the original radix of the nuptiality and mortality table gives the average family size for the generation. Application of the ratio of female to male births yields the number of female births to replace each original female birth, viz. the generation-replacement rate.

8.51   A close approximation to the rate may be obtained by using a procedure similar to that outlined above for the marriage cohort. The difference is that in the column headed 'number of spinster marriages' the actual numbers of marriages of the cohort are replaced by the numbers relating to a particular generation (derived from an abridged nuptiality table). As we are dealing with the marriage experience of the whole generation, there is no longer any need for the factor 0·9082 of Table 8.9, which allowed for replacement of unmarried females (this factor will be implicit in the relationship between the size of the generation—the radix of the nuptiality table—and the total number of marriages up to the end of the reproductive period). Otherwise the calculation follows the same procedure.

Differential fertility

8.52   Fertility varies not only with age and duration of marriage but also with occupation and social class, area of residence (rural or urban, say), religion and many other factors. These factors are clearly of interest to those who may have to estimate the possible effect of steps taken by the community to influence fertility through any of them, e.g. family allowances or social changes such as urbanization.

8.53   Features which have to be borne in mind are heterogeneity of occupational classes, differing average age of marriage (professional men may defer marriage until attainment of a certain status), and changes in occupation between the ages of highest fertility and those at which the fertility is recorded.

8.54   Studies of differential fertility associated with the population censuses in England and Wales indicate that generally the lower social classes have always had, and continue to have, larger families than the higher social classes. The social gradient is becoming less pronounced and the underlying influences and attitudes tend to be different as fertility becomes more widely under voluntary control. Groups with the largest mean family size and smallest proportion childless are the manual workers, especially the unskilled and semi-skilled, members of the armed forces (other ranks) and farmers and agricultural workers. At the other end of the scale there are the clerical workers, managerial and professional workers, traders and shop assistants (Table 8.10). Fertility also varies with length of full-time education (Table 8.11).

Table 8.10   *England and Wales. Census, 1961—ratio (per cent) of mean family size to that for all women married once only (standardized for age at marriage)*

Socio-economic group of husband	Duration of marriage (years)		
	10–14	15–19	20–24
Employers and managers			
Large establishments	95	92	92
Small establishments	93	91	91
Professional workers			
Self-employed	114	115	109
Employees	96	94	96
Intermediate non-manual workers	92	90	91
Junior non-manual workers	88	89	90
Personal service workers	103	103	95
Foremen and supervisors, manual	97	95	95
Skilled manual workers	100	101	101
Semi-skilled manual workers	104	104	106
Unskilled manual workers	120	120	118
Own account workers (other than professionals)	98	97	93
Farmers			
Employers and managers	117	117	120
Own account	109	109	110
Agricultural workers	106	112	117
Armed forces	119	120	115

Sources of data

8.55 The numbers of births and marriages which provide the numerators of the rates referred to in this chapter are derived from registration records. In England and Wales the information recorded

Table 8.11 *England and Wales. Census, 1961—ratio (per cent) of mean family size to that of all women married once only (standardized for age at marriage and marriage duration)*

Terminal education age of husband	Terminal education age of wife			
	Under 15	15–16	17–19	20 and over
Under 15	103	93	95	91
15–16	93	90	91	87
17–19	92	88	95	100
20 and over	93	93	102	102

by a registrar at civil marriages, or by the person solemnizing a religious marriage and transmitted to the registrar, comprises:

1 Date of marriage.
2 Names and surnames.
3 Ages.
4 Marital conditions.
5 Occupations.
6 Residences at time of marriage.
7 Fathers' names and surnames.
8 Occupation of fathers.
9 Precise place of marriage and form of ceremony.

By law it is required that the father and mother of every child born alive, or, in their default by death or inability, 'the occupier of the house in which a child was, to the knowledge of that occupier, born' or 'any person present at the birth' or 'any person having charge of' the child, shall give to the Registrar within 42 days from the date of the birth information of the particulars required to be registered. These are:

(a) Date and place of birth.
(b) Name, if any.
(c) Sex.
(d) Name and surname of father.
(e) Name and maiden surname of mother.
(f) Father's occupation.
(g) Signature, description and residence of informant.

In addition, the following information, which is required for statistical purposes only and is treated as confidential, is also sought:

1   In all cases the age of the mother.
2   Where the name of any person is to be entered in the register of births as father of the child, the age of that person.
3   Except where the birth is of an illegitimate child,
    (i) the date of the parents' marriage;
    (ii) whether the mother has been married before her marriage to the father of the child;
    (iii) the number of children of the mother by her present husband and by any former husband, and how many of them were born alive or were still-born.

8.56   It is, therefore, possible for the Registrar General to produce tables of births separately for once-married and remarried women, and to classify births by year of marriage, age at marriage, age at maternity, duration of marriage, number of children previously born (parity) or any combination of these variables. These tables appear in a special annual volume of statistics of fertility prepared by the Office of Population Censuses and Surveys and published by H.M.S.O.

8.57   The same volume contains the relevant populations at risk and the derived fertility rates. The populations are estimated by using the previous population census as a bench mark and taking account of marriage and mortality experiences since the date of the census. Those married women who survive from the middle of one year to the next will add one year to their age and one year to their duration of marriage, and a proportion who have given birth to a child will add one to their parity.

REFERENCES

Office of Population Censuses and Surveys.
   (Published annually) Series FM, *Birth Statistics*, H.M.S.O.
   (Published quarterly) *Population Trends*, H.M.S.O.
   (1967) *Population Census 1961, Fertility Tables*, H.M.S.O.

EXERCISES FOR CHAPTER EIGHT

1   The data in Table 8.12 have been provided in respect of a pension fund which pays a lump sum benefit to women employees who leave on marriage. Assuming that mortality may be ignored at these ages, calculate a

Table 8.12

Age l.b.	Unmarried women in service		Marriages of women in service, 1976–8	Withdrawals from service *before* marriage 1976–8
	1.1.76	31.12.78		
20	2,500	2,700	1,900	300
21	2,400	2,500	2,000	200
22	2,200	2,400	2,100	150
23	2,000	2,000	1,800	100
24	1,900	1,800	1,700	100

nuptiality table, net of withdrawals *before* marriage, applicable to the unmarried female staff, from age 20 exact to age 25 exact.

2   Write a brief note on the trend of marriage rates in England and Wales during the period 1950–5, indicating the salient features of this trend and the factors responsible for them.

3   Define the various measures of fertility in common use. In respect of specific rates explain the reason for the specificity.

4   In the German F.R. in 1976 the period total fertility rate for women was 1.56. Would it have been possible to make any inference about the replacement of the population? Would you wish to have additional information before making any inference? If so, what?

5   What information is recorded at the registration of a live birth in England and Wales to enable the Registrar General to measure current fertility in the country?

6   In respect of the measures referred to in question 3, how are the populations at risk derived?

7   In general terms what changes have taken place in average completed family size in Great Britain since 1870?

8   To what extent was the rise in the annual number of births in England and Wales between 1955 and 1965 due to an increase in family size? To what other causes could the rise be attributed?

CHAPTER NINE

TRENDS AND FORECASTING

Mortality

9.1 It has been pointed out in Chapter 1 that, although mortality measurements are necessarily made retrospectively, it is, or should be, well understood that past experience is unlikely to be reproduced in the future. We live in a changing world. Mortality is constantly varying. It has been pointed out that for many purposes the 'error' in using past mortality for calculations relating to the future, as for insurance contracts or population forecasts, is less important than margins which have to be introduced. Nevertheless there are occasions when, because the period of time is long, it is important to look at the pace and direction of systematic change in mortality in order that any likely substantial changes can be taken into account.

9.2 The aim then is to establish trends. This immediately creates an apparent dilemma in the choice of the indicator for assessing trends. Clearly one would wish to employ the most inert indicator, i.e. the rate or index whose movement is either slow or at least continuous in pace and direction over a long period of time, so that extrapolation is least hazardous. Such indices are generally not very specific. Yet in order to be able to form a judgement as to the validity of extrapolation one wishes to understand fully the causes of the established trend. This calls for fairly refined analysis and for indices having a high degree of specificity. How does one choose between stability and specificity?

9.3 Fortunately the dilemma is more apparent than real. Judging from the intermittent publicity given to dramatic advances in drugs or surgery or preventive medicine, one would expect to find it necessary to establish mortality trends for specific causes for each sex separately and for narrow age-groups in order to take account of sharp dramatic falls in these rates. One would expect to form a judgement, for example, as to how soon there will be a drug which can destroy cancer cells *in situ*, and to decide whether or not for some causes of death that arise from the operation of genetic or environmental factors there may be an increase in the risk of death in the future. Such trends are, however, much too unstable, and such judgements much too speculative to form a sound basis for forecasting. This was well illustrated by Pollard's comparison (1949) of different methods of forecasting. Pollard demonstrated that, in forecasting mortality separately for specific causes of death caution naturally led to the arbitrary levelling off of rates for causes where there had been improvement and to margins for worsening where there had not. The trend of age-specific rates for all causes combined was consequently forecast to be rising, although other methods indicated a declining trend.

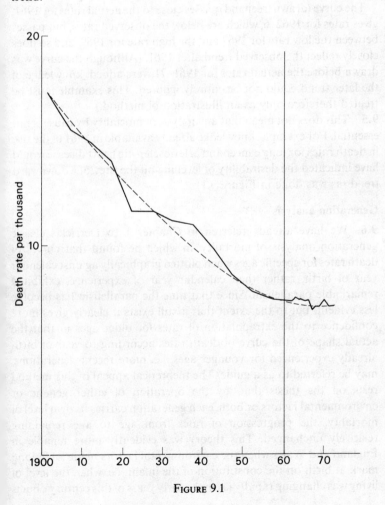

FIGURE 9.1

9.4   It is generally found, however, at least in developed countries, that dramatic medical advances have little impact on age-specific death rates when all causes of death are combined, and it is usually as satisfactory a method as any other to extrapolate the trends of these rates for each sex separately. This is often carried out by simple graphical means. Figure 9.1 shows the actual death rates for men age 45–54 in England and Wales from 1901 to 1971, together with a graphical extrapolation that might have been made as at 1961 (rates for the period 1901–61 are for intervals of 5 calendar years).

The curve (drawn freehand) passes close to the actual rates for 1961, gives rates for 1962–6, which are below the observed rates, but passes between the low rate for 1967 and the high rate for 1969, and so does closely reflect the observed trend after 1961. (Although the curve was drawn before the actual rates for 1961–71 were added, knowledge of the later trend could not be entirely ignored. This example must be treated therefore only as an illustration of method.)

9.5   This does not mean that an analysis of mortality by cause is not essential. For example, knowledge already available in 1961 of the rise in death rates for lung cancer and arteriosclerotic heart disease would have indicated the desirability of levelling off the previous downward trend (as was done in Figure 9.1).

Generation analysis *Death rate plotted against calendar year of birth*

9.6   We have already referred in Chapter 1 to Derrick's classic generation analysis of mortality, in which he found that curves of death rates for specific ages when plotted graphically against calendar year of birth, rather than calendar year of experience, exhibited remarkable parallelism. Since that time the parallelism has become less evident, but to the extent that it still exists it clearly gives more confidence to the extrapolation of rates for older ages in that the actual shape of the curve of death rates according to year of birth already experienced for younger ages, i.e. more recent generations, may be referred to as a guide. The theoretical appeal of this method rests on the thesis that, by the operation of either genetic or environmental factors or both, each generation carries its own level of mortality, the progression of rates from age to age remaining relatively unchanged. This theory was evidently more tenable in England and Wales when the environmental factors made a life-long mark at birth on the constitution of the infant, i.e. when the level of living was changing rapidly (as in the early years of this century), but is less tenable when factors operating in adult life assume relatively greater importance (e.g. cigarette smoking).

9.7 We must distinguish between the employment of generation analysis as a step in the process of forecasting of secular rates and the use of generation life tables in the application of forecast rates not necessarily forecast by generation analysis to financial calculations such as the purchase of annuities. In whatever way rates are forecast, it has to be borne in mind that a group of persons purchasing annuities at the age of 60 in 1970 will experience q_{70} in 1980 and q_{80} in 1990, so that the forecast is 10 years further ahead for q_{80} than for q_{70}. We are concerned, in valuing annuities, with using a series of q_x likely to be experienced by a particular generation

Mathematical methods

9.8 So far we have considered only the employment of freehand graphical methods of extrapolation. It might be considered more reliable or more reasonable to fit a curve to the past rates of mortality and to extend this curve by reference to its parameters in order to calculate rates expected in the future (rather than reading the rates from a freehand graphic extrapolation). The question as to the form of curve to be fitted then arises. The possibilities are as follows. For simplicity we assume first that the trend to be investigated is that of the force of mortality $_y\mu_x$, where y is a variable calendar year of experience (or birth in the case of a generation analysis) and x is a fixed age.

1 A polynomial $_y\mu_x = a_x + b_x y + c_x y^2 + d_x y^3 \ldots w_x y^n$, where n is not greater than a number one less than the number of actual rates plotted and the curve is fitted by least squares or moments. This is laborious if n is large (unless a computer is available and a standard program), and it may turn in the wrong direction at the end of the forecast period by too faithfully following previous fluctuations. Some judgement has to be exercised to keep n as small as possible.

2 Where some gradual levelling off of a descending trend is desired, an exponential function $_y\mu_x = a_x + b_x e^{-c_x y}$, either alone or in combination with a low order polynomial or straight line. Unless the exponential function alone is appropriate, this could be a tedious operation.

3 If, for a number of years, the mortality rates have been graduated by a formula such as Makeham's ($\mu_x = A + Bc^x$), we may then treat

the formula constants as functions of time to be varied for future years on their trend in the past. For example Cramer and Wold (1935), working on Swedish data, found that log c and log B could be fitted to logistic curves and that a straight line could be fitted to A. The same technique could be applied where a Perks graduation formula $\mu_x = A + Bc^x/(Kc^{-x} + 1 + Dc^x)$ has been applied or indeed where any other formula has been consistently applied. Where there are more parameters in the basic graduation formula, one has to balance the likelihood of getting closer fits to the trends of the individual parameters against the labour of fitting an increased number of curves to these trends.

9.9 Another possibility is to use not $_y\mu_x$ but some transform of the mortality rate that is less curvilinear. For example, Brass (1971) uses a logit transform W, where $W_x = \frac{1}{2}\log[q_x/(1-q_x)]$. Because the trend of $_y\mu_x$ with respect to y tends often to be exponential, the trend of the logit with respect to y tends to be mainly linear, and a straight line is clearly easier to fit than a curve. Brass actually employs a two-parameter curve $_yW_x = \alpha_y + \beta_y \cdot _0W_x$, where α_y is a linear function of y but β_y may be a more complex function.

9.10 Before deciding upon the effort to be expended in exercises of this kind, it is important to consider the use to which the forecast rates will be applied and whether spurious precision is justified. The term 'spurious' is used here to remind the reader that precision in the method of extrapolation does not necessarily increase the likelihood that the past trend will be maintained. The really important part of the exercise lies in the appreciation of the mortality changes that are taking place. Getting the 'feel' of the figures and assessing the relative importance of factors which are at work (increase in road accidents, campaigns against infectious diseases, etc.) is of paramount importance in gaining appreciation of the origin of past mortality changes and in judging whether or not to make allowance for changes in the future. It also helps to make it possible to distinguish short-term fluctuations from long-term trends and, for example, to decide whether, in a particular period of years of experience for which it is desired to calculate a life table, short-term fluctuations may have rendered the data unrepresentative of longer-term conditions. As Redington (1949) pointed out at an Institute of Actuaries discussion, the aim is to separate what is non-random from what is random. 'The elements into which a mortality experience was divided—duration, age, or, it might be, size of sum assured—were chosen because they were unlikely to enter into the experience in a random way.' Only if we are satisfied from our study of trends that, for example, changes in social and economic conditions have entered into the determination of mortality in a non-random way, do we project the effect of further changes in conditions. We should not concentrate on time itself as a factor but upon what changes non-randomly with time.

9.11 The approach to the forecasting of mortality rates will be influenced by the use to which the forecast rates will be put. In the valuation of life-assurance liabilities or in premium calculations for life assurance it is not usual to forecast improvement in rates of mortality. Monetary tables are based on recent investigations (see Chapter 18 for an account of the Continuous Mortality Investigation) and any improvement subsequent to their calculation forms an inherent margin (though not the only margin) against unfavourable experience; there may be general deterioration rather than improvement in mortality in future years and even if there has been general improvement, a particular group of policy-holders may deviate from the general trend either as a sampling fluctuation or as a result of selection against the office (see para. 10.7). In the calculation of premiums for annuities future mortality improvement would work in the other direction: the annuity would be underpriced. Explicit allowance is therefore made for mortality improvement. To the extent that recent trends are extrapolated without reservation the forecast is on the safe side financially. The process is illustrated in detail in Chapter 18. For national population projection purposes in a developed country (e.g. the United Kingdom, see para. 9.36) the current mortality trend is projected, though if the term of projection is long (40 or 50 years), it may often be regarded as prudent to level off the trend after, say, 20 to 30 years and to assume constant rates thereafter. This is because where rates of mortality are already low, there is less elasticity for further improvement; the limitless extension of the current trends might produce forecast rates which are regarded as unacceptably low. However, a developing country concerned with the problem of mounting population pressure arising directly from a transition from a condition of high mortality and high fertility to a condition of lowered mortality without reduction of fertility would wish to know the full implications of this change. It would be unwise, in these circumstances, deliberately to underestimate future mortality improvement. For some purposes special attention would be paid to mortality rates in particular age-groups: for annuity valuation purposes (already referred to) the interest is largely confined to mortality at older adult ages, and those concerned with the planning of maternity and infant health services would be particularly interested in perinatal mortality trends (see para. 1.40).

Forecasting sickness rates

9.12 The basic methodology for forecasting sickness rates is the same as for forecasting mortality rates, but it has to be remembered that sickness rates are claim rates, so that, as well as health factors, administrative and economic factors have to be taken into account. If the rules for admission of claims or the rates of benefit (in real terms) are likely to be changed, and especially if they are already in process of change, then the likely effect of these changes in the volume of claims must be estimated. If a change in the level of unemployment or in general labour conditions appears likely, then this too will have its effect upon readiness to 'go sick'. As to health factors, account must be taken not only of trends in the incidence of disease but also trends in the extent of loss of activity associated with particular diseases. The latter may be effected by the introduction of new forms of therapy (e.g. drugs for the rapid healing of peptic ulcers).

Fertility

9.13 The estimation of a series of annual numbers of births $_yB$ in the future (where y is the calendar year and $_yB$ the total births in that year) strictly means estimating the number of married women of each age x in year y, $_yP_x^{mw}$, and their fertility rates, i_x^{mw}, summing the products $_yP_x^{mw} \cdot i_x^{mw}$ for all values of x, and making a fractional allowance k for births to unmarried women,

i.e. $_yB = \Sigma \cdot _yP_x^{mw} \cdot i_x^{mw}(1+k)$.

9.14 This in turn would mean projecting $_yP_x^{mw}$ from year to year. An expression for $_yP_x^{mw}$ as a function of $_{y-1}P_{x-1}^{mw}$ can be written down. It is very complicated, since it includes losses from $_{y-1}P_{x-1}^{mw}$ by death, divorce or widowhood, and gains by new marriages of spinsters widows and divorcees and by net immigration (or loss by net out-migration) of married women. Further, the terms in this expression concerned with changes of status, such as divorce or widowhood would have to allow for mortality in the remainder (half a year on the average) of the year of experience. Moreover the whole operation including the estimation of births, ought to be carried out with reference to age at marriage, so that fertility rates specific for age and duration of marriage can be applied.

9.15 It is usual to eschew this degree of refinement and complication, which is not appropriate to such a process as population projections, whose purpose is to provide only an illustration of the effects of long-term continuation of current trends (in the knowledge that they are rarely so continued). The separate elements of the calculation are usually examined in order to form a judgement about the trend in the total flow of births, but they are brought into an integrated calculation.

9.16 In the official projections of England and Wales the examination is carried out in the following stages for the first 15 years of the projection period (usually 40 years):

Births on the assumption of no migration after the starting date of the projections:
(a) to women married once only,
(b) to remarried women,
(c) to unmarried women.
2. Effect of assumed net migration.

9.17 For (1a) it is necessary to estimate the female population at annual intervals for 15 years by marital status, and for married women by age at marriage and duration of marriage. This itself necessitates a number of stages:

1 Examination of the trend of marriage rates.
2 Derivation of the expected proportions married by age last birthday in each future year, and therefore of spinster populations.
3 Estimates of number of marriages of spinsters in successive years, by age at marriage (maintaining consistency with the effect of bachelors' marriage-rate trends).
4 Derivation, from (3) and records of past marriages, of an analysis of married women by age at marriage and duration of marriage, for each year in the 15 years. For example, the women married once only, age at marriage 25 and duration of marriage 10 years in year y, will be the survivors of spinsters married at 25 in year $y - 10$ (i.e. of the results of applying the spinster marriage rate at age 25 to the population of spinsters aged 25 in year $y - 10$), with allowance for

the relatively small numbers of deaths, widowhoods, and divorces subsequently occurring.

9.18 To this population matrix (we use the term to describe a large cross-tabulation of numbers of women by age at marriage and marriage duration for each calendar year) we apply a matrix of fertility rates specific for age at marriage and marriage duration for each calendar year to generate the expected births in each calendar year. In deriving these fertility rates it is usual to have regard to the most stable of all fertility indicators (mean ultimate family size); to extrapolate this (by year of marriage) after taking account of likely changes in the factors affecting fertility (changes in level of living, changes in extent of use and efficiency of contraceptive methods) and the results of any population surveys that may have been carried out to gauge the fertility intentions of couples in the early stages of family building; and to adjust the current pattern of age-duration-specific fertility rates to be consistent with the projected mean ultimate family size figures.

9.19 The mean ultimate family size for a particular year of marriage is the result of adding together the rates in the diagonal of a table of fertility rates (live births per married woman) by marriage duration and calendar year of attaining that duration: for example, for age at marriage 20 and year of marriage 1955, figures (which are hypothetical) are shown in Table 9.1. Thus the adjustment referred to in para. 9.18 is an adjustment of each diagonal of tables such as 9.1. The mean ultimate family size is projected first and then the diagonal of rates is made to add to it.

9.20 This adjustment is usually effected rateably over the whole of each diagonal of the table unless there is clear evidence of a change in the pattern of rates, e.g. further concentration of family building into the early years of marriage, necessitating an increase in rates at early marriage durations and a decrease at later durations. In the latter event the adjustment of rates to a particular family size would be a matter of judgement.

9.21 When the diagonals for future years of the type of tabulation shown in Table 9.1 have been adjusted to yield the expected family sizes, the horizontal lines of the completed table (as illustrated for 1980) form the set of rates to be applied to the population in 1980 of women married for the first time at age 20 to yield expected births, for item (1a) referred to in para. 9.16.

Table 9.1 Fertility rates by duration of marriage

Age at marriage	Year of attaining duration	Duration of marriage										
		0	1	2	3	4	5	6	7	8	9	10 etc.
20	1955	0·31										
	1956		0·29									
	1957			0·28								
	1958				0·27							
	1959					0·25						
	1960						0·23					
	1961							0·20				
	1962								0·16			
	1963									0·13		
	1964										0·10	
	1965											0·08
	etc.											
	1980	0·29	0·26	0·25	0·23	0·22	0·21	0·18	0·13	0·08	0·06	0·04——2·10

Total (diagonal, over all durations for year of marriage 1955)   2·40

9.22 It is usual to work in groups of marriage ages, e.g. under 20, 20–4, 25–9, etc. to cut down the amount of detail.

9.23 Item (1b) in para. 9.16, the births to remarried women, would probably be a round figure addition, having regard to the recent run of annual births in this population segment.

9.24 The allowance for illegitimate births, item (1c), is normally a percentage addition of legitimate births based on current experience (in England and Wales 7–8 per cent).

9.25 As to the special fertility allowance for migrants (item 2 in para. 9.16), we have to remember that they are included in (1a), so that the only consideration is whether they bring with them any substantial fertility differential. Migrants from less developed areas usually have higher fertility on arrival than those of the receiving country if the receiving country is economically developed, as is commonly the case; it is also usual for their descendants to assimilate the family-size attitudes of the population into which they are born. It is therefore necessary, if there has been a large influx of such migrants, to quantify that influx in terms of women in the fertile age groups in successive years and to allow for their fertility being initially, say, 50 per cent higher than the indigenous female population, the loading being justifiably assumed to decrease as time passes. Although item 2 in para. 9.16 may be significant and not to be ignored, it is likely to be small relative to item 1, and very approximate methods would be adequate to estimate the future annual addition to births from the differential fertility of migrants.

Migration

9.26 The balance of migration is an element liable to considerable variation from year to year as a result of changes in world economic conditions or of political decisions by governments. It is necessary to make a judgement as to the annual figure which, over the longer run, is likely to represent average conditions. This figure has then to be distributed by sex and age on the basis of recent experience.

9.27 The principal source of information about migration in the United Kingdom (which does not maintain a continuous population register, as in Scandinavian countries, in which all movements are recorded) is the *National Travel Survey*. This is a continuously maintained sample survey conducted by the Office of Population Censuses and Surveys of travellers passing through the sea and airports of the United Kingdom. A migrant is defined as a traveller who declares his intention of staying at least 1 year in the country of ultimate destination. Because of the labour necessary, and, especially, the need to avoid hindrance to passengers, the sampling fractions are small, so that the data do not permit very detailed analysis. Nevertheless over the years much useful information of the population structure of migrants has been accumulated and published by O.P.C.S.

9.28 In 1975 the migration balance of the United Kingdom was estimated to be 41,000 outward.

Population projection

9.29 In making forward as distinct from current* estimates of the population of the country the term 'projection' is used rather than 'forecast'. The reason is an important one. Demographers can do no more than analyse existing trends of births, deaths, migration, and throw them forward (extrapolate them) into the future. Hence the term 'projection'. This is a purely mechanical operation, carrying no expectation of fulfilment, as would be implied by the term 'forecast'. In projecting existing trends we are doing no more than spell out the implications in terms of what must happen if these trends are maintained. There is no implication that they *will* be maintained. Indeed there is often an expectation that they will not be maintained. Trends do change, sometimes quite suddenly, as when births began to rise steeply in this country in 1955 and when they later began to fall (this was more a change in the timing of fertility than in the level of fertility, but still a change in trend of numbers of births.) Sometimes the projections (the implication of existing trends) stimulate actions which alter trends. There is no doubt that the publicity given to the effect of continuing rapid population growth in the less developed regions of the world has stimulated, in a number of countries (India, Pakistan, for example) the institution of official population policies aimed at restricting growth. Conversely the virtual cessation of growth in the population of France in the late 1930s, when deaths actually exceeded births, led to drastic economic measures to

*Current estimates are made, inter-censally, by taking account of births, deaths and migration actually recorded since the date of the last population census. They are estimates only in the sense, first, that the population census itself is an estimate subject to error and, second, that migration data are derived from a sample survey of travellers. There is no projection element in the calculation; it is wholly retrospective.

encourage fertility. Projections soon become out of date, therefore, and have to be regularly revised to take account of changes in the underlying trends. Sometimes the need for revision arises not so much from changes in trends as from improved information of these trends. In the United Kingdom information about migration is still scanty, and the available data on fertility, though substantial, is not yet such as to permit analyses of motivation towards, and intentions about, family planning which would permit surer assumptions to be made about long-term trends. There is, therefore, always scope for sharper definition of trends and, on these grounds alone, a new look at the projection.

Method

9.30 In the following formulae the prefix relates to the calendar year and the suffix relates to age last birthday.

9.31 The calculation moves forward from year to year separately for each sex and for each single year of age by the formulae:

$$_yP_x = {}_{y-1}P_{x-1}(1 - {}_{y-1}q_{x-\frac{1}{2}}) + {}_yM_x$$

where $_yP_x$ = number of persons at mid-year y aged x last birthday,

         $_yM_x$ = net migrants inward (if outward, it becomes a negative quantity) in the period mid-year $y-1$ to mid-year y aged x last birthday at mid-year y, and

$_{y-1}q_{x-\frac{1}{2}}$ = probability of death within a year for a person aged $(x-1)$ last birthday at mid-year $y-1$.

9.32 It is usual to ignore the mortality of migrants between the date of migration and mid-year y.

9.33 At age 0 the formula is

$$_yP_0 = {}_yB \cdot (1 - \tfrac{1}{2} \cdot {}_{y-1}q_0) + {}_yM_0$$

where $_yB$ = the number of live births in the period mid-year $y-1$ to mid-year y, and

$\frac{1}{2}({}_{y-1}q_0)$ = probability that a baby born in the period mid-year $y-1$ to mid-year y will die before the end of that period

9.34 The base population will be the latest available mid-year estimate of the *total* population. The *total* population includes forces overseas but excludes foreign forces stationed in this country. The reason for this is that if the process were to be applied to the civilian population or to the 'home' (or actual) population resident in the country (i.e. including national and foreign forces in the country but excluding national forces temporarily stationed overseas), the gap in the age structure caused by the temporary absence of this young segment of the population would be a distortion which would be moved on to older age groups over the years, whereas by virtue of its continuous replenishment the age structure in the *total* population remains virtually the same from year to year and the gap in the *home* population structure remains at the same ages from year to year. Projections of the total population are therefore derived as basic data, and the civilian and home (or actual) populations are obtained by making appropriate additions or subtractions (which have themselves to be projected). The total population may be looked upon, approximately, as the population owing allegiance to the Government of the country (it omits visitors abroad and includes visitors to this country, but these roughly balance). The home population is the population which would be counted in a national census.

9.35　We have already discussed the projection of mortality rates and fertility rates. Migration is a very small element in the population projection (fertility is the most important factor), and numbers are usually maintained at current levels unless there are clear indications of significant changes, in which case some judgement would have to be exercised as to the extent and persistence of the change.

9.36　In the United Kingdom national population projections are revised annually by the Government Actuary's Department and the Office of Population Censuses and Surveys in joint consultation, and they are published by the latter office. A discussion of the assumptions is published as a special issue of the O.P.C.S. *Monitor*, and the projections themselves appear as a volume entitled *Population Projections*.

REFERENCES

Brass, W. (1971). *On the scale of mortality. The Biological aspects of Demography* (ed. W. Brass), Taylor & Francis, London, 69–110.

Cramer, H. and Wold, H. (1935). Mortality variations in Sweden. A study in graduation and forecasting. *Skandinavisk Aktuarietidskrift*, **18**, 161.

Office of Population Censuses and Surveys (annually). Series MN. *International Migration*, HMSO.

Pollard, A. H. (1949). Methods of forecasting mortality using Australian data. *J. Inst. Actu.*, **75**, 151.

Redington, F. M. (1949). In discussion of 'Some thoughts on the analysis of numerical data' by L. G. K. Starke, *J. Inst. Actu.*, **75**, 227.

EXERCISES FOR CHAPTER NINE

1 What are the main causes of mortality in men aged 45–54 in England and Wales? What is the present outlook for these causes?

2 How do the current trends of mortality at middle adult ages compare for males and females in England and Wales?

3 Describe any one mathematical method of extrapolating mortality trends for particular age-groups, and employ it to provide a 10-year projection of the following data:

Year	Rate of mortality per 1,000 for males
1910	15·0
1920	13·0
1930	12·0
1940	11·0
1950	9·0
1960	8·5
1965	8·1
1970	7·9
1975	8·0

4 You are required to make a projection of the future population to mid-year 1994 of Exton, a New Town of 80,000 population, which is completely built and is experiencing a small net annual loss of population, which is partly because dwellings vacated by households leaving Exton are filled by second-generation households formed within Exton and partly because some young individual members of households leave each year to look for employment elsewhere. Mortality rates, sub-divided by sex and 5-year age-groups, are available. Fertility rates for women are available by age (5-year groups) but not by marital status or duration of marriage. Numbers of migrants are available, both inward and outward, for recent calendar years, subdivided by sex and 5-year age-groups. The population, sub-divided by sex and 5-year age-groups, has been established by a special census at mid-year 1979. How would you proceed? Set out your working sheets.

5 The present annual death rate for Exton is 5·9 per 1,000 and the birth rate is 14·0. How would you explain to the Exton Town Council why these rates differ from the national rates and why they are likely to change considerably in the future?

CHAPTER TEN

SELECTION

10.1 There has already been some discussion, in this textbook, of the way in which mortality is influenced by a number of factors such as sex, age, marital status, social and economic conditions, and it has been stressed that, before useful comparisons can be made between rates, we do have to be sure that we are comparing like with like. Although this chapter refers to mortality it should be understood that the principles apply equally to other contingencies, e.g. fertility, marriage, sickness. If we calculate the general rates of mortality for two population groups A and B and find that the rate for A is higher than that for B, we do not know whether this means that in general the risk of death is higher in group A or whether A has more men, or more old people. Before we can make fair comparisons of mortality itself rather than of population characteristics, we must eliminate the influence of these characteristics from the comparison. In respect of two of these characteristics we have already spoken of standardization (see Chapter 1). This is for the calculation of single figure indices.

Hetero-geneity

10.2 For most comparative work, however, single figure indices do not suffice, especially when it is desired to effect a comparison in such a way that it leads to practical action (for example, in underwriting life-assurance contracts) to take account of the significant difference revealed. For this reason the actuary, or the statistician in population work divides the data, before comparison, into groups which are homogeneous in relation to factors known to affect mortality. He compares two groups which are similarly composed, in respect of these factors. The most obvious illustration is the calculation of rates specific for age and sex. For males or females separately we compare q_x at each integral age x before forming a view about the relationship between the two mortality experiences.

10.3 Statisticians working outside the actuarial field do not use the term 'selection'. They talk more directly about adequate classification to remove heterogeneity. In actuarial practice the term has become applied to the operation of factors which influence mortality rather than to the classification of data with different characteristics. The reader should have no difficulty with the terminology but the distinction is important.

Temporary initial selection

10.4   We have already discussed one form of selection in Chapter 6. The methods of constructing mortality tables which take account of this factor have also been set out in that chapter. This form of separation is the separation of a 'select' group of lives of various ages who share one particular attribute: they have, on entry, passed a medical examination. They do, however, attain any particular age at varying durations of time from this initial examination. Each such duration sub-group is subject to different mortality rates. This is not a separation of those who have been medically examined from those who have not. It is a separation, within those who have been medically examined, of those whose examination is more recent (and from whom people with severe impairments have been excluded) from those whose examination is more distant. Some of this latter group now suffer from impairment which would prevent them from passing a further medical examination. Those who have recently passed a medical examination can, therefore, be regarded as having a mortality advantage over those whose examination is more distant. If this mortality advantage were not temporary, i.e. diminishing to insignificant proportions within a short period of years after entry to assurance, this kind of separation would not be necessary. This is because if the benefit of initial medical selection were constant with time, all lives of a particular attained age would be equally affected, irrespective of the duration since entry, and there would be no problem of heterogeneity (with regard to this particular factor) to worry about.

Class selection

10.5   Normally when actuaries talk of class selection they are concerned with more permanent attributes, like level of education or occupation, which may have to be differentiated to secure homogeneity within groups to be compared. It has to be borne in mind, however, that often the permanence is only relative. Many effects do wear off in time, if only slowly, and it may be necessary to analyse data durationally (in the conventional manner) in order to establish the degree of permanence. Possible examples might be previous service in a tropical climate, or a limited period of employment in an occupation bringing one into contact with a poisonous substance.

10.6 While the objective will always be to separate classes that are significantly different in their mortality experience but homogeneous within themselves, there is clearly a difficulty in that sub-divisions may reduce the numbers in each class to a point where sampling errors render the resulting mortality rates too unreliable even after graduation for practical use. It depends, of course, upon what this practical use is to be.

10.7 A life office might, and usually does, argue that the degree of homogeneity among its policy-holders with regard to mortality results from a constant form of selection of insurable lives from the general population, and that this changes in character only slowly, if at all; and that, therefore, a broad general approach to the calculation of premiums, which may be more reliable and certainly more convenient, is justifiable. On the other hand, it would be inequitable to charge the same average premium for two classes which differ widely in mortality. There would also be a risk of an option being exercised against the office. The high mortality group (which is being undercharged by the premium based on averaged mortality) would be attracted; the low mortality group would find it possible to get better terms elsewhere. The average rates of mortality subsequently experienced would be more and more weighted by the high mortality group and would consequently rise. The office would have to increase its premiums and the low mortality group would be further discouraged from making proposals. So unless all offices increased their premiums, the situation would get worse. The actuary in a life office has therefore to make a judgement (in relation to the practice of other offices) as to how far it is necessary to go, in the interests of equity and the avoidance of options, in differentiating mortality rates for life-assurance premium rates.

10.8 If the practical use of the mortality rates is to establish occupational or socio-economic factors in mortality (as in the Registrar General's periodic occupational mortality investigations) or to establish impairment risks (as in the American studies carried out jointly by the Society of Actuaries and the Association of Life Insurance Medical Officers) then refinement in classification is essential (see Chapter 18).

10.9 As an example, reference may be made to recent work by Capildeo et al. (1977), who found it necessary in studying the subsequent mortality of men who had suffered a stroke to classify the population with respect to (1) the anatomy of the stroke, e.g. cerebellum, brain stem, etc., (2) pathology, e.g. aneurysm, (3) method of investigation, (4) associated conditions, (5) disability on admission, (6) disability on discharge, and (7) outcome.

Time selection

10.10   One of the factors giving rise to heterogeneity is time itself. Mortality rates change with the passage of time, sometimes quite rapidly. If, therefore, an investigation is extended over a long period of time in order to increase the years of life in the experience, the resulting mortality rates would be an average of different levels of mortality. The point of time to which they related would depend on the relative weight of various years of experience. In any case they would not represent reasonably up to date mortality experience. This was one of the major criticisms of the British Offices' Experience, which covered the period 1863–93. Care is usually taken, therefore, to keep the period of investigation as short as is compatible with a reasonable volume of data, in order to minimize heterogeneity due to time changes.

10.11   A. H. Pollard (1970) has discussed the problem of random mortality fluctuations and concluded, *inter alia*, that while for some diseases (e.g. neoplasms) the rate of mortality and the incidence in the community do not vary to any extent from year to year, for others (e.g. diseases of circulatory system at higher ages) either the rate of mortality or the incidence of the relative impairments (or both) vary significantly from year to year. G. C. Taylor (1973), in a paper on optimizing the term of an investigation into decremental rates, concluded that the optimal term was determined by size of experience, level of mortality, and the rate at which mortality has been changing. For a given level and rate of change of mortality the optimal term is inversely proportional to the cube root of size of experience. For a given size of experience and rate of change of mortality the optimal term increases as the level of mortality rises. For a given size of experience and level of mortality the optimal term decreases as the rate of change in mortality increases.

10.12   Even if a short period of investigation is used, consideration must be given to likely subsequent mortality changes which may render it necessary to use the rates merely as a base for projecting rates applicable to the future. This has already been discussed in Chapter 9 and is further referred to in Chapter 18.

10.13 Time may also affect the extent to which other factors operate. Improvement in underwriting practice may alter the effect of temporary initial selection by increasing both its intensity and its duration. On the other hand, the general vitality of the population could so improve as to render initial selection of only marginal importance. Changes in financial conditions may make certain types of insurance contracts more or less attractive to particular sections of the population, and so bring about changes in the general constitution of the population associated with any particular type of contract. Other risks, such as those associated with particular occupations or particular impairments, may also change with time. Action may be taken to remove a hazard (e.g. a dangerous chemical); as a result of advances in medical treatment an impairment may cease to affect mortality to the same extent as hitherto. The possibility of these time changes must always be borne in mind before accepting the results of an investigation at their face value.

Spurious selection Revision text 2 Q 3

10.14 In this sort of situation a statistician will be on guard against the confounding of one factor by another. A particular example in actuarial practice arises where temporary initial selection appears when it does not really exist, or its effect is inflated or diminished by the operation of other factors. Actuaries refer to this as spurious selection.

10.15 Suppose we have a mortality investigation of an experience which combines two groups of lives A and B, the mortality of A being heavier at all ages than that of B. Let us suppose that the experience is analysed by duration but that there are relatively more A lives at duration $t+1$ than at duration t. If this happens, $q_{[x-1]+t+1}$ will tend to be greater than $q_{[x]+t}$, on account of the additional weight of the A lives, even if real initial selection is no longer present in either the A or the B lives. See Table 10.1.

10.16 In Table 10.1 the difference between A and B may be one of time (year of entry into assurance) or a difference in some such characteristic as sex, socio-economic group, etc., or even of proportions at integral ages within an age-group.

10.17 A major difficulty is that past experience has never been free of some source of spurious selection, so that there has never been a clear

Table 10.1

Group	$E_{[x]+t}$	$\theta_{[x]+t}$	$q_{[x]+t}$	$E_{[x-1]+t+1}$	$\theta_{[x-1]+t+1}$	$q_{[x-1]+t+1}$
A	1,000	30	0·030	2,000	60	0·030
B	2,000	40	0·020	1,000	20	0·020
Total	3,000	70	0·023	3,000	80	0·027

guide as to how long initial selection should persist, i.e. the period after which apparent initial selection should be suspect. In the $0^{[M]}$ table, based on the experience of assured lives in Great Britain during the period 1863–93, the select period was taken as 10 years but no account was taken of spurious selection, about which less was then known, and it is now thought that the effect of initial selection was over stated. In the A 1924–29 experience the possibility of spurious selection was accepted, but it was not possible to assess its influence. The select period was restricted to 3 years, but it is possible that this was too restrictive and that, actually, the effect of initial selection persisted longer. Despite this risk of choosing too restricted a period of selection, later tables produced by the Continuous Mortality Investigation Bureau all have select periods of less than 3 years on the grounds that a short period would pay adequate attention to the main mortality effect and avoid difficulties over the run in of select rates to the ultimate rates but for A 1967–70 a table based on a 5-year select period was prepared, in addition to a 2-year select period, (see para. 18.35). For the A1949–52 table the compilers faced considerable difficulty in interpreting the somewhat irregular approach of the select rates to the ultimate rates and wondered whether to publish an aggregate table only. (See paras 18.26 and 18.27.)

10.18 A strong indication to spurious selection is given by the failure of the select rates to converge to ultimate rates; a 'permanent' durational effect is likely to be something other than initial selection, which on general reasoning must wear off.

10.19 What are these 'permanent' durational effects likely to be? Variation of mortality with calendar year of entry is a fairly obvious and expected one. It should be borne in mind that this is a mixture of generation and secular effects. Two persons born respectively in 1920 and 1930 were not only born into different social and economic environments, which may determine their subsequent relative vitalities, but they also, for example, will attain age 60 in calendar years divided by a decade, between which times mortality conditions may be very different.

10.20 The use of group rates, as we have seen, can give rise to spurious selection if the age-weighting of the group changes with time. If this means, for example, that the weighting is in favour of older ages in the ultimate data as compared with the select data, this will create the appearance of temporary initial selection. If group rates are used, therefore, one should always look carefully at the average ages of any groups, especially those which are used to establish the difference between select and ultimate rates of mortality.

10.21 All this comes down to a very old rule in statistical investigations—that one should never accept statistically significant differences between rates without asking the question 'statistically significant of what?' and without suspecting that the answer may be 'of heterogeneity in the data'. Sub-divide first, combine later, is a good working rule, provided that the sub-division is not taken to the point at which numbers become too small to provide any reliable indication of underlying rates. The accessibility of computers makes it possible to carry out a considerable amount of preliminary analysis without inordinate work-load, but the caution against excessive sub-division still applies.

REFERENCES

Capildeo R., Haberman, S. and Clifford Rose, F. (1977). New Classification of Stroke. *Brit. Med. J.*, **2**, 1578–80.

Pollard, A. H. (1970). Random Mortality Fluctuations and the Binomial Hypothesis. *J. Inst. Actu.*, **96**, 251.

Taylor, G. C. (1973. Optimising the Term of an Investigation into Decremental Rates. *J. Inst. Actu.*, **99**, 69.

EXERCISES FOR CHAPTER TEN

1   What is meant by 'temporary initial selection'?

2   What is the usual method for determining the period of time during which initial selection continues to operate significantly?

3   Explain what is meant by 'spurious selection'.

4   Give an example of an analogue of initial selection in fertility statistics.

5   In a recent paper to the Royal Statistical Society it was proposed that mortality rates should be standardized by fitting them to a regression function which would correlate known sources of variation, e.g. socio-economic conditions, urbanization, etc., the residual representing the standardized rate. Criticise this procedure.

Learn philosophy behind graduation.

INFERENCES FROM MORTALITY AND OTHER INVESTIGATIONS; PRINCIPLES OF GRADUATION

Introduction

11.1 Actuaries and demographers need mortality tables for many of their calculations. The table used in any particular instance must be applicable to the lives under consideration. Thus, the actuary must choose a mortality basis suitable for ordinary life-assurance proposers when he sets premium rates for ordinary assurance contracts, and a different mortality basis appropriate to annuitants when he determines annuity purchase prices; he may use a national mortality table to calculate industrial assurance premiums. The demographer will use a national mortality table when he projects the population of a country.

11.2 Although we shall confine our attention for the most part to mortality rates in this chapter, the methods we describe are applicable to all decremental rates (e.g. withdrawal, ill-health retirement, marriage, etc.). Many of the techniques can also be applied to non-decremental rates like sickness.

11.3 Before selecting a mortality basis for his calculations, the actuary (or demographer) needs to examine the mortality experience of lives similar to those in question. Two alternatives are then open to him. He may either

(a) adopt a particular standard table as his mortality basis, or
(b) construct a special new table.

11.4 It is obviously easier to use an existing table, and a number of statistical tests have been devised to determine whether the lives in a particular mortality experience can be regarded as coming from a population whose mortality rates have already been accurately determined (i.e. a mortality table has already been prepared). These tests are described in paras. 11.8–11.43.

11.5 The construction of a new table is rather more complicated

The main problem is the adjustment of the observed rates to produce smooth decrement rates which are accurate estimates of the underlying mortality. The adjustment procedure that reduces the random errors in the observed rates as well as smoothing them is known as graduation, and various methods are described in Chapters 12–16. The statistical tests for comparing a mortality experience with a given standard table are also used for examining the goodness-of-fit of a graduation, but there are certain difficulties when the tests are used for this purpose. We therefore devote the earlier part of the chapter to the simpler problem of comparing a mortality experience with a standard table, and return to the problem of graduation in the latter part (paras 11.49–11.83).

11.6 The purpose for which the mortality table is required must be kept clearly in mind, and the final choice of standard table or graduation is always a matter of judgement. The statistical tests we describe should therefore be regarded as aids in the assessment of the standard table or graduation, and not interpreted too rigidly.

Special considerations

11.7 In the choice of standard table, or method of graduation, special considerations sometimes apply, such as a desire to err on the side of safety either over the whole table or over a particular range of ages. It is important, for example, that mortality for ordinary assurances should not be underestimated. Annuitant mortality, on the other hand, must not be overestimated. The tests we describe examine whether the experience represents a random sample from a population with a given mortality; they make no allowance for practical considerations like these, which are a matter of judgement to be introduced at a later stage.

The chi-square test

11.8 The chi-square test is one of the most widely used statistical tests, and it is frequently employed for testing the null hypothesis that the lives in a mortality experience came from a population with given mortality rates. It does have certain serious limitations when applied to mortality data, however (paras 11.12–11.14), and a number of less sophisticated statistical tests have been devised to overcome these shortcomings (paras 11.15–11.43). These tests are generally simpler to apply than the chi-square test, and for this reason are probably better performed *prior* to the chi-square calculation, which can be avoided if the earlier calculations reveal either an inadequate fit or an extremely good fit.

11.9   To appreciate the need for the other tests, however, it is necessary to understand first the chi-square test and its limitations. Under the null hypothesis that the mortality experience is from a population with given known mortality rates (q_x), the number θ_x of deaths at age x is binomially distributed with parameters E_x and q_x. Provided the expected number of deaths $E_x q_x$ is not too small (less than 5, say), the distribution of θ_x is approximately normal with mean $E_x q_x$ and variance $E_x p_x q_x$, and

$$\chi^2_n = \sum_x \frac{(\theta_x - E_x q_x)^2}{E_x p_x q_x} \tag{11.1}$$

has the chi-square distribution with n degrees of freedom, where n is the number of separate ages or age-groups in the calculation. (This is only strictly true when the age-groupings are chosen without reference to the data. An unknown deduction from the number of degrees of freedom should really be made in other cases.) The right-hand side of equation (11.1) is the sum of the squares of the standardized deviations of the deaths at each age and an example of the more general formula

$$\chi^2 = \sum_{\substack{\text{age} \\ \text{groups}}} \left(\frac{\text{observed} - \text{expected}}{\text{standard deviation}} \right)^2 \tag{11.2}$$

11.10   The null hypothesis that the underlying mortality is according to the standard table is usually rejected if the chi-square value falls in the upper 5 per cent region of the distribution.

Example 11.1

The results of a mortality investigation are shown in columns (2) and (3) of Table 11.1. Let us test whether the underlying mortality is the same as English Life Table Number 10 (Males).

We begin by calculating the expectations and variances of the deaths on the basis of the English Life Table Mortality. We then calculate the standardized deviations of the deaths in column (7), and the contributions to chi-square in column (8).

The chi-square value on 36 degrees of freedom turns out to be 34·48 which is not significant. We have no reason, therefore, to reject the

Table 11.1 *A chi-square example*

Age	Exposed	Deaths	E.L.T. 10 (Males)	Expected Deaths	Variance	Standardized deviation	χ^2 contrib.
x	E_x	θ_x	q_x	$E_x q_x$	$E_x p_x q_x$	$[(3)-(5)]/\sqrt{(6)}$	$(7)^2$
(1)	(2)	(3)	(4)	(5)	(6)	(7)	(8)
35	1051	1	·00421	4·42	4·41	−1·63	2·66
36	940	6	·00447	4·20	4·18	0·88	0·77
37	1048	2	·00474	4·97	4·94	−1·33	1·78
38	716	3	·00502	3·59	3·57	−0·31	0·10
39	719	2	·00531	3·82	3·80	−0·93	0·87
40	1051	4	·00562	5·91	5·87	−0·79	0·62
41	1042	4	·00598	6·23	6·19	−0·90	0·80
42	1804	12	·00639	11·53	11·45	0·14	0·02
43	1468	7	·00687	10·09	10·02	−0·97	0·95
44	1576	16	·00741	11·68	11·59	1·27	1·61
45	1647	18	·00799	13·16	13·05	1·34	1·79
46	1861	16	·00861	16·02	15·89	−0·01	0·00
47	1669	13	·00925	15·44	15·30	−0·62	0·39
48	1624	14	·00990	16·08	15·92	−0·52	0·27
49	1157	11	·01057	12·23	12·10	−0·35	0·12
50	2193	19	·01128	24·74	24·46	−1·16	1·35
51	1803	20	·01206	21·74	21·48	−0·38	0·14
52	2402	31	·01295	31·11	30·70	−0·02	0·00
53	2120	27	·01393	29·53	29·12	−0·47	0·22
54	2406	38	·01499	36·07	35·52	0·32	0·11
55	1975	37	·01614	31·88	31·36	0·91	0·84
56	2564	38	·01744	44·72	43·94	−1·01	1·03
57	1798	36	·01890	33·98	33·34	0·35	0·12
58	2536	51	·02050	51·99	50·92	−0·14	0·02
59	2511	71	·02224	55·84	54·60	2·05	4·21
60	1858	32	·02415	44·87	43·79	−1·95	3·78
61	1835	54	·02630	48·26	46·99	0·84	0·70
62	1393	47	·02875	40·05	38·90	1·11	1·24
63	1462	40	·03150	46·05	44·60	−0·91	0·82
64	1245	34	·03455	43·01	41·53	−1·40	1·96
65	1064	46	·03791	40·34	38·81	0·91	0·83
66	1502	74	·04162	62·51	59·91	1·48	2·20
67	875	36	·04568	39·97	38·14	−0·64	0·41
68	927	38	·05014	46·48	44·15	−1·28	1·63
69	497	29	·05502	27·34	25·84	0·33	0·11
70	983	60	·06033	59·32	55·74	0·09	0·01
Total	–	–	–	–	–	–	34·48

null hypothesis that the underlying mortality is the same as English Life Table Number 10 (Males).

A useful approximation

11.11 The survival probability p_x is very close to one for all except the very old ages, and the expectation $E_x q_x$ is therefore often used as an approximation for the variance $E_x p_x q_x$ of the number of deaths at age x. Some of the calculations are simplified, and the effects on the statistical tests are small (χ^2, for example, is slightly understated). The approximation is equivalent to using the Poisson limit for the binomial distribution of rare events. $\lambda = np = var = mean$

Limitations of the chi-square test

11.12 Even when the chi-square test indicates reasonable adherence to the standard table, closer examination of the individual deviations sometimes reveals serious discrepancies between the experience and the standard table. The test statistic (11.1) in fact comprises the *sum* of the *squares* of the standardized deviations for the individual ages or age-groups. It is not surprising, therefore, that it sometimes fails to detect

(a)   the existence of a number of excessively large deviations counter-balanced by a large number of small deviations;
(b)   a large cumulative deviation over part or the whole of the age range;
(c)   an excess of positive (or negative) deviations over part or the whole of the age range;
(d)   an excessive clumping of deviations of the same sign.

These discrepancies are not necessarily mutually exclusive.

11.13 Discrepancies of type (a) can be detected by comparing the contributions to χ_n^2 of individual ages with chi-square on one degree of freedom. The method we describe in paras 11.15–11.19 is equivalent, however, and possibly easier to apply.

11.14 The use of a standard table for premium and valuation purposes when discrepancies such as these remain undetected can have serious financial consequences: (b), (c) and (d), for example, indicate that the true mortality curve for the office is higher (or lower) than the standard table over a significant portion of the age range. We conclude, therefore, that while the chi-square test does provide a useful comparison of the experience and standard table in the form of a single statistic, further tests are necessary, and some of these may be of greater importance than the chi-square test. Six such tests are described in this chapter, examining respectively

- (i) individual standardized deviations;
- (ii) absolute deviations;
- (iii) cumulative deviations;
- (iv) signs of deviations;
- (v) grouping of signs;
- (vi) changes of sign.

Tests (i), (ii) and (iv) examine the standardized deviations for normality, while (iii), (v) and (vi) test whether the deviations are randomly distributed with respect to age.

Individual standardized deviations

11.15 Under the null hypothesis that the standard table represents office mortality, the observed number of deaths at age x, θ_x is a binomial random variable with parameters E_x and q_x, and its distribution can be approximated by a normal random variable with mean $E_x q_x$ and variance $E_x p_x q_x$. Deaths at successive ages are independent, and it follows that the standardized deviations

$$(\theta_x - E_x q_x)/\sqrt{(E_x p_x q_x)} \tag{11.3}$$

should resemble independent observations on the unit normal distribution.

11.16 The actuary should check, therefore, that not more than about 5 per cent of the standardized deviations exceed two in absolute size.

11.17 According to the unit normal distribution, the percentages of standardized deviations expected to lie in the ranges $(-\infty, -3)$, $(-3, -2)$, $(-2, -1)$, $(-1, 0)$, $(0, 1)$, $(1, 2)$, $(2, 3)$ and $(3, \infty)$ are 0%, 2%, 14%, 34%, 34% 14%, 2% and 0% respectively. The numbers of standardized deviations falling in these ranges should be compared with the expected numbers calculated on this basis. A chi-square test can sometimes be used for this comparison (example 11.2).

11.18 Discrepancies of type (a) in para. 11.12 will usually be detected by means of these methods.

11.19 The actuary will not usually be concerned if the distribution of the standardized deviations is concentrated closer to zero than predicted by the unit normal curve. He will have doubts about the appropriateness of the standard mortality table, however, if the spread of the standardized deviations is too great or their distribution appears to have non-zero mean.

Example 11.2

The standardized deviations in example 11.1 are exhibited in column (7) of Table 11.1 and the distribution of these standardized deviations is summarized in Table 11.2. Only one standardized deviation out of the 36 exceeds 2·0 in absolute value, and this is quite reasonable. According to para. 11.17, we should expect

$$
\begin{aligned}
0{\cdot}00 \times 36 &= 0{\cdot}00 \text{ standardized deviations in the range } (-\infty, -3), \\
0{\cdot}02 \times 36 &= 0{\cdot}72 \text{ standardized deviations in the range } (-3, -2), \\
0{\cdot}14 \times 36 &= 5{\cdot}04 \text{ standardized deviations in the range } (-2, -1), \\
0{\cdot}34 \times 36 &= 12{\cdot}24 \text{ standardized deviations in the range } (-1, 0), \\
0{\cdot}34 \times 36 &= 12{\cdot}24 \text{ standardized deviations in the range } (0, 1), \\
0{\cdot}14 \times 36 &= 5{\cdot}04 \text{ standardized deviations in the range } (1, 2), \\
0{\cdot}02 \times 36 &= 0{\cdot}72 \text{ standardized deviations in the range } (2, 3), \\
0{\cdot}00 \times 36 &= 0{\cdot}00 \text{ standardized deviations in the range } (3, \infty).
\end{aligned}
$$

Table 11.2   *The distribution of standardized deviations in example 11.1*

Range	Observed number	Expected number
less than −3	0	0·00
−3 to −2	0	0·72
−2 to −1	7	5·04
−1 to 0	15	12·24
0 to 1	9	12·24
1 to 2	4	5·04
2 to 3	1	0·72
over 3	0	0·00

These expectations are also included in Table 11.2, and we see that none of the observed frequencies deviates substantially from its expected value.

The expected numbers below −2 and above +2 are very small, and in order to compare the observed and expected frequencies in the various ranges, using a chi-square test, we amalgamate the tail ranges so that the expectations are not less than one (W. G. Cochran, 1954). The test criterion is

$$\chi^2 = \frac{(7-5\cdot76)^2}{5\cdot76} + \frac{(15-12\cdot24)^2}{12\cdot24} + \frac{(9-12\cdot24)^2}{12\cdot24} + \frac{(5-5\cdot76)^2}{5\cdot76} = 1\cdot85$$

on three degrees of freedom (one less than the number of 'cells' in the calculation of χ^2).

It is not significant. The distribution of the standardized deviations appears therefore to be unit normal, as it should be if the underlying mortality is the same as English Life Table Number 10 (Males).

Absolute deviations

11.20 The probability that a unit normal random variable lies between $-2/3$ and $2/3$ is almost exactly $0\cdot5$. It follows that approximately half the absolute standardized deviations

$$|(\theta_x - E_x q_x)/\sqrt{(E_x p_x q_x)}| \tag{11.4}$$

should be less than $2/3$, and half should be greater.

11.21 In the case of n ages or age groups, the number N of absolute standardized deviations exceeding $2/3$ will be a binomial random variable with parameters n and $1/2$. The actuary is not usually concerned if the distribution of standardized deviations is concentrated closer to zero than predicted by the unit normal distribution. He will, therefore, only have doubts about the appropriateness of the standard table if N falls in the upper 5 per cent region of the binomial $(n, \frac{1}{2})$ distribution.

11.22 The upper percentage points of the binomial $(n, \frac{1}{2})$ distribution are given in Table 11.3 for $n = 5, 6, 7, ..., 20$. For n greater than 20 the normal approximation to the binomial can be used. The appropriateness of the standard table will be suspect if

$$T = (2N - n)/\sqrt{n} \; = \; \frac{(N - \frac{1}{2}n)}{\sqrt{\frac{1}{2} \cdot \frac{1}{2} \cdot n}} \tag{11.5}$$

falls in the upper 5 per cent region of the unit normal distribution (i.e. greater than about $1\cdot65$).

11.23 This test will usually detect discrepancies of type (a) in para. 11.12. It is simpler to apply than the method of paras 11.15–11.19, but not quite as thorough.

Example 11.3

Examination of column (7) in Table 11.1 reveals that twenty-one of the thirty-six absolute standardized deviations are greater than $2/3$

and 15 are less. To test whether the number exceeding 2/3 is excessive, we compute

$$T = (2 \times 21 - 36)/\sqrt{36} = 1.00$$

This value is not significant at the 5 per cent level. We have no evidence, therefore, to contradict the null hypothesis that the underlying mortality is according to the English Life Table Number 10 (Males).

Table 11.3   *The upper* 100α per cent points of the*
binomial distribution† with parameters n *and* $\frac{1}{2}$
The critical region includes the tabled value

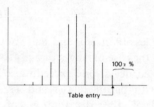

Table entry

n	α = 0·005	0·01	0·025	0·05
5	–	–	–	5
6	–	–	6	6
7	–	7	7	7
8	8	8	8	7
9	9	9	8	8
10	10	10	9	9
11	11	10	10	9
12	11	11	10	10
13	12	12	11	10
14	13	12	12	11
15	13	13	12	12
16	14	14	13	12
17	15	14	13	13
18	15	15	14	13
19	16	15	15	14
20	17	16	15	15

* The lower 100α per cent point is obtained by subtracting the table entry from the binomial parameter *n*.
† Reproduced with permission from *Handbook of Numerical and Statistical Techniques*, by J. H. Pollard (1977), Cambridge University Press.

Cumulative deviations

11.24 Deaths at successive ages are independent, and under the null hypothesis that mortality is according to the standard table, θ_x is approximately a normal random variable with mean $E_x q_x$ and variance $E_x p_x q_x$. It follows that the accumulated deviation for ages x_1 to x_2

$$\sum_{x=x_1}^{x_2} (\theta_x - E_x q_x) \qquad (11.6)$$

is a normal random variable with zero mean and variance

$$\sum_{x=x_1}^{x_2} E_x p_x q_x \qquad (11.7)$$

11.25 The use of the standard table may be regarded as suspect if the absolute value of the accumulated deviation over the whole table is greater than about twice the square root of the variance as given by (11.7), or the accumulated deviations over sections of the table are too large in absolute value.

11.26 The accumulated deviation test should be applied to the whole table and to all age ranges of financial importance to detect discrepancies of type (b) in para. 11.12. The reader should note, however, that it is incorrect to apply this test to an age range determined by the data (e.g. a range of ages all having deviations of the same sign). The age range must be chosen without reference to the data. Furthermore accumulated deviation tests on various age ranges are only independent if the age ranges do not overlap. Cumulative deviations for overlapping age intervals are positively correlated, and if tests are applied to such overlapping intervals, the expected proportion of tests producing significant results when the null hypothesis is true is not necessarily 5 per cent.

Example 11.4

The best way to study accumulated deviations is to form a table like 11.4, showing the accumulated deviations from the youngest age in the investigation and the corresponding variance. The accumulated deviations and variances in Table 11.4 are those of example 11.1 and were obtained by summing respectively the differences between columns (3) and (5), and column (6) of Table 11.1. All the absolute accumulated deviations in the table are less than twice their standard deviation.

Table 11.4   *Accumulated deviations for example 11.1*

Age x	Accumulated deviation	Variance	Age x	Accumulated deviation	Variance
35	− 3·42	4·41	53	− 20·47	244·04
36	− 1·62	8·59	54	− 18·54	279·56
37	− 4·59	13·53	55	− 13·42	310·92
38	− 5·18	17·10	56	− 20·14	354·86
39	− 7·00	20·90	57	− 18·12	388·20
40	− 8·91	26·77	58	− 19·11	439·12
41	− 11·14	32·96	59	− 3·95	493·72
42	− 10·67	44·41	60	− 16·82	537·51
43	− 13·76	54·43	61	− 11·08	584·50
44	− 9·44	66·02	62	− 4·13	623·40
45	− 4·60	79·07	63	− 10·18	668·00
46	− 4·62	94·96	64	− 19·19	709·53
47	− 7·06	110·26	65	− 13·53	748·34
48	− 9·14	126·18	66	− 2·04	808·25
49	− 10·37	138·28	67	− 6·01	846·39
50	− 16·09	162·74	68	− 14·49	890·54
51	− 17·83	184·22	69	− 12·83	916·38
52	− 17·94	214·92	70	− 12·15	972·12

All the cumulative deviations in Table 11.4 are negative. This is not so surprising, when we recall that they are not independent, but positively correlated (para. 11.26).

The standardized accumulated deviation for the whole table is

$$\frac{-12\cdot15}{\sqrt{(972\cdot12)}} = -0\cdot39$$

which is not significant.

When we apply the cumulative deviation test to the four age ranges (35, 43), (44, 52), (53, 61) and (62, 70), which were chosen arbitrarily without reference to the data, we find that none of the tests produce a significant result. The standardized deviation over the age range (44, 52), for example, is

$$[(-17\cdot94)-(-13\cdot76)]/\sqrt{(214\cdot92 - 54\cdot43)} = -0\cdot33.$$

The underlying mortality would appear to be the same as English Life Table Number 10 (Males). The final decision as to the suitability of the standard table, however, must wait until all the statistical tests have been completed.

Sign test

11.27 Under the null hypothesis that mortality is according to the given standard table, the deviations of the observed deaths from the expected are independent normal random variables. The signs of the individual deviations are therefore independent, and equally likely to be positive or negative.

11.28 The actuary will be concerned if an examination of the experience reveals an abnormally large number of positive or negative deviations. In the case of n age-groups he will begin to doubt the null hypothesis if the number of positive deviations N falls in the upper or lower $2\frac{1}{2}$ per cent region of the binomial $(n, \frac{1}{2})$ distribution.

11.29 The percentage points of the binomial $(n, \frac{1}{2})$ distribution are given in Table 11.3 for $n = 5, 6, 7,..., 20$. For n greater than 20, the normal approximation (11.5) can be used; the null hypothesis is rejected if T falls in the upper or lower $2\frac{1}{2}$ per cent regions of the unit normal distribution (i.e. greater than about $2 \cdot 0$ in absolute size).

11.30 This test should detect discrepancies of type (c) in para. 11.12.

Example 11.5

$$\frac{2}{N} \int_{0}^{\infty} \frac{N}{\sigma \sqrt{2\pi}} \, e^{-x^2/2\sigma^2} \, x \, dx \doteq 0.80 \qquad \text{see reason 6}$$
$$\text{pg 7}$$

Fourteen of the thirty-six deviations in example 11.1 are positive and twenty-two are negative. To see whether the number of positive signs is abnormal, we compute

$$T = (2 \times 14 - 36)/\sqrt{36} = -1 \cdot 33. \quad \left(\text{see } (11.5) \right)$$

The number of positive signs is not abnormal. We have no reason, therefore, to doubt the null hypothesis that the underlying mortality is according to English Life Table Number 10 (Males).

Stevens' test for the grouping of signs

11.31 Under the null hypothesis that mortality is according to the given standard table, the signs of the individual deviations are independent and equally likely to be positive or negative. The numbers of positive and negative deviations might be reasonable according to the sign test of paras 11.27–11.30, but we should still have doubts about use of the standard table if the number of groups of positive signs (and consequently the number of negative groups) is small.

11.32 It is possible to divide n_1 positive signs into t non-empty groups by placing barriers between the signs in $t-1$ of n_1-1

positions (Figure 11.1). The number of ways of doing this is

$$\binom{n_1-1}{t-1}.$$

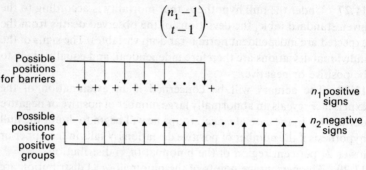

FIGURE 11.1   An explanation of Stevens' test

11.33 With n_2 negative signs, there are $n_2 + 1$ possible positions for the t positive groups (Figure 11.1), and the number of ways of selecting t positions is

$$\binom{n_2+1}{t}.$$

11.34 The total number of ways of arranging n_1 positive and n_2 negative signs is

$$\binom{n_1+n_2}{n_1}$$

and we deduce that the probability of obtaining t positive groups, given n_1 and n_2 is

$$\binom{n_1-1}{t-1}\binom{n_2+1}{t}\bigg/\binom{n_1+n_2}{n_1}$$

which may be written

$$\binom{n_1-1}{t-1}\binom{n_2+1}{n_2+1-t}\bigg/\binom{n_1+n_2}{n_2} \qquad (11.8)$$

This is a hypergeometric probability of the form

$$\binom{R}{r}\binom{B}{b}\bigg/\binom{R+B}{r+b}.$$

11.35 Let us imagine that our experience has g positive groups. The probability of obtaining g or fewer positive groups is obtained by summing (11.8) for t less than or equal to g. If this probability turns out to be less than 0·05, we shall have serious doubts about the appropriateness of using the standard table, because of the excessive clumping of signs.

11.36 Except when n_1 and n_2 are very small, the evaluation and summation of terms like (11.8) is very tedious. Hypergeometric tables can be used. The mean and variance of the hypergeometric distribution are known, however (J.H. Pollard, 1977, p. 119), and it is possible to deduce that the mean and variance of the number of positive groups are given by

$$\text{mean} = n_1(n_2+1)/(n_1+n_2); \tag{11.9}$$

$$\text{variance} \doteqdot (n_1 n_2)^2/(n_1+n_2)^3 \tag{11.10}$$

11.37 Stevens' test can be performed approximately by comparing

$$G = (g-\text{mean})/\sqrt{(\text{variance})} \tag{11.11}$$

with the lower 5 per cent region of the unit normal curve (i.e. less than $-1\cdot65$). Daw (1954) has pointed out that different results can be obtained by applying the test to the negative signs rather than the positive signs. The effect is of little consequence except when the total numbers of signs is small, when it is debatable whether a formal test should in fact be applied. A test similar to Stevens', but counting both positive and negative runs, has been proposed by David (1949).

11.38 An alternative approach is to represent the outcome from the hypergeometric distribution by the 2×2 contingency table.

n_2-g+1	$g-1$	n_2
g	n_1-g	n_1
n_2+1	n_1-1	n_1+n_2

A very small value of g suggests that the signs are excessively clumped. A large value of g, on the other hand, is quite acceptable. If the observed number of positive groups exceeds the expectation (11.9), we can be quite satisfied with the grouping of signs. If the observed number turns out to be less than the expected number, we apply the usual χ_1^2 test to the 2×2 table and conclude that the clustering is excessive if the chi-square value exceeds the upper 10 per cent point of χ_1^2. The procedure is essentially the same as the normal method of para. 11.37.

11.39 The distinction between Stevens' test of the grouping of signs and the binomial test of signs should be kept clearly in mind. Stevens' test is designed to test clumping—discrepancy (d) in para. 11.12. It is a conditional test, given the numbers of positive and negative signs, and does not, for example, produce a significant result with thirty-nine negative signs and a single positive sign (the probability of one or less positive groups is certain); the binomial sign test would produce a very significant result with these data. A single group of twenty positive signs among twenty negative and twenty positive signs (a total of forty signs) would, on the other hand, produce a very significant result with Stevens' test and a non-significant result in the binomial sign test. Stevens' test is essentially the same as the perhaps better-known Wald and Wolfowitz runs test, a 'run' being the same as a 'group', (see, for example, Kendall and Stuart, 1967, p. 463.)

Example 11.6

In example 11.1, there are fourteen positive deviations, twenty-two negative deviations and nine positive groups. The expected number of positive groups is 8.94 and the variance is approximately 2·03.

The observed number of positive groups exceeds the expected number; so we do not need to compute G. There is no evidence of excessive clumping of signs.

Binomial test of change of sign

11.40 Under the null hypothesis that mortality is according to the given standard table, the signs of successive deviations are equally likely to be the same or opposite. The number of sign changes in a sequence of n deviations is therefore binomial with parameters $n - 1$ and $\frac{1}{2}$.

11.41 The actuary will be concerned if an examination of the experience reveals too few sign changes. He will be inclined to reject the standard table if the number of sign changes N falls in the lower 5 per cent region of the binomial $(n - 1, \frac{1}{2})$ distribution.

11.42 It is apparent that this test examines both the numbers of positive and negative signs and their grouping, and would produce significant results in both the extreme situations mentioned in para. 11.39. In a sense, it combines Stevens' test and the sign test. However, it is not as efficient as the sign test in detecting an abnormal number of positive or negative signs, or as efficient as Stevens' test in detecting clumping.

11.43 Percentage points for the binomial distribution are given in

Table 11.3. When $n-1$ is greater than 20, the normal approximation to the binomial can be used; we reject the standard table if

$$S = (2N - n + 1)/\sqrt{n-1} \qquad (11.12)$$

falls in the lower 5 per cent region of the unit normal distribution.

Example 11.7

There are seventeen sign changes among the thirty-six deviations in example 11.1. The expected number of changes is 17·5. We do not need a formal statistical test to see that the result is not significant.

This is the final test we shall apply in our comparison of the data in Table 11.1 with English Life Table Number 10 (Males). None of the tests produced a significant result. It would seem, therefore, that the underlying mortality of lives in the experience is the same as English Life Table Number 10 (Males).

Tests over sections of the table

11.44   The tests of paras 11.8–11.43 are often applied to sections of the mortality table as well as the overall table. Discrepancies barely discernible in the whole-table tests are sometimes detected.

Heterogeneity—the Redington–Michaelson test

11.45   The basic assumption in all the above tests is that the lives are independent and that mortality is the same for all lives of the same age. The number of deaths at age x is then binomial with mean $E_x q_x$ and variance $E_x p_x q_x$.

11.46   A group of lives in an experience can be heterogeneous with respect to mortality in a number of ways, and this can upset the assumption of a binomial distribution of the number of deaths at a particular age. The effect of heterogeneity is not always to increase the variance above $E_x p_x q_x$, however. Fluctuations in the underlying mortality rates over time increase the variance; mortality differences among lives of the same age, on the other hand, *reduce* the variance (A. H. Pollard, 1970; R. H. Daw, 1974). Life office experiences usually include multiple policies on the same life, and these increase the variance.

11.47   Occasionally knowledge of the data will suggest the possibility that the binomial variance is incorrect. A test which examines the appropriateness of the binomial variance was devised by Redington and Michaelson (1940). The test is an example of the variate-difference method described by Kendall and Stuart (1968), and makes use of the fact that the third difference of the underlying mortality rate, $\Delta^3 q_x$ is zero for all practical purposes. The expected value of the third difference of the crude mortality rate $\mathring{q}_x$ is therefore zero. If the binomial variance is appropriate for the deaths in the experience, the third difference of $\mathring{q}_x$ will have variance

$$\text{Var } (\Delta^3 \mathring{q}_x) = p_x q_x / E_x + 9 p_{x+1} q_{x+1} / E_{x+1}$$
$$+ 9 p_{x+2} q_{x+2} / E_{x+2} + p_{x+3} q_{x+3} / E_{x+3} \quad (11.13)$$

11.48 When heterogeneity is present, the variance of $\Delta^3 \mathring{q}_x$ becomes $K^2 \text{Var } (\Delta^3 \mathring{q}_x)$, where K is assumed to be independent of age, at least within a certain age range. To test whether K is one and the binomial variance is appropriate, we calculate

$$\chi^2 = \sum_{j=0}^{r} (\Delta^3 \mathring{q}_{x+4j})^2 / \text{Var } (\Delta^3 \mathring{q}_{x+4j}) \quad (11.14)$$

and reject the null hypothesis if χ^2 falls in the upper or lower $2\frac{1}{2}$ per cent regions of the chi-square distribution on $r + 1$ degrees of freedom. The terms in (11.14) are for every fourth age to ensure independence. If the test produces a significant result, we need to replace the binomial variances in the standard tests by $K^2 E_x p_x q_x$. An estimate of K^2 is provided by $\chi^2 / (r+1)$.

Construction of a new mortality table

11.49 It is not always possible to find a standard table for the underlying mortality of a particular group of lives, and in this situation a new table must be constructed. New standard tables (e.g. national life tables and assured lives mortality tables) are also needed from time to time.

11.50 When we construct a new life table or a sickness table, we actually begin (perhaps unconsciously) by formulating a model. The model has unknown parameters such as q_x and z_x. These are population values. The life table and sickness values which we compute and use are *estimates* of the true parameters, based on the finite amount of data available to us. Indeed, any body of data examined by the actuary should be regarded as a sample (even though all the available data have been included in the investigation), and actuarial estimates based on the data will be subject to sampling errors.

The purposes of graduation

11.51 In the course of time the term 'graduation' has been both extended and narrowed in its application, according to the particular interests of different writers. For example, the process of fitting trend curves, as in the previous chapter, with the view to projection into the future might be embraced by 'graduation'. On the other hand, the actual process of graduating the observed rates might be a subject for a general philosophical discussion on laws of mortality (as, for example, in the work referred to in paras 1.48–1.53). Our present purpose, however, is much more mundane and practical, and these wider implications of 'graduation' will be ignored. Our concern is mainly with the principles and methods of adjusting a set of observed rates to provide a suitable basis for actuarial and demographic calculations of a practical nature. In fact, our interest will be still further narrowed because it is sufficient for practical purposes to assume that mortality is not changing with time. It must be admitted immediately that the relatively meticulous processes of graduation may often be inappropriate because the needs of the practical situation may be met either by minimal smoothing or, perhaps, by a hypothetical set of mortality rates differing from the observed rates by much more than would usually be tolerated in a set of graduated rates. It is important to keep a sense of proportion. Most actuarial problems require assumptions regarding future interest rates as well as future mortality or other statistical rates. The result is that from a strictly practical point of view graduation has come to be regarded as a refined technique whose application is not often justified. Nevertheless the principles of graduation are of importance to a proper appraisal of the behaviour of actuarial statistics and to the development of a sound judgement in the selection of a statistical basis for dealing with practical problems.

The rationale of graduation *See also lesson 6 pg 2*

11.52 Let us assume that we observe θ_x deaths amongst E_x persons all aged x last birthday, and that our experience is limited to this single age. The best estimate of the mortality rate q_x would be the observed mortality rate (and maximum likelihood estimate)

$$\mathring{q}_x = \theta_x / E_x \tag{11.15}$$

which may lie above or below the true underlying value.

11.53 Most mortality experiences cover a range of ages, and (11.15) may be applied at each age. Some of the maximum likelihood estimates will lie above the corresponding population values and some will lie below, and the progression of maximum likelihood estimates from age to age will be quite uneven.

11.54 But for certain prior information we have about the mortality curve, the separate maximum likelihood estimates (11.15) would be the best possible estimates of the underlying $\{q_x\}$ values.

11.55 We have reason to believe, however, that if the numbers of individuals we had observed at the various ages had been much larger, the estimated rates would have shown a much more regular progression from age to age, and that in the limit, if the numbers in the groups had been indefinitely large, the estimates would have exhibited a smooth progression from age to age (i.e. the underlying q_x curve is smooth). Indeed, there is a saying, *Natura non agit per saltum*, expressing the fact that natural forces operate gradually and that their effects become apparent continuously and not in sudden jerks.

11.56 It follows that the data for several ages on either side of age x can be used to augment the basic information we have at age x, and an improved estimate of q_x can be obtained by smoothing the individual estimates (11.15). The art of smoothing the separate maximum likelihood values to obtain the best possible estimates of the underlying population values is called *graduation*.

11.57 The ability to smooth out random sampling errors may enable us to calculate valid rates from relatively scanty data. The important proviso is that the sampling errors *are* random. Non-random errors in a sample (i.e. bias) are *not* progressively reduced by increasing the size of the sample and the statistical rationale for graduation does not apply to them. It is, of course, true that in a very large sample, a source of bias may be swamped but there is no basis for estimating just how large the sample has to be before such bias can be effectively ignored. In any case this would be a 'sledge hammer' method of dealing with bias. It would be more economical to revise the method of drawing the sample so as to avoid bias altogether. The essential point here is that the underlying statistical theory of graduation cannot apply to bias. If, for example, the experience on which the investigation is based contains a sub-group of lives with atypical mortality rates which distort the shape of the progression of q_x, it would not be permissible, and would probably not be possible, to remove this distortion by any smoothing process. First, it would be difficult to identify the distortion by mere inspection; second, removal of the distortion would leave the resulting rates unrepresentative of the experience actually investigated. One might as well adopt an entirely hypothetical set of rates.

11.58 A number of different graduation methods are available. The principal ones covered in this book include the graphic method, summation and adjusted average methods, graduation by mathematical formula, graduation by reference to a standard table, and osculatory interpolation and spline functions. A single data set (Table 12.1) will be used to demonstrate all the methods. This will facilitate comparisons among the methods and an assessment of the advantages and disadvantages of each.

so graduate because of age misstatement

Smoothness

11.59 The concept of 'smoothness' has been used in paras 11.55–11.57 without actually being defined. It is in fact a very difficult concept to define mathematically. We all have an intuitive idea about what we mean by 'smooth', and scientists have been smoothing crude data for centuries. Yet there does not seem to be a completely satisfactory definition.

11.60 A mathematician might call a continuous curve smooth if it is continuously first differentiable. Such a definition is of little practical use to the experimenter, who is unlikely to accept as 'smooth' the polynomial of degree 15 passing through his original 16 data points. A mathematical curve with only a small number of parameters is therefore advocated by some authorities. Such a definition eliminates the higher-order polynomial, but it still allows certain curves which offend intuition. For example, the curve

$$y = a + b \sin c/x \qquad (11.16)$$

can hardly be described as smooth near the origin.

11.61 M. T. L. Bizley (1958) describes a car being driven along a narrow lane only just wide enough to allow the car's passage. If the track of the lane is a smooth curve, it will not turn *suddenly* to the left or to the right, and when it is bending, it will not *suddenly* straighten out. It will be possible to keep the car on the track by making only gradual adjustments to the steering wheel. Bizley also observes that smoothness is intimately concerned with predictability, and proposes the following definition of smoothness: *a plane continuous curve is smooth at those points which are such that the absolute value of* *the rate of change of curvature with respect to distance measured along the curve is small.*

11.62 Bizley's requirement of a small rate of change of curvature turns out to be equivalent in the mortality context to a requirement that third-order differences be small, which is consistent with the widely held view that low-order polynomials are smooth. We shall concentrate our attention on the first three orders of differences.

11.63 Apart from the improvements in the estimates of the underlying population parameters brought about by smoothing, there are also good practical reasons why a table which is to be extensively used should have a high degree of smoothness. Complicated functions such as policy values will be calculated by means of the table, and if a high degree of smoothness has not been achieved, these more complicated functions may show alarming and even embarrassing irregularities.

Test for smoothness

11.64 It is usually found desirable to examine the first three orders of differences of the graduated values. Generally speaking, third-order differences will be small, and it is customary in comparing two different graduations for smoothness to calculate the sum of the absolute values of the third differences in each table, and to accept as the better graduation (on grounds of smoothness) that which gives rise to the smaller total. The implied smoothness criterion in the case of a mortality graduation is therefore

$$\sum_x |\Delta^3 q_x| \tag{11.17}$$

11.65 Mortality rates at the older ages tend to be about a hundred times as great as the rates at younger ages, and third differences vary in about the same proportion (exercise 4). 'Smoothness' in the successive orders of differences is thus more important than smallness.

Random error and 'intrinsic' roughness

11.66 It would be wrong to assume that *all* roughness in the progression of rates of mortality—for example, from age to age—was due to random errors and should be eliminated by graduation *on this account*. Roughness might be of two totally different kinds. It might be due (1) to what we may call 'intrinsic' roughness, or sharp changes in the course of the rates, which have nothing whatever to do with chance or randomness, and (2) to random variations of the kind we have been discussing, the incidence of which from age to age we should not expect to be repeated if the experience itself could be repeated. The presence or otherwise of 'intrinsic' roughness is usually determinable, from a practical point of view, from our general knowledge of the circumstances of the group of lives and from the knowledge of the progression of the rates of mortality of other groups of lives of not widely dissimilar constitution and in not widely dissimilar circumstances of environment and period of observation. By the same token this information provides some guidance as to whether the intrinsic roughness is a feature likely to be reproduced in the future. It is perhaps worth observing that in a number of early life tables attempts were made to remove by graduation the now familiar 'accident hump' near age 20. This was clearly wrong.

Circumstances in which 'intrinsic' roughnesses may be removed

11.67 When 'intrinsic' roughness exists in a set of rates, the decision as to whether or not it should be smoothed out by a graduation process would depend on the knowledge available concerning the reasons for its existence and on the purpose which the graduation is to serve. This amounts to asking whether this roughness in the progression of the rates (when the assumed random errors have been removed) is indeed a natural feature of the underlying experience from which our sample of data (and it is only a sample) has been drawn; and if it is a natural feature, would its smoothing out be a justifiable practical convenience—for example, in achieving a smooth progression of life-assurance premiums from age to age. To put it another way, if we *could* estimate the random errors otherwise than by smoothing, would we still smooth? Strict fidelity to the data would compel a negative answer to this question. It is, however, an academic question, for there is no other way than by graduation to assess the actual random errors that have arisen (as distinct from their possible range, which could be estimated on some hypothesis about their underlying distribution). The next question is whether smoothing is liable to remove more than the unknown actual random errors, i.e. to remove 'intrinsic' roughness; and if so whether this is desirable or undesirable. If the purpose of smoothing is to produce a statistical basis for actuarial calculations relating to the future and if, as is usual, the reasons for the 'intrinsic' roughness were not thought likely to persist or to be of any practical importance, the obvious course would be to remove it in the process of graduation. If the purpose of a graduation is merely to exhibit the experienced rates with the random roughness removed or at least reduced, a graduation process which avoids smoothing out the 'intrinsic' roughness should be adopted, and the resulting 'graduated' rates would not, therefore, be expected to exhibit complete smoothness. An example of this kind is provided by the methods used for the earlier English Life Tables, where the aim was to preserve the 'inherent' features of the experience as far as possible. These methods are discussed in Chapter 16.

11.68 For the rest of the discussion we shall assume that our data do not exhibit any 'intrinsic' roughness or at least that, in so far as 'intrinsic' roughness exists in the data, its removal by the graduation process is not objectionable.

Fidelity to data

11.69 An infinite number of smooth curves can be drawn near a set of data points, and any degree of smoothness can be achieved by choosing the appropriate curve. Smoothing alone, however, is not graduation. Graduated rates must be representative of the underlying data.

11.70 The two qualities 'smoothness' and 'goodness-of-fit' tend to conflict, in the sense that smoothness may not be improved beyond a certain point without some sacrifice of goodness-of-fit, and vice versa. Thus, a graduation will often turn out to be a compromise between optimal fit and optimal smoothness. To be of general use, a graduation method must allow the graduator some latitude in choosing the relative emphasis to place on smoothness and fit. All the methods we describe in Chapters 12–16 meet this requirement.

11.71 The trade-off between fit and smoothness is most explicit in the case of the Whittaker–Henderson method of graduation. Graduated mortality rates $\{\hat{q}_{x+j}\}$ are chosen to minimize the quadratic form

$$Q = \sum_{j=0}^{n} w_j (\hat{q}_{x+j} - \mathring{q}_{x+j})^2 + K \sum_{j=0}^{n-3} (\Delta^3 \hat{q}_{x+j})^2 \qquad (11.18)$$

where the $\{w_j\}$ and K are fixed positive weights. The relative importance of smoothness and fit is determined by the graduator when he selects the value of K. A large value will result in optimized smoothness and a quadratic mortality curve. The choice $K = 0$, on the other hand, optimizes fit, and the graduated and observed mortality rates coincide. The weights $\{w_j\}$ are the reciprocals of the estimated variances of the crude mortality rates, and Q is minimized by solving a set of simultaneous linear equations (exercise 12).

11.72 The statistical tests of paras. 11.8–11.44 were designed to test whether the lives in a mortality investigation came from a population with a particular mortality curve. The same tests are also used to check the adequacy of fit of a graduation.

11.73 It should be noted, however, that graduated rates are calculated from the actual experience, and because of this they tend to exhibit closer adherence to data than would the true underlying mortality rates. Strictly speaking, the tests should be modified to take this into account. The modification is straightforward in the case of the chi-square test: a reduction in the number of degrees of freedom, although the test must then be regarded as approximate. The amount of the reduction depends on the method of graduation, and the problem is discussed separately for each method. One degree of freedom is almost always lost because the graduation method constrains the total expected and total observed deaths to be approximately equal.

11.74 The other tests have no known modifications. Fortunately the fact that the graduated rates are calculated from the data has little effect on the sign tests. Beard (1951) has suggested an approximate modification for the remaining tests: the replacement of the variance $E_x p_x q_x$ by

$$\{(n-k)/n\}E_x p_x q_x \qquad (11.19)$$

where n and $n-k$ are respectively the number of age-groups and the number of degrees of freedom in the chi-square test. The adjustment is not usually of great consequence.

11.75 The reader should note that in the case of an unadjusted test the criterion is always slightly more significant than the nominal level would suggest. Thus, a test value which appears to be not quite significant may in fact be just significant, and a value which is marginally significant is actually of greater significance than it appears.

11.76 When a statistical test of adherence to data produces a significant result, we may reject the graduation as inadequate. The significant test result tells us that there is strong evidence that one or more of the assumptions inherent in the graduation procedure is invalid. In the case of an adjusted-average graduation (Chapter 13), which assumes that sections of the mortality curve can be represented by third-degree polynomial arcs and that along these sections of the curve the variances of the observed mortality rates are constant, a significant test value provides strong evidence that at least one of these assumptions is not valid. A significant test result in respect of a graduation by mathematical curve probably indicates that the assumed mathematical form (e.g. Makeham's curve) is not appropriate.

11.77 A comment should be made about applying more than one statistical test to the same set of data. If two different tests are applied to the same data to test the same null hypothesis (or very similar hypotheses) and a 5 per cent significance level is used in each case, the probability that at least one of the tests will lead to an incorrect rejection of the null hypothesis is somewhat greater than 5 per cent. If two very different hypotheses are tested by means of the same data, the probability of an incorrect rejection of at least one null hypothesis is considerably greater than 5 per cent and often closer to 10 per cent. The tests we propose all relate to the one basic null hypothesis. They should be regarded as aids in the assessment of a graduation and not interpreted too rigidly.

Undergraduation

11.78 Graduated rates sometimes adhere too closely to the data. The problem usually only arises in connection with the graphic method of graduation, and is referred to as undergraduation. The rates are said to be undergraduated. Undergraduation is indicated by lack of smoothness, a very small chi-square value, and an excess of small absolute deviations.

Heterogeneity

11.79 The Redington–Michaelson test of paras 11.45–11.48 can be used to test whether heterogeneity has had any effect on the assumed binomial variances. The underlying mortality rates are, however, unknown and we need to estimate the variance (11.13) using

$$V(x) = \mathring{p}_x \mathring{q}_x / E_x + 9\mathring{p}_{x+1}\mathring{q}_{x+1}/E_{x+1}$$
$$+ 9\mathring{p}_{x+2}\mathring{q}_{x+2}/E_{x+2} + \mathring{p}_{x+3}\mathring{q}_{x+3}/E_{x+3} \quad (11.20)$$

The test criterion becomes

$$\chi^2 = \sum_{j=0}^{r} (\Delta^3 \mathring{q}_{x+4j})^2 / V(x+4j). \quad (11.21)$$

If the test proves significant, the adjustment of para. 11.48 should be applied to all the statistical tests on the graduation.

Choice of function to be graduated

11.80 The rough data derived from the investigation are usually available in the form of the exposed to risk at each age or group of ages and the corresponding decrements (deaths, retirements, marriages, etc.). It is usual to compute ungraduated rates of decrement directly from the rough data and then graduate the rates.

11.81 In considering mortality tables, the rate of mortality q_x is often chosen for graduation, but the form of the curve, with its gentle gradient at the younger ages and its very rapidly increasing gradient at higher ages, makes it unsuitable for some purposes. For this reason $\log q_x$ and $\log(q_x + 0.1)$ have sometimes been used, since these functions tend to be much flatter and can therefore be represented more easily in the graphic form.

11.82 'Laws' of mortality generally bring in mortality functions such as μ_x and m_x (paras 1.48–1.49); μ_x, m_x and $-\log p_x$ are therefore frequently chosen for graduation by mathematical formula.

11.83 There are occasions when it is appropriate to graduate the exposed to risk and decrements separately, and obtain the graduated rate by division. This approach was used in connection with the earlier English Life Tables to overcome the problem of age misstatements in the exposed to risk and in the deaths. It should be remembered, however, that

(a) in many experiences the exposed to risk is essentially a discontinuous function;
(b) a slight distortion of the exposed to risk may coincide with a slight distortion of the decrement in the opposite direction, and the combined effect may be quite appreciable.

Example 11.8

Table 11.5 is typical of a graduation based on scanty data. The graduated rates have been calculated to four rather than five decimal places. The columns for $\Delta \hat{q}_x$ and $\Delta^2 \hat{q}_x$ are inspected for smoothness, but on this occasion $\Delta^3 \hat{q}_x$ has not been found, since only three significant figures of $\hat{q}_x$ are available and $\Delta^2 \hat{q}_x$ is clearly smooth.

From Table 11.6, we see that 8.15 is the chi-square value on about 15 degrees of freedom (see paras 12.26–12.27 and 13.92). We also see

Table 11.5

Age (1)	Exposed (2)	Actual deaths (3)	$10^4 \times \hat{q}_x$ graduated (4)	$\Delta(4)$ (5)	$\Delta^2(4)$ (6)
47	166	2	144	1	1
48	187	2	145	2	−1
49	218	4	147	1	1
50	243	6	148	2	0
51	276	2	150	2	0
52	302	4	152	2	1
53	347	7	154	3	1
54	390	3	157	4	1
55	430	9	161	5	1
56	494	9	166	6	2
57	558	8	172	8	2
58	628	11	180	10	2
59	701	14	190	12	3
60	813	18	202	15	3
61	917	18	217	18	3
62	1040	24	235	21	4
63	1181	30	256	25	3
64	1299	43	281	28	3
65	1432	41	309	31	3
66	1596	54	340	34	
67	1752	64	374		
Total		373	—	—	—

that the observed and expected standardized deviations in various ranges are as shown in Table 11.7. Six of the absolute standardized deviations lie above 2/3 and fifteen lie below. The absolute values of the cumulative deviations in column (6) of Table 11.6 are all much less than twice the square root of their variances in column (7). There are thirteen negative deviations in the twenty-one ages and ten sign changes. None of these results are significant. Nor is the number of positive groups, because the observed number, 5, exceeds the expected number 4.3.

The graduation appears satisfactory both from the smoothness point of view and from the adherence to data criterion. The statistical tests suggest undergraduation; it is not possible to investigate smoothness more fully, however, because the graduated rates are only given correct to three significant figures.

Table 11.6

Age (1)	Actual deaths (2)	Expected deaths (3)	Deviation (2)−(3) (4)	Approximate standardized deviation (4)/√(3) (5)	Cumulative deviation Σ(4) (6)	Approximate variance Σ(3) (7)	Contrib. to χ^2 (5)² (8)
47	2	2·4	−0·4	−0·26	−0·4	2·4	0·07
48	2	2·7	−0·7	−0·43	−1·1	5·1	0·18
49	4	3·2	0·8	0·45	−0·3	8·3	0·20
50	6	3·6	2·4	1·25	2·1	11·9	1·60
51	2	4·1	−2·1	−1·04	0·0	16·0	1·08
52	4	4·6	−0·6	−0·28	−0·6	20·6	0·08
53	7	5·3	1·7	0·74	1·1	25·9	0·55
54	3	6·1	−3·1	−1·26	−2·0	32·0	1·58
55	9	6·9	2·1	0·80	0·1	38·9	0·64
56	9	8·1	0·9	0·32	1·0	47·0	0·10
57	8	9·6	−1·6	−0·52	−0·6	56·6	0·27
58	11	11·3	−0·3	−0·09	−0·9	67·9	0·01
59	14	13·3	0·7	0·19	−0·2	81·2	0·04
60	18	16·4	1·6	0·40	1·4	97·6	0·16
61	18	19·9	−1·9	−0·43	−0·5	117·5	0·18
62	24	24·4	−0·4	−0·08	−0·9	141·9	0·01
63	30	30·3	−0·3	−0·05	−1·2	172·2	0·00
64	43	36·5	6·5	1·08	5·3	208·7	1·16
65	41	44·2	−3·2	−0·48	2·1	252·9	0·23
66	54	54·3	−0·3	−0·04	1·8	307·2	0·00
67	64	65·5	−1·5	−0·19	0·3	372·7	0·03
Total							8·15

Table 11.7

Range	Observed	Expected
$(-\infty, -3)$	0	0·00
$(-3, -2)$	0	0·42
$(-2, -1)$	2	2·92
$(-1, 0)$	11	7·14
$(0, 1)$	6	7·14
$(1, 2)$	2	2·92
$(2, 3)$	0	0·42
$(3, \infty)$	0	0·00

REFERENCES

Barnett, H. A. R. (1951). Graduation tests and experiments. *J. Inst. Actu.* **77**, 15–54.

Beard, R. E. (1951). Some notes on graduation. *J. Inst. Actu.* **77**, 382–418.

Bizley, M. T. L. (1958). A measure of smoothness and some remarks on a new principle of graduation. *J. Inst. Actu.*, **84**, 125–65.

Cochran, W. G. (1954). Some methods for strengthening the common x^2 tests. *Biometrics*, **10**, 417–51.

David, F. N. (1949). A x^2 'smooth' test for goodness of fit. *Biometrika*, **34**, 299.

Daw, R. H. (1945). On the validity of statistical tests of the graduation of a mortality table. *J. Inst. Actu.*, **72**, 174–88.

Daw, R. H. (1954). Statistical tests of random order. *J. S. S.*, **12**, 167.

Daw, R. H. (1974). A study of the variance of mortality rates. *J. Inst. Actu.*, **101**, 415–34.

Kendall, M. G. and Stuart, A. (1967). *The Advanced Theory of Statistics*, Vol. 2, second edition, Griffin, London, 463.

Kendall, M. G. and Stuart, A. (1968). *The Advanced Theory of Statistics*, Vol. 3, second edition, Griffin, London, 384–96.

Pollard, A. H. (1970). Random mortality fluctuations and the binomial hypothesis. *J. Inst. Actu.*, **96**, 251–64.

Pollard, J. H. (1977). *A Handbook of Numerical and Statistical Techniques*, Cambridge University Press.

Redington, F. M. and Michaelson, R. L. (1940). An aspect of the 'a priori' probability theory of mortality. *Trans. of the Twelfth International Congress of Actuaries*, **1**, 225.

Seal, H. L. (1941). Tests of a mortality table graduation, *J. Inst. Actu.*, **71**, 5–47.

Stevens, W. L. (1939). Distribution of groups in a sequence of alternatives. *Ann. Eugen., Lond.*, **9**, 10.

Taylor, G. C. (1976) Allowance for heterogeneity in the testing of a graduation of mortality rates. *Bull. Inst. Actu. of Australia and New Zealand*, 403–12.

EXERCISES FOR CHAPTER ELEVEN

1   Prove that the cumulative deviations for ages x to $x + n$ and ages x to age $x + n + 1$ have correlation

$$\rho \doteq 1 - \frac{E_{x+n+1} q_{x+n+1}}{2 \sum_{j=x}^{x+n} E_j q_j}$$

2   Stevens' test has been criticized on the ground that it is concerned only with the signs of the deviations and not with the relative magnitude of the positive and negative deviations. It has been suggested therefore that the test be applied to the signs of the accumulated deviations. Is it correct to do this?

3 Plot the curve (11.16) with $a = 0$ and $b = c = 1$ for values of x near the origin.

4 The underlying mortality of a group of lives is known to follow Gompertz's law

$$\mu_x = Bc^x$$

Prove that the third differences of μ_x are small, but that they follow an increasing geometric progression with age.

5 (a) Prove that the sum of the absolute deviations over the $n+1$ ages x to $x+n$ has

$$\text{expectation} = \frac{4}{5} \sum_{j=x}^{x+n} \sqrt{(E_j p_j q_j)}$$

$$\text{and standard deviation} = \frac{3}{5} \sqrt{\left(\sum_{j=x}^{x+n} E_j p_j q_j \right)}$$

(b) The sum of the absolute deviations is sometimes compared with the expectation and standard deviation in (a). This test has been superseded by one of the tests in this chapter. Which one?

6 The rates of mortality observed among a body of lives have been graduated in three ways. Table 11.8 shows in quinary age-groups the actual numbers of deaths experienced and the expected numbers according to each graduation. Examine the graduations with regard to their fidelity to the experience (ignoring smoothness) and comment on their relative merits.

Table 11.8

	Actual	Expected deaths by		
Age-group	deaths	Graduation A	Graduation B	Graduation C
20–24	15	10	12	14
25–29	28	21	22	26
30–34	39	41	42	40
35–39	54	64	62	58
40–44	84	85	81	81
45–49	93	107	102	99
50–54	97	90	93	93
55–59	80	75	78	78
60–64	55	52	57	54
Total	545	545	549	543

7 Criticize the graduation in Table 11.9 from the point of view of fidelity to the data.

Table 11.9

Age-group	Exposed to risk	Actual deaths	Expected deaths
40–44	15,518	65	73·9
45–49	19,428	144	134·6
50–54	21,594	219	223·9
55–59	21,890	378	346·3
60–64	19,174	465	468·1
65–69	15,775	557	600·2
70–74	11,414	685	675·5
75–79	6,993	644	637·4
80–84	3,276	471	458·7
85–89	1,096	217	240·6
90–94	201	67	61·4

8 Criticize the section of a graduation in Table 11.10 from the point of view of smoothness and test the adherence to the data.

Table 11.10

Age	Exposed to risk	Actual deaths	Expected deaths	Graduated rate of mortality
71	8,292	401	423·7	·0511
72	8,156	432	461·0	·0565
73	7,905	518	497·3	·0629
74	7,588	532	528·8	·0697
75	7,214	592	556·1	·0771
76	6,713	567	566·1	·0843
77	6,205	548	571·5	·0921
78	5,704	565	568·3	·0996
79	5,196	562	563·7	·1085
80	4,664	549	548·4	·1176
81	4,142	558	532·2	·1285
82	3,576	479	497·5	·1391
83	3,070	481	467·0	·1521
84	2,575	399	425·4	·1652
85	2,146	404	388·4	·1810
86	1,706	342	332·8	·1951

9 A small Life Office has examined its mortality experience over a recent period of time. The total actual deaths number 471, while the total expected according to the A1967–70 Table was 450. In respect of the Without Profit business the actual deaths were 31 and the expected deaths 50. It is accordingly suggested that the Without Profit business must attract a much better class of life than the With Profit business.

Criticize this suggestion and state carefully the assumptions underlying any tests you might consider it necessary to make.

10 (a) Show how the results of paras 7.17–7.27 can be used to modify the statistical tests in paras 11.8–11.43 so that they are applicable to sickness rates.

(b) A friendly society sickness experience is shown in Table 11.11. The proportion of members sick, first 2 years of sickness, is obtained by dividing the figures in column (2) by the corresponding figures in column (1). Column (3) shows the results of graduating the proportion thus obtained. The number of weeks of sickness per member per annum, first 3 months of sickness, is obtained by dividing the figures in column (4) by the corresponding figures in column (1). Column (5) shows the results of graduating the resultant rates.

Criticize the two graduations.

11 Prove that the chi-square approach to Stevens' test in para. 11.38 is equivalent to the normal method of para. 11.37.

12 In the Whittaker–Henderson method of graduation (para. 11.71) a quadratic function Q is minimized. Write down the partial derivatives of Q with respect to the $\{\hat{q}_{x+j}\}$ and deduce the system of linear equations which the graduated mortality rates must satisfy.

Table 11.11 *A sickness experience*

Age	No. of years of life exposed to risk of sickness (1)	No. of sickness claims. First 2 years of sickness (2)	Graduated proportion of members sick. First 2 years of sickness (3)	No. of weeks of sickness claim. First 3 months of sickness (4)	Graduated weeks of sickness per member per annum. First 3 months of sickness (5)
35	61,632·5	13,108	·213	42,432	·685
36	59,473	12,701	·214	41,436	·696
37	57,380·5	12,406	·215	40,518	·709
38	54,741·5	11,777	·217	39,411	·726
39	52,911	11,642	·220	39,767	·744
40	51,478	11,434	·222	39,323	·764
41	49,835·5	11,378	·226	39,613	·784
42	48,199	10,929	·227	38,737	·803
43	46,818·5	10,737	·230	38,413	·821
44	45,418	10,563	·232	38,105	·839
45	43,483	10,168	·235	37,115	·858
46	41,654·5	9,828	·237	36,675	·879
47	40,328·5	9,749	·241	36,521	·904
48	39,107	9,481	·244	35,735	·932
49	37,723·5	9,441	·249	36,304	·962
50	36,510	9,194	·252	37,251	·994

CHAPTER TWELVE

THE GRAPHIC METHOD

12.1 Although not generally used for standard tables and therefore seldom discussed in actuarial literature, the graphic method is perhaps the most widely used graduation technique. It can give good results even when the data are so scanty that the use of any other method would be out of the question, and it is commonly used in pension funds and friendly societies (where the data are often scanty) for functions such as rates of withdrawal or retirement. An important advantage of the method is that it is easy to make allowance for special features, e.g. discontinuities in retirement rates.

Graphical graduation of rates of decrement

12.2 Rates of decrement are calculated from the available data and represented graphically by points. A smooth curve, its shape suggested by the lie of the points, is drawn to pass as near to these points as possible while still providing a reasonable progression of rates, and smoothed decrement rates are read from the curve. The progression of the rates may be further improved by examination and adjustment of the first few orders of differences to obtain graduated rates which satisfy the prescribed requirements of smoothness and adherence to data. This process is referred to as 'hand-polishing'. The principles underlying the graphical method of graduation are straightforward, but the process can be tedious, and skill and patience are required.

12.3 Standard tables may be available, giving an indication of the general trend of the rate of decrement (i.e. to assist in the choice of shape of curve). These are particularly useful at the ends of the table, where the data are bound to be so scanty that the rates brought out are especially unreliable, and the curve has to be sketched in the light of previous experience. There is usually some information of the likely behaviour of the curve that is being drawn.

Approximate confidence limits

12.4 In performing a graphical graduation of a set of mortality rates it is usually helpful to record on the graph approximate 95 per cent confidence limits for the observed mortality rate at each age. There is usually no need for complete precision in computing the limits, since they are only to be used as a rough guide. Provided that the actual deaths at any given age are not fewer than about ten, the 95 per cent confidence limits may be taken as

$$\mathring{q}_x \pm (2\sqrt{\theta_x})/E_x$$

A series of straight lines can be drawn connecting consecutive pairs of upper limit points and another such line connecting the lower limit points. These two limit lines provide a convenient guide when drawing the smooth curve for the graduation. The smooth curve should not, of course, pass outside the limit lines more often than about once for every twenty observations.

12.5 Confidence limits automatically provide a graphical expression of the weight of the data at successive ages. In an unusual case where E_x shows large variations from age to age, they show clearly by the narrowness of the gap between them which observed rates should most influence the drawing of the smooth curve.

Grouping sparse data

12.6 Sparse data need to be grouped. This will give fewer observations but with relatively smaller sampling errors. (There will also be greater imprecision as to the ages to which the grouped observations relate.)

12.7 The choice of group is usually a difficult matter and calls for considerable experience and skill. Different groupings may, in fact, lead to widely differing results. Some authorities maintain that grouping with a fixed class interval (e.g. quinquennial groups) gives the best results. The general opinion seems to be, however, that it is preferable to select groups in such a way that the group rates progress more smoothly. This almost invariably means the use of groups of unequal range. They can be found approximately as follows:

(i)   Plot the rough rates of decrement, without grouping, as a series of points and sketch in lightly a smooth curve representing the general run of values. This may prove difficult, but refinement is unnecessary, as a moderate degree of smoothness is quite sufficient.

(ii)   Now choose groupings in such a way that points above this guide curve are balanced by points below it: i.e. so that a point some distance above may be offset by grouping it with the next two, or even three, points lying slightly below the curve. The aim should be to ensure that the group rate will lie close to the general run of values. Generally speaking, if the curvature seems to be changing rapidly, groups should be of short range; if the curve rises to a peak and falls again, care should be taken to ensure that this peak is not cut off by the method of grouping adopted.

12.8 For each group the total deaths (or other decrements) are divided by the total exposed to risk, and the resulting rate is plotted as corresponding to the middle age of the range. This is not strictly accurate, but for graphical graduation purposes any refinement in age estimation is not really justified. The statistical tests of adherence to data should reveal any systematic errors, and these can be corrected during hand-polishing.

12.9 The points representing the group rates should progress more regularly than those representing the original data, and it should not be difficult to draw a smooth curve passing close to them. The importance of grouping to produce a smoother curve should not be underestimated, because, although it may be said that the final graduation takes place in the hand-polishing, this latter process is at the best of times a laborious business and may well become very lengthy unless the initial curve has produced a set of values which are in themselves fairly satisfactory before any further adjustment is carried out.

12.10 Confidence limits cannot be computed for group rates because of the non-random balancing achieved in the selection of the ages for grouping. If, however, a uniform interval of grouping were employed (e.g. quinary groups) there would be no such loss of randomness and a suitable set of approximate confidence limits would be given by

$$(\text{group } \mathring{q}) \pm 2 \{ \sqrt{(\text{group decrements})} \} / (\text{group exposed}).$$

Sketching the curve

12.11 Inexperienced operators tend to adhere to the data too closely in sketching their curves and, as a result, the rates are undergraduated. Undergraduation will usually be detected by the tests of adherence to data (para. 11.78). See also example 11.8.

12.12 If it is found that an appreciable section of the table is unsatisfactory by, say, overstating the mortality, it will probably be quicker in the long run to redraw that part of the curve and deduce fresh values rather than to attempt to adjust the bias by hand-polishing.

Hand-polishing

12.13 Rates of decrement should be read from the curve for individual ages, and the first two or three orders of differences tabulated. Scrutiny of these differences reveals not only where the smoothness is unsatisfactory but also where points of inflexion occur. If the first differences are positive, a positive second difference shows that the gradient is increasing, while a negative second difference shows that the curve is becoming flatter. Consequently a change in the sign of the second difference indicates a point of inflexion, and this also applies when all the first differences are negative. Although points of inflexion are not unknown in mortality curves, particularly between the ages of 15 and 35, they always require investigation and, if found to be unacceptable, they can often be eliminated by a bolder drawing of the curve; this will also usually improve the graduation generally.

12.14 The statistical tests of Chapter 11 should be applied to check adherence to data. Grouping is usually necessary because of scanty data, and care should be taken to avoid using the same groupings as those adopted in drawing the curve.

12.15 In the light of these tests of smoothness and adherence to data, the rates are adjusted and readjusted until a satisfactory table is obtained. If, for instance, there is a run of positive deviations at one section, greater than could be accounted for by sampling fluctuations, the curve would appear to be too low and might with advantage be redrawn.

12.16 Even with skilled hand-polishing, a high degree of smoothness is sometimes difficult to achieve. It is worth noting, however, that the methods of Chapter 13 applied to rates which have been graphically graduated will often produce very smooth rates.

Example 12.1

Use the graphic method to graduate the mortality data in Table 12.1. The crude mortality rates for ages 35 to 70 are plotted in Figure 12.1. Approximate 95 per cent confidence intervals can be calculated for each individual age from 44 to 70, using the method of para. 12.4. These are also shown in Figure 12.1. Confidence intervals are not given below age 44 because the numbers of observed deaths are too small and the simple approximate method becomes unreliable.

A smooth curve is drawn near to the crude mortality rates, and the smoothed mortality rates are read from the curve (Table 12.2). It is immediately apparent from first differences that the smoothness of these rates is far from satisfactory—column (4) in Table 12.2. Considerable hand-polishing will be necessary.

First differences tend to follow a geometric progression over the adult ages of a mortality table. The graduated rates in column (5) of Table 12.2 were obtained by adjusting the first differences of the smoothed rates in column (3) until the progression of the differences was approximately geometric, at least over sections of the table. The differences in columns (6), (7) and (8) of Table 12.2 indicate that the resultant rates are quite smooth.

Apart from a possible slight overestimation of mortality rates for ages 35–44, the graduated rates adhere to the data reasonably well (Table 12.3). The chi-square value on about 30 degrees of freedom (para. 12.27) is 35.1. A full investigation of goodness-of-fit is set as exercise 1.

Although the data are not particularly sparse in this example, the crude rates do jump around considerably. A better graduation might be obtained by grouping the exposed to risk and deaths, and graduating the group mortality rates (exercises 2 and 3).

Table 12.1   *A mortality experience*

x	E_x	θ_x	x	E_x	θ_x	x	E_x	θ_x
35	1051	1	47	1669	13	59	2511	71
36	940	6	48	1624	14	60	1858	32
37	1048	2	49	1157	11	61	1835	54
38	716	3	50	2193	19	62	1393	47
39	719	2	51	1803	20	63	1462	40
40	1051	4	52	2402	31	64	1245	34
41	1042	4	53	2120	27	65	1064	46
42	1804	12	54	2406	38	66	1502	74
43	1468	7	55	1975	37	67	875	36
44	1576	16	56	2564	38	68	927	38
45	1647	18	57	1798	36	69	497	29
46	1861	16	58	2536	51	70	983	60

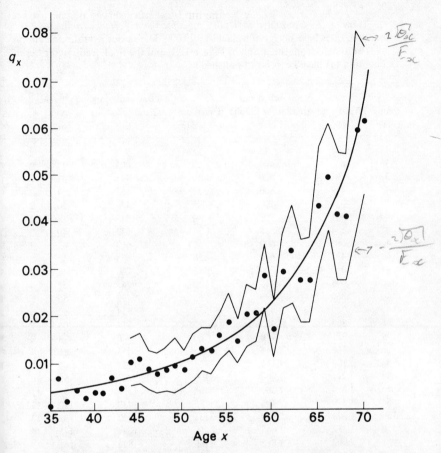

FIGURE 12.1   A graphical graduation of the data in Table 12.1

Example 12.2

The data in Table 12.4 represent the marriage experience of a group of unmarried males. Use the graphic method to obtain graduated marriage rates for ages 17 to 49 inclusive.

The crude central marriage rates are plotted in Figure 12.2. The data for ages 17–20 are sparse and have therefore been combined to produce a more meaningful rate for age $18\frac{1}{2}$. The approximate 95 per cent confidence limits shown in the figure were calculated by means of the formula

$$(M_x \pm 2\sqrt{M_x})/E_x^c \qquad (12.1)$$

260 CHAPTER TWELVE

Table 12.2 *Graduated mortality rates for the experience in Table* 12.1
All the rates have been multiplied by 100,000. The smoothed rates in column
(3) were read from the graph in Figure 12.1, and the final graduated rates in
column (5) have been hand-polished

Age (1)	Crude rate (2)	Smoothed rate (read from graph) (3)	Difference (4) = Δ(3)	Graduated rate (hand-polished) (5)	Differences of (5) Δ (6)	Δ² (7)	Δ³ (8)
35	95	375	25	375	28	2	C
36	638	400	20	403	30	2	C
37	191	420	40	433	32	2	C
38	419	460	30	465	34	2	C
39	278	490	25	499	36	2	C
40	381	515	50	535	38	2	C
41	384	565	35	573	40	2	
42	665	600	50	613	42	3	
43	477	650	50	655	45	3	
44	1,015	700	45	700	48	3	
45	1,093	745	50	748	51	4	
46	860	795	55	799	55	5	
47	779	850	55	854	60	6	
48	862	905	75	914	66	7	
49	951	980	60	980	73	8	
50	866	1,040	75	1053	81	9	
51	1,109	1,115	85	1134	90	9	
52	1,291	1,200	100	1224	99	10	
53	1,274	1,300	105	1323	109	11	
54	1,579	1,405	125	1432	120	12	
55	1,873	1,530	135	1552	132	13	
56	1,482	1,665	150	1684	145	16	
57	2,002	1,815	165	1829	161	19	
58	2,011	1,980	145	1990	180	22	
59	2,827	2,125	205	2170	202	25	
60	1,722	2,330	230	2372	227	29	
61	2,942	2,560	260	2599	256	33	
62	3,374	2,820	285	2855	289	38	
63	2,735	3,105	315	3144	327	43	
64	2,751	3,420	355	3471	370	50	
65	4,323	3,775	375	3841	420	58	10
66	4,926	4,150	450	4261	478	68	12
67	4,114	4,600	520	4739	546	80	14
68	4,099	5,120	680	5285	626	94	
69	5,835	5,800	950	5911	720		
70	6,143	6,750		6631			

Table 12.3 Comparison of observed and expected deaths

Using the data of example 12.1 and the graduated rates given in column (5) of Table 12.2

Age (1)	Deaths Exp. (2)	Obs. (3)	Dev. (3)−(2) (4)	(4)/√(2) (5)*	Cum. Dev. (6)	Age (1)	Deaths Exp. (2)	Obs. (3)	Dev. (3)−(2) (4)	(4)/√(2) (5)*	Cum. Dev. (6)
35	3·9	1	−2·9	−1·5	−2·9	53	28·0	27	−1·0	−0·2	−4·9
36	3·8	6	2·2	1·1	−0·7	54	34·5	38	3·5	0·6	−1·4
37	4·5	2	−2·5	−1·2	−3·2	55	30·7	37	6·3	1·1	4·9
38	3·3	3	−0·3	−0·2	−3·5	56	43·2	38	−5·2	−0·8	−0·3
39	3·6	2	−1·6	−0·8	−5·1	57	32·9	36	3·1	0·5	2·8
40	5·6	4	−1·6	−0·7	−6·7	58	50·5	51	0·5	0·1	3·3
41	6·0	4	−2·0	−0·8	−8·7	59	54·5	71	16·5	2·2	19·8
42	11·1	12	0·9	0·3	−7·8	60	44·1	32	−12·1	−1·8	7·7
43	9·6	7	−2·6	−0·8	−10·4	61	47·7	54	6·3	0·9	14·0
44	11·0	16	5·0	1·5	−5·4	62	39·8	47	7·2	1·1	21·2
45	12·3	18	5·7	1·6	0·3	63	46·0	40	−6·0	−0·9	15·2
46	14·9	16	1·1	0·3	1·4	64	43·2	34	−9·2	−1·4	6·0
47	14·3	13	−1·3	−0·3	0·1	65	40·9	46	5·1	0·8	11·1
48	14·8	14	−0·8	−0·2	−0·7	66	64·0	74	10·0	1·3	21·1
49	11·3	11	−0·3	−0·1	−1·0	67	41·5	36	−5·5	−0·9	15·6
50	23·1	19	−4·1	−0·9	−5·1	68	49·0	38	−11·0	−1·6	4·6
51	20·4	20	−0·4	−0·1	−5·5	69	29·4	29	−0·4	−0·1	4·2
52	29·4	31	1·6	0·3	−3·9	70	65·2	60	−5·2	−0·6	−1·0

* Note that the approximate standard deviation described in para. 11.11 has been used.

Table 12.4   *A marriage experience*

Age x (1)	Central exposed E_x^c (2)	Marriages M_x (3)	Central marriage rate (3)/(2) (4)	$(2\sqrt{(3)})/(2)$ (5)
17	39	0	0·000	—
18	57	4	0·070	—
19	93	5	0·054	—
20	137	7	0·051	—
21	152	25	0·164	0·065
22	165	32	0·194	0·069
23	140	26	0·186	0·073
24	115	24	0·209	0·085
25	97	23	0·237	0·099
26	81	20	0·247	0·110
27	63	16	0·254	0·127
28	50	13	0·260	0·144
29	38	8	0·211	0·149
30–4	137	27	0·197	0·076
35–9	44	9	0·205	0·136
40–4	40	4	0·100	0·100
45–9	34	3	0·088	0·102
Totals	1,482	246	—	—

where M_x is the observed number of marriages in age-group x. This formula could not be used to obtain confidence limits at age $18\frac{1}{2}$ because the crude central marriage rate at that age was obtained by combining the exposed to risk and marriages for ages 17–20 *after* an examination of the data (para. 12.10).

A smooth curve was drawn near to the crude marriage rates and smoothed rates were read from the curve (Table 12.5). Although the first three orders of differences progress remarkably well, considering the shape of the curve, the task of hand-polishing is not particularly easy. Problems are caused by

(a)   the two points of inflexion;
(b)   the peak near age 28;
(c)   the fact that the smoothed rates read from the graph for ages 17–24 tend to overestimate the true underlying rates.

Considerable effort was required to produce the graduated rates in

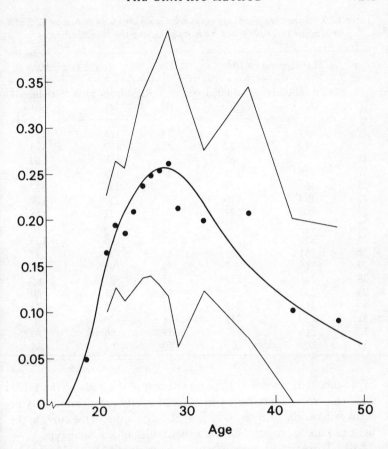

FIGURE 12.2 A graphical graduation of the marriage data of Table 12.4

Table 12.5. It will be noted that these rates are reasonably smooth (Table 12.6) and that they adhere to data adequately (Table 12.7). There is some evidence of intrinsic roughness in the data around age 21, and the question arises as to whether or not we wish to remove it (para. 11.66). The answer depends upon the ultimate purpose of the table (para. 11.67).

Advantages of the graphic method

12.17 The main advantages of the graphic method were outlined in para. 12.1. It allows great scope for individual judgement, based on

Table 12.5 *Smoothed marriage rates read from the curve in Figure 12.2 and graduated rates obtained by hand-polishing the smoothed rates*

| Age | Marriage rate × 10³ | | Age | Marriage rate × 10³ | |
| | Read from curve | Graduated | | Read from curve | Graduated |
(1)	(2)	(3)	(1)	(2)	(3)
17	14	2	34	186	187
18	40	32	35	172	173
19	72	65	36	160	160
20	115	101	37	149	148
21	155	137	38	139	137
22	184	170	39	130	127
23	208	198	40	121	118
24	226	221	41	114	110
25	240	239	42	106	103
26	251	251	43	99	97
27	256	257	44	93	91
28	256	257	45	87	85
29	252	252	46	81	80
30	243	243	47	75	75
31	230	231	48	70	70
32	216	217	49	66	66
33	200	202	50	63	63

experience. Experience is important because the ends of the table, which always cause difficulty because of scanty data, can usually be dealt with satisfactorily by sketching these portions of the curve in the light of knowledge gained from other tables of a similar type.

12.18 There is so reason why the graduation should not be adequate, since the hand-polishing is assumed to continue until the criteria for both smoothness and adherence to data have been satisfied.

Disadvantages of the method

12.19 In practice the method is much more difficult to apply than it would seem to be and demands considerable skill and patience from the operator.

12.20 It is unsuitable for standard tables based on extensive data, since a very high degree of smoothness is difficult to achieve. It is usually impossible to obtain sufficient places of decimals in the graduated rates because of the difficulty of reading more than three

Table 12.6 *The first three orders of differences of the graduated marriage rates in Table 12.5*

Age	Graduated marriage rate × 10³	Δ	Δ²	Δ³	Age	Graduated marriage rate × 10³	Δ	Δ²	Δ³
17	2	30	3	0	31	231	−14	−1	1
18	32	33	3	−3	32	217	−15	0	1
19	65	36	0	−3	33	202	−15	1	0
20	101	36	−3	−2	34	187	−14	1	0
21	137	33	−5	0	35	173	−13	1	0
22	170	28	−5	0	36	160	−12	1	0
23	198	23	−5	−1	37	148	−11	1	0
24	221	18	−6	0	38	137	−10	1	0
25	239	12	−6	0	39	127	−9	1	0
26	251	6	−6	1	40	118	−8	1	0
27	257	0	−5	1	41	110	−7	1	−1
28	257	−5	−4	1	42	103	−6	0	0
29	252	−9	−3	1	43	97	−6	0	1
30	243	−12	−2	1	44	91	−6	1	−1
31	231	−14	−1	1	45	85	−5	0	0
32	217	−15	0	1	46	80	−5	0	1
33	202	−15	1		47	75	−5	1	
34	187	−14			48	70	−4		
35	173				49	66			

figures from a graph. The methods of Chapter 13 can, however, be used to smooth the results of the graphic graduation further.

12.21 Owing to difficulties of scale, it is usually necessary in graduating rates of mortality to draw the curve in two parts, namely one curve up to age 65 or 70 and another from age 60 or 65 to the end of life. When this is done, it is desirable to make the curves overlap so as to ensure continuity. (See paras 14.57–14.68 for a discussion of methods of joining curves.)

12.22 By leaving scope for individual judgement the method also leaves scope for individual bias and prejudice, and it must be confessed that by means of the graphic method equally experienced workers might obtain widely differing results from the same data.

12.23 Although a graphic process can be used to graduate the ultimate portion of a mortality table, it is not very satisfactory for dealing with select data. These are usually so scanty that it is

Table 12.7 *Comparison of observed and expected marriages*

Using the data of example 12.2 and the graduated rates given in column (3) of Table 12.5

Age (1)	Graduated rate (2)	Exposed to risk (3)	Expected marriages (4) $(2) \times (3)$	Actual marriages (5)	Deviations (5)–(4) (6)	(6) $\sqrt{\{(4)[1-(2)]\}}$ (7)*	Accumulated deviations (8)
17	0·002	39	0·1	0	−0·1	−0·3	−0·1
18	0·032	57	1·8	4	2·2	1·7	2·1
19	0·065	93	6·0	5	−1·0	−0·4	1·1
20	0·101	137	13·8	7	−6·8	−1·9	−5·7
21	0·137	152	20·8	25	4·2	1·0	−1·5
22	0·170	165	28·1	32	3·9	0·8	2·4
23	0·198	140	27·7	26	−1·7	−0·4	0·7
24	0·221	115	25·4	24	−1·4	−0·3	−0·7
25	0·239	97	23·2	23	−0·2	−0·0	−0·9
26	0·251	81	20·3	20	−0·3	−0·1	−1·2
27	0·257	63	16·2	16	−0·2	−0·1	−1·4
28	0·257	50	12·9	13	0·1	0·0	−1·3
29	0·252	38	9·6	8	−1·6	−0·6	−2·9
30	0·243						
31	0·231						
32	0·217	137	29·7	27	−2·7	−0·6	−5·6
33	0·202						
34	0·187						
35	0·173						
36	0·160						
37	0·148	44	6·5	9	2·5	1·1	−3·1
38	0·137						
39	0·127						
40	0·118						
41	0·110						
42	0·103	40	4·1	4	−0·1	−0·1	−3·2
43	0·097						
44	0·091						
45	0·085						
46	0·080						
47	0·075	34	2·6	3	0·4	0·3	−2·8
48	0·070						
49	0·066						
Total	–	1,482	248·8	246	−2·8	–	–

* The approximation outlined in para. 11.11 has not been used in this case, because the marriage rate is not close to zero.

impossible to form an idea of the trend until they have been grouped in quinquennial or decennial groups of ages.

12.24 If the group rates are plotted on the same sheet as the curve representing the graduated ultimate rates, it is often possible to form an idea of how the select rates run into the ultimate rates, and by working back from the ultimate rates a judgement may be formed of the select rates themselves.

Statistical Tests

12.25 All the usual tests of adherence to data should be applied to a graphical graduation.

12.26 There is a difficulty with the chi-square test, however, since we cannot know how many degrees of freedom to assume. The graduating curve has to some extent been forced to fit the rough data, and the necessary deduction that should be made on this account from the total number of groups cannot be precisely determined.

12.27 With a reasonably large experience, the graphic graduation involves the drawing of a smooth curve near observed mortality rates at n individual consecutive ages. Along each section of the curve approximately one degree of freedom will be lost on account of the fitted height of the curve, one because of the slope, and possibly one more because of the curvature. A reduction of about two or three degrees of freedom for every ten or so ages is probably appropriate. This is in line with the conclusions reached in respect of the summation formulae in para. 13.92.

12.28 With sparse data, the graduation will be based on a few broad groupings. Approximately one degree of freedom will be lost along the whole curve on account of the fitted height, one because of the slope, and possibly one more because of the curvature. A reduction of about two or three degrees of freedom from the number of cells in the chi-square test would seem to be appropriate.

12.29 The reader should note that, even with the correct adjustment to the number of degrees of freedom, the chi-square test is approximate (para. 11.73).

EXERCISES FOR CHAPTER TWELVE

1 Examine thoroughly the goodness-of-fit of the graduation in example 12.1.
2 Combine the exposed to risk and deaths in Table 12.1 into quinquennial groups and graduate the grouped rates.

3 Group the exposed to risk and deaths in Table 12.1 so that the grouped rates progress in a reasonably smooth fashion. Graduate these rates.

4 Hand-polish the smoothed mortality rates which were read from the graph in example 12.1.

5 Hand-polish the smoothed marriage rates which were read from the graph in example 12.2.

6 Obtain graduated mortality rates for ages 47–67 using the graphic method and the data in Table 12.8.

Table 12.8

Age	Exposed to risk	Deaths	$10^5 xq_x$	Age	Exposed to risk	Deaths	$10^5 xq_x$
47	166	2	1,205	58	628	11	1,752
48	187	2	1,070	59	701	14	1,997
49	218	4	1,835	60	813	18	2,214
50	243	6	2,469	61	917	18	1,963
51	276	2	725	62	1,040	24	2,308
52	302	4	1,325	63	1,182	30	2,538
53	347	7	2,017	64	1,299	43	3,310
54	390	3	769	65	1,432	41	2,863
55	430	9	2,095	66	1,596	54	3,383
56	494	9	1,822	67	1,752	64	3,653
57	558	8	1,434				

7 Obtain graduated mortality rates for ages 30 to 95 using the graphic method and the data in Table 12.9.

Table 12.9

Age-group	Exposed to risk of death	Actual deaths	Age-group	Exposed to risk of death	Actual deaths
30–34	9	–	65–69	829	40
35–39	22	–	70–74	864	51
40–44	24	–	75–79	796	85
45–49	54	–	80–84	488	69
50–54	194	9	85–89	217	54
55–59	395	10	90–94	49	16
60–64	678	27	95 and over	3	2
			Total	4,622	363

8　The figures in Table 12.10 are the male deaths in Australia in 1970 from 'all other accidents'. Use the graphic method to obtain graduated rates of 'all other accidents' mortality for ages 1 to 50.

Table 12.10

Age Group	Crude 'all other accidents' death rate $\times 10^6$	Central Exposed (000s)	Age Group	Crude 'all other accidents' death rate $\times 10^6$	Central Exposed (000s)
0	47	127	45–49	69	393
1–4	8	483	50–54	78	321
5–9	6	634	55–59	40	304
10–14	8	610	60–64	45	243
15–19	23	563	65–69	40	176
20–24	52	557	70–74	65	122
25–29	35	461	75–79	40	76
30–34	45	402	80–84	47	43
35–39	37	376	85 +	217	18
40–44	73	408			

CHAPTER THIRTEEN

SUMMATION AND ADJUSTED-AVERAGE GRADUATION FORMULAE

13.1 It is convenient in this chapter to regard any ungraduated value v_x as consisting of two parts, the true or universal value u_x and a superimposed error e_x. Thus

$$v_x = u_x + e_x$$

The error e_x may be positive or negative. We shall for the most part consider only sampling errors, in which case the $\{v_x\}$ are independent unbiased estimators of the underlying $\{u_x\}$, and the $\{e_x\}$ are independent random variables with zero expectations.

13.2 The $\{e_x\}$ will in practice contain inaccuracies in addition to sampling errors, and since the two sources of contribution to $\{e_x\}$ cannot be differentiated, they will both be redistributed by the graduation formulae we develop. The inaccuracies may be purely random or they may be systematic. In the case of systematic inaccuracies the $\{e_x\}$ cease to be independent random variables with zero expectations, and summation and adjusted-average graduation methods are not applicable. When the form of the bias and its approximate magnitude is known, an appropriate graduation method can sometimes be devised. A method which was developed to deal with a particular form of systematic inaccuracy is described for example in paras 16.1–16.20. If the inaccuracies are purely random and not too large, good results can often still be obtained by summation and adjusted-average formulae, and other graduation methods.

13.3 An ideal graduation would of course eliminate all the $\{e_x\}$. In practice the most that can be attained is a reduction of the error and a smooth progression of the graduated rates.

The smoothing effect of a running average

13.4 In analysing series of observations which show irregularities in the form of ripples or undulations, statisticians often tabulate moving or 'running' averages as a means of showing the general trend of the observations. By taking an average of, say, five consecutive values, the ripples are greatly reduced.

13.5 Let us apply this technique to the observed mortality rates in Table 12.1 and use the running average formula

$$V_x = \frac{1}{5}(v_{x-2} + v_{x-1} + v_x + v_{x+1} + v_{x+2})$$

The symbol V_x denotes the smoothed value at the point x. The crude mortality rates and the smoothed rates are shown graphically in Figure 13.1, and the improvement in smoothness is immediately apparent.

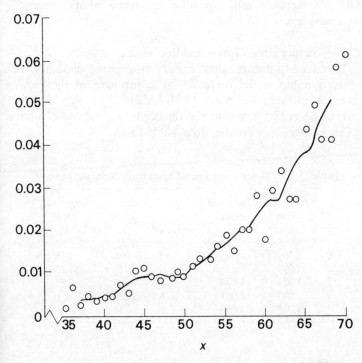

FIGURE 13.1   The smoothing effect of a running average

Distortion of smooth values

13.6 There is a difficulty, however: as well as smoothing a set of data, moving averages distort values that already follow a smooth progression and do not require adjustment. The distortion will not affect the smoothness of these values but may introduce a downward or upward bias to them.

13.7 Consider the quadratic curve

$$v_x = 1100 + 2x - 5x^2$$

which may be considered ideally smooth because it is a low-order polynomial. Numerical values of this function are listed in Table 13.1, and smoothed values using the above five-term moving average formula are also listed. The distortion is obvious: each value has been reduced by 10.

13.8 We therefore note the following three points concerning moving averages:

1. They reduce irregularities and fluctuations.
2. They tend to distort values already progressing smoothly. This distortion has to be corrected by adjustment of the moving average operation (see paras 13.21–13.22).
3. They do not provide values at the beginning and end of a table. (This is clear, for example, from Table 13.1.)

Table 13.1   *The distortion caused by a simple 'running' average*

x	Quadratic value v_x	Smoothed value V_x	x	Quadratic value v_x	Smoothed value V_x
0	1,100		5	985	975
1	1,097		6	932	922
2	1,084	1,074	7	869	859
3	1,061	1,051	8	796	
4	1,028	1,018	9	713	

Summation n

13.9 A special short-hand notation has been developed to represent moving averages. The operator $[n]$ or 'summation n' is defined by

$$[n]v_0 = v_{-\frac{n-1}{2}} + v_{-\frac{n-3}{2}} + \ldots + v_{\frac{n-3}{2}} + v_{\frac{n-1}{2}}.$$

Thus, for example

$$[3]\,v_0 = v_{-1} + v_0 + v_1$$

$$[4]\,v_0 = v_{-3/2} + v_{-1/2} + v_{1/2} + v_{3/2}$$

$$[5]\,v_0 = v_{-2} + v_{-1} + v_0 + v_1 + v_2$$

In each case $[n]\,v_0$ represents the sum of n consecutive v's, unit distance apart and with an equal number on each side of v_0.

13.10 The five-term moving average in para. 13.5 can be written

$$V_x = \frac{[5]}{5}\,v_x$$

and a moving average of n terms is represented by

$$V_x = \frac{[n]}{n}\,v_x$$

13.11 It is possible to prove that the moving average of n terms

$$\frac{[n]}{n}\,v_x = \left\{ 1 + \frac{(n^2 - 1^2)}{2^2\,3!}\delta^2 + \frac{(n^2 - 1^2)(n^2 - 3^2)}{2^4\,5!}\delta^4 + \ldots \right\}v_x \quad (13.1)$$

where the second and fourth *central* differences of v_x are defined as follows:

$$\delta^2 v_x = v_{x+1} - 2v_x + v_{x-1}$$

$$\delta^4 v_x = v_{x+2} - 4v_{x+1} + 6v_x - 4v_{x-1} + v_{x-2}$$

See, for example, Kendall and Stuart (1968).

13.12 Formula (13.1) shows the distortion inherent in the use of a simple moving average. The quadratic function in Table 13.1, for example, has a constant second difference of -10 and zero fourth and higher differences. According to (13.1), the distortion introduced by applying a moving average of five to this quadratic will be -10, and this is confirmed by our earlier calculation.

13.13 Formula (13.1) also allows us to construct summation formulae having no first-, second- or third-difference distortion (paras 13.21–13.22).

Summation formulae

13.14 British actuaries have used the smoothing properties of moving averages to develop summation graduation formulae. Most of

Table 13.2 *Graduation of the mortality data in Table 12.1 by Spencer's 21-term formula*

Age (1)	Crude rate (2)	[3](2) (3)	[5](2) (4)	[7](2) (5)	(2)+(3) + (4)−(5) (6)	[5](6) (7)	[5](7) (8)	[7](8) (9)	(9)÷350 (10)
35	·00095								
36	·00638	·00924							
37	·00191	·01248	·01621						
38	·00419	·00888	·01907	·02386	·00828				
39	·00278	·01078	·01653	·02956	·00053				
40	·00381	·01043	·02127	·02795	·00756	·02837			
41	·00384	·01430	·02185	·03619	·00380	·03402			
42	·00665	·01526	·02922	·04293	·00820	·05786	·28937		
43	·00477	·02157	·03634	·04875	·01393	·07564	·36027		
44	·01015	·02585	·04110	·05273	·02437	·09348	·42411		
45	·01093	·02968	·04224	·05751	·02534	·09927	·45453	2·86122	·00817
46	·00860	·02732	·04609	·06037	·02164	·09786	·45922	3·00757	·00859
47	·00779	·02501	·04545	·06426	·01399	·08828	·44377	3·11552	·00890
48	·00862	·02592	·04318	·06520	·01252	·08033	·42995	3·21774	·00919
49	·00951	·02679	·04567	·06718	·01479	·07803	·43572	3·35799	·00959
50	·00866	·02926	·05079	·07132	·01739	·08545	·46822	3·57513	·01021
51	·01109	·03266	·05491	·07932	·01934	·10363	·52633	3·88078	·01109
52	·01291	·03674	·06119	·08943	·02141	·12078	·59478	4·26953	·01220
53	·01274	·04144	·07126	·09474	·03070	·13844	·67636	4·71384	·01347
54	·01579	·04726	·07499	·10610	·03194	·14648	·74942	5·21394	·01490
55	·01873	·04934	·08210	·11512	·03505	·16703	·81870	5·73446	·01638
56	·01482	·05357	·08947	·13048	·02738	·17669	·88003	6·26431	·01790
57	·02002	·05495	·10195	·13496	·04196	·19006	·96832	6·78632	·01939
58	·02011	·06840	·10044	·14859	·04036	·19977	1·04685	7·34284	·02098
59	·02827	·06560	·11504	·16360	·04531	·23477	1·12463	7·93746	·02268
60	·01722	·07491	·12876	·17613	·04476	·24556	1·19837	8·59878	·02457
61	·02942	·08038	·13600	·18342	·06238	·25447	1·30594		
62	·03374	·09051	·13504	·20654	·05275	·26380	1·41332		
63	·02735	·08840	·16105	·22753	·04927	·30734	1·54135		
64	·02731	·09789	·18089	·25145	·05464	·34215			
65	·04323	·11980	·18829	·26302	·08830	·37359			
66	·04926	·13363	·20193	·28763	·09719				
67	·04114	·13139	·23297	·32131	·08419				
68	·04099	·14048	·25077						
69	·05835	·16037							
70	·06103								

the well-known formulae involve three summation operators $[l]$, $[m]$ and $[n]$, and a fourth operator which is a linear combination of two or more summation operators. The formulae are designed to be free of second-difference distortion (paras 13.21–13.22).

13.15 Spencer's 21-term formula is probably the most famous and generally satisfactory of all summation formulae and it takes the form

$$V_x = \frac{[5][5][7]}{350}\{[1]+[3]+[5]-[7]\}\,v_x \qquad (13.2)$$

13.16 The summation method of graduation is demonstrated in Table 13.2, using Spencer's formula and the data of Table 12.1. The reader should note that apart from the final division by 350, all the other operations are additions. This simplicity of calculation was a very important consideration in the days before modern electronic calculators and computers. Note also that because of the commutative properties of finite difference operators, the operations $[5]$, $[5]$, $[7]$ and $\{\ \}$ may be performed in any order.

13.17 An examination of the first three orders of differences of the graduated rates in Table 13.2 reveals that not all the roughness in the crude rates has been removed by the graduation process, and the graduation is unsatisfactory in this respect. Discussion of this problem is continued in para. 13.89 and example 13.4.

Second- and fourth-difference distortion

13.18 The distortion caused by using Spencer's 21-term formula can be readily calculated by means of (13.1). We note that

$$\frac{[5][5][7]}{5\times5\times7} \equiv \left(1+\delta^2+\frac{1}{5}\delta^4\right)^2 (1+2\delta^2+\delta^4+\ldots)$$

$$\equiv 1+4\delta^2+\frac{32}{5}\delta^4+\ldots;$$

$$\frac{1}{2}\{[1]+[3]+[5]-[7]\} \equiv \frac{1}{2}\left\{1+3\left(1+\frac{1}{3}\delta^2\right)+5\left(1+\delta^2+\frac{1}{5}\delta^4\right)\right.$$

$$\left. -7(1+2\delta^2+\delta^4+\ldots)\right\}$$

$$\equiv 1-4\delta^2-3\delta^4+\ldots.$$

So $\dfrac{[5]^2[7]}{350}\{[1]+[3]+[5]-[7]\}v_x$

$$= \left(1+4\delta^2+\frac{32}{5}\delta^4+\ \dots\ \right)(1-4\delta^2-3\delta^4+\ \dots)v_x$$

$$= \left(1-\frac{63}{5}\delta^4+\ \dots\ \right)v_x$$

13.19 Spencer (1904) designed the formula so that it would not introduce any second-difference distortion, and we have confirmed that this is in fact true. The formula does produce fourth- and higher-difference distortion. Most smooth curves can be approximated reasonably well by third degree polynomials, at least over sections of their lengths; so the fourth- and higher-difference distortion causes us little concern. In the case of a function with non-negligible fourth differences, a transformation of the function to one which is more accurately represented by third-degree polynomial arcs over sections of its length is sometimes practicable. Although such a transformation is not really necessary for a mortality curve, the graduation of $\log q_x$ rather than q_x ought at least be considered (para. 11.81).

13.20 The method of para. 13.18 can be used to calculate the distorting effects of other summation formulae.

Summation formulae with zero second-difference distortion

13.21 We have already noted that most summation formulae involve three operators $[l]$, $[m]$ and $[n]$, and a fourth operator which is a linear combination of two or more summation operators. Once the operators $[l]$, $[m]$ and $[n]$ have been chosen, the final linear compound operator can be selected so as to eliminate completely at least second-difference distortion.

13.22 Let us imagine that the operators $[5]$, $[5]$ and $[7]$ have been chosen. We already know from para. 13.18 that the second-difference distortion resulting from the operations $[5][5][7]/175$ is $4\delta^2$. If a linear compound operator is chosen to produce second-difference distortion of $-4\delta^2$, the resulting summation formula will have zero second-difference distortion.

Example 13.1

Find a suitable linear compound operator, which, used in conjunction with the operator $[5][5][7]/175$, will produce a summation graduation formula with zero second-difference distortion.

The operations $[5]^2[7]/175$ produce second-difference distortion of $4\delta^2$. The linear compound operator must be such that when it operates on v_x, it will produce second-difference distortion of $-4\delta^2 v_x$. That is, it must change v_x into

$$v_x - 4(v_{x+1} - 2v_x + v_{x-1}) \tag{13.3}$$

or $$13v_x - 4(v_{x+1} + v_x + v_{x-1})$$

A suitable linear compound operator is therefore $\{13[1] - 4[3]\}$, and the graduation formula is

$$V_x = \frac{[5]^2[7]}{175}\{13[1] - 4[3]\}$$

13.23 The reader will note that the summation formula derived in example 13.1 is not that of Spencer, even though the three summation operators are the same. The number of possible summation formulae having the same operators $[l]$, $[m]$ and $[n]$ and zero second-difference distortion is in fact infinite. Alternative formulae can be derived by adding multiples of the fourth, sixth, eighth, etc., differences to the linear compound operator $\{\ \}$. as the following example shows.

Example 13.2

Find a suitable linear compound operator, which, used in conjunction with the operator $[5][5][7]/175$, will produce a summation graduation formula with no second- or fourth-difference distortion.

We need to add a multiple of the fourth central difference to (13.3). The multiple A must be chosen so that the resulting summation formula has no fourth-difference distortion. That is, we must choose A so that

$$\left(1 + 4\delta^2 + \frac{32}{5}\delta^4 + \ldots\right)(1 - 4\delta^2 + A\delta^4)$$

contains no term in δ^4. It is easy to see that $A = \dfrac{48}{5}$.

The required linear compound operator must therefore be such that it will change v_x into

$$v_x - 4(v_{x+1} - 2v_x + v_{x-1}) + \frac{48}{5}(v_{x+2} - 4v_{x+1} + 6v_x - 4v_{x-1} + v_{x-2})$$

or

$$109v_x - 52(v_{x+1} + v_x + v_{x-1}) + \frac{48}{5}(v_{x+2} + v_{x+1} + v_x + v_{x-1} + v_{x-2})$$

A suitable linear compound operator is therefore

$$\left\{ 109[1] - 52[3] + \frac{48}{5}[5] \right\},$$

and the resulting summation graduation formula is

$$V_x = \frac{[5]^2[7]}{875} \{545[1] - 260[3] + 48[5]\} v_x$$

The range

13.24 The meaning of the 'range' of a formula is almost self-evident. It may be defined as the span of the number of ungraduated v's involved in the calculation of a single graduated value. This may be greater than the number of v's if some of the coefficients are zero when the formula is fully expanded (see para. 13.28). For instance, the range of the expression

$$-v_{x-3} + v_{x-1} + v_x + v_{x+1} - v_{x+3}$$

is seven, although only five terms are apparently involved.

13.25 The range of a summation formula is readily determined by means of the following obvious rule: take the number of terms implied by the widest summation operator in the linear compound operator; then for each individual summation operator $[n]$ outside the linear compound operator add $n - 1$ to the range. Spencer's formula (13.2) has range 21.

13.26 Most summation graduation formulae produce no first-, second- or third-difference distortion, but they usually involve fourth- and higher-difference distortion. In the case of a formula of range r, fourth- and higher-difference distortion will be negligible, provided any given set of r consecutive underlying values to be graduated by the formula can be accurately represented by a polynomial of degree three or less. A different approximating polynomial will usually be implied for each different set of r terms.

13.27   Other things being equal, the shorter the range of the formula the better, because

(1)   it is easier to apply;

(2)   the assumption that fourth and higher differences are negligible over the range is more likely to be accurate;

(3)   a smaller number of terms at the ends of the series of graduated values remain to be filled in by other methods.

Expansion of a formula

13.28   Little use is found for summation formulae of even range, and we shall confine our attention to formulae of odd range. Any summation formula of range $2r+1$ can be written in the simple explicit form

$$K_0 v_x + K_1(v_{x+1} + v_{x-1}) + K_2(v_{x+2} + v_{x-2}) + \ldots + K_r(v_{x+r} + v_{x-r})$$

13.29   Although every summation formula can be so expressed, there are an infinite number of formulae of this expanded type which cannot be derived from summation formulae. They are referred to as 'adjusted-average' graduation formulae in the North American literature, and are often excellent for graduation purposes (paras 13.65–13.75). Summation formulae, as distinct from formulae of the expanded type, have owed their importance to the ease with which they can be applied, but with modern electronic calculators and computers, this advantage is much less important.

13.30   To obtain the expansion of a summation graduation formula, we apply the formula to a long column of zeros containing a single 1 in the middle. The technique is demonstrated with Spencer's 21-term formulae in Table 13.3, and we deduce the following expanded form for that formula:

$$\frac{1}{350}\{60 v_x + 57(v_{x+1} + v_{x-1}) + 47(v_{x+2} + v_{x-2})$$

$$+ 33(v_{x+3} + v_{x-3}) + 18(v_{x+4} + v_{x-4}) + 6(v_{x+5} + v_{x-5})$$

$$- 2(v_{x+6} + v_{x-6}) - 5(v_{x+7} + v_{x-7}) - 5(v_{x+8} + v_{x-8})$$

$$- 3(v_{x+9} + v_{x-9}) - (v_{x+10} + v_{x-10})\} \tag{13.4}$$

13.31   Note that the sum of the coefficients must be exactly one

Table 13.3 *Expansion of Spencer's 21-term formula*

Zeros have been suppressed to make the table more readable

[3](1)	[5](1)	[7](1)	(1)	(1)+(2)+(3)−(4)	[5](5)	[5](6)	[7](7)
(1)	(2)	(3)	(4)	(5)	(6)	(7)	(8)
							−1
							−3
							−5
						−1	−5
						−2	−2
					−1	−2	6
					−1	0	18
			1	−1	0	3	33
		1	1	0	2	8	47
	1	1	1	1	3	12	57
1	1	1	1	2	4	14	60
	1	1	1	1	3	12	57
		1	1	0	2	8	47
			1	−1	0	3	33
					−1	0	18
					−1	−2	6
						−2	−2
						−1	−5
							−5
							−3
							−1

(otherwise the formula would distort polynomials of degree zero). The entries in column (8) of Table 13.3 sum to 350 because the divisor 350 has been omitted from the calculations.

13.32 In practice it is not necessary to complete the second half of the final column, since the coefficients repeat in reverse order, and the earlier columns can be abbreviated accordingly. Calculation of the complete series of coefficients does, however, provide a useful check (the expanded formula must be symmetric about the central coefficient and the sum of the coefficients is exactly one).

The coefficient curve

13.33 The *coefficient curve* is obtained by plotting graphically the coefficients $K_{-r}, \ldots, K_0, \ldots, K_r$ and joining them with a smooth curve, of which those in Figure 13.2 are typical. There is no need for refinement in the drawing of the curve.

(a)   (b)

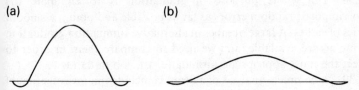

FIGURE 13.2   Typical coefficient curves

13.34 The smoothing properties (paras 13.46–13.56) and wave-cutting properties (paras 13.57–13.59) of a graduation formula are determined largely by the shape of the coefficient curve.

13.35 The general characteristics are that the curve is symmetrical: it usually rises to a peak in the middle, cuts the axis towards each end and thereafter lies below it. The sum of the coefficients must be unity, so that they will tend to be mainly positive proper fractions with a few negative ones (para. 13.36).

13.36 Formula (13.1) can be used to derive a formula for $v_x + v_{-x}$ in terms of v_0 and its differences as follows:

$$v_x + v_{-x} = \{[2x+1] - [2x-1]\}v_0$$

$$= (2 + x^2\delta^2 + \frac{1}{12}(x^4 - x^2)\delta^4 + \dots)v_0 \quad (13.5)$$

This formula contains a second difference term $x^2\delta^2 v_0$. It follows that for a summation graduation formula to have zero second-difference distortion,

$$\Sigma x^2 K_x = 0$$

Some of the K's, must therefore be negative, and in order to counteract the predominantly positive K's, they must occur for the higher values of x: i.e. the negative coefficients will occur at the ends of the coefficient curve where they are weighted with the largest values of x^2. This is not a rigid demonstration; it is a discussion of the general form of the coefficient curve, and there may be exceptions.

Effect of a summation formula on superimposed errors

13.37 Hitherto we have considered only the way in which a summation formula affects the underlying true values, and we have seen that it is a simple matter to ensure that, apart from fourth- and higher-difference error, it will reproduce them without distortion.

13.38 The whole purpose of graduation is to eliminate the superimposed random errors as far as possible and obtain a smooth series of values. A large number of alternative summation graduation formulae are available, and we need to compare them in order to select the most appropriate formula for the job in hand.

13.39 A complete analysis of a formula includes an investigation of the following features:

1 The range.
2 The second-difference distortion.
3 The fourth-difference distortion.
4 The error-reducing power of the formula.
5 Its smoothing power.
6 Its 'wave-cutting' properties.

The first three, which deal with the underlying true values have already been described, and of these the third is probably the least important. We now examine the last three.

Error-reducing power

13.40 Clearly one of the most important functions of a summation formula is to reduce the superimposed errors $\{e_x\}$.

13.41 When a summation graduation formula with the expanded form

$$V_x = K_0 v_x + K_1(v_{x+1} + v_{x-1}) + \ldots + K_r(v_{x+r} + v_{x-r})$$

is applied to observed data, the ungraduated errors $\{e_x\}$ are smoothed to yield graduated errors $\{e'_x\}$. In fact

$$e'_x = K_0 e_x + K_1(e_{x+1} + e_{x-1}) + \ldots + K_r(e_{x+r} + e_{x-r}).$$

13.42 The $\{e_x\}$ can be positive or negative. If the $\{v_x\}$ are unbiased observations, the expectations of the $\{e_x\}$ will all be zero and the expectations of the $\{e'_x\}$ will also be zero.

13.43 The summation graduation formula will be successful as an error-reducer if the $\{e'_x\}$ tend to be concentrated closer to zero than the $\{e_x\}$. For this to be true, the variance of e'_x must be considerably smaller than the variance of e_x.

13.44 Let us imagine that the $\{e_x\}$ are independent and have a common variance σ^2. Then e_x has variance σ^2, and e'_x has variance

$$(K_0^2 + 2K_1^2 + \ldots + 2K_r^2)\sigma^2$$

A measure of the error-reducing power of a formula is provided by ϕ_E, the ratio of the standard deviation of e'_x to the standard deviation of e_x:

$$\phi_E = \sqrt{(K_0^2 + 2K_1^2 + 2K_2^2 + \ldots + 2K_r^2)} \tag{13.6}$$

The smaller this *error-reducing index*, the greater the error-reducing power of the formula.

13.45 Spencer's 21-term formula has an error-reducing index of 0·378. We shall see later in para. 13.69 that this value is very satisfactory.

Smoothing power

13.46 This may at first seem synonymous with error-reducing power, since when errors are brought closer to zero, the graduated values will tend to progress more smoothly. There is an important distinction, however.

13.47 Consider Spencer's 21-term formula in the expanded form (13.4), and a particular observed value

$$v_{37} = u_{37} + e_{37}$$

The error e_{37} will first appear in the formula for V_{27} and it will contribute $K_{10}e_{37}$ to that graduated rate. Subsequently it will contribute K_9e_{37} to V_{28}, K_8e_{37} to $V_{29}, \ldots$, rising to a maximum contribution of K_0e_{37} in V_{37}. After V_{37}, the contributions of e_{37} to V_{38}, $V_{39}, \ldots$ decline, disappearing from the formula after V_{47} has been calculated.

13.48 Similar remarks apply to the other errors $e_{36}, e_{35}, e_{34}, \ldots$ and $e_{38}, e_{39}, e_{40}, \ldots$ It follows that if the coefficient curve is smooth, i.e. if the successive coefficients K_j change only gradually, the graduated errors will themselves change only gradually, however irregular the ungraduated errors $\{e_x\}$ may be. Since the underlying 'true' values $\{u_x\}$ are supposed to be smooth, it follows that a formula which when expanded has a smooth run of coefficients will produce smoothly progressing graduated values.

13.49 Thus, the smoothing power of a summation graduation formula depends upon the size of the coefficients *and* upon their order.

The error-reducing index depends only upon the size of the coefficients. It takes no account of their order.

13.50 The usual way of examining smoothness is to consider the various orders of differences (para. 11.62), and it is conventional to concentrate on third differences, although the choice of third differences is to some extent arbitrary.

13.51 A summation graduation formula has good smoothing properties if the third differences of the graduated errors $\{e'_x\}$ tend to be concentrated closer to zero than those of the $\{e_x\}$. For this to be true the variance of $\Delta^3 e'_x$ must be considerably smaller than the variance of $\Delta^3 e_x$.

13.52 A measure of the smoothing power of a formula is provided by the *smoothing index* ϕ_S, which is the ratio of the standard deviation of $\Delta^3 e'_x$ to the standard deviation of $\Delta^3 e_x$ under the assumption that the $\{e_x\}$ are independent and have a common variance σ^2.

13.53 Because $\Delta^3 e_x = e_{x+3} - 3e_{x+2} + 3e_{x+1} - e_x$

$$\text{var}(\Delta^3 e_x) = \sigma^2 + 9\sigma^2 + 9\sigma^2 + \sigma^2 = 20\sigma^2$$

13.54 To find the variance of $\Delta^3 e'_x$ we form a table. The first column contains the coefficients in the expanded formula. The second column is obtained by multiplying the first column by -3 and shifting the entries down one position. The third column is the same as the second apart from a change of sign and a shift down of one position. Column 4 is the same as column 1 apart from a change of sign and a shift down of three places. We then form column 5 by adding the previous columns, and column 6 by squaring the entries in column 5. The variance of $\Delta^3 e'_x$ is equal to the total of column 6 multiplied by σ^2.

13.55 The smoothing index is then given by

$$\phi_S = \sqrt{\left\{\frac{\text{total of column (6)}}{20}\right\}} \tag{13.7}$$

13.56 Certain short-cuts are possible in this calculation procedure. The first is to note that because of the symmetry of the graduation formula, the entries in column 6 repeat themselves in reverse order; so we only need form the first half of the table and double the sum for the first half of column 6. The second simplification is to note that although the coefficients $\{K_j\}$ are usually fractions, the fractions are in fact the result of dividing integer coefficients by a certain integer denominator; the tabular calculations are simpler if we operate with the integer coefficients and divide the total of column 6 by the square of the denominator at the end. These short-cuts are included in the following example.

Example 13.3

Find the smoothing index for Spencer's 21-term formula.

We begin by listing the integer coefficients in column 1 of Table 13.4. The coefficients are obtained from (13.4). The methods of paras 13.54 and 13.56 are then used to complete the table, and we deduce that

$$\phi_S = \sqrt{\left\{\frac{96/(350)^2}{20}\right\}} = 0{\cdot}00625$$

We shall see later in para. 13.73 that this value is very satisfactory.

Wave cutting

13.57 The first coefficient curve in Figure 13.2 rises steeply to a narrow peak, while the second rises very gradually to a broad flat top. The use of a formula represented by the first curve will mean that any particular ungraduated error will have a marked influence on the graduated values close to it but very little effect on the others. Such a formula will tend to localize the effect of the errors, and a wave in the ungraduated errors will be repeated, although to a lesser extent in the graduated values. A formula typified by the second curve will spread the effect of an ungraduated error over a much wider field and will be said to have good wave-cutting properties.

13.58 *The wave-cutting index* ϕ_W *of a graduation formula is conventionally defined as the sum of the five central coefficients.* This is somewhat arbitrary, and breaks down if there is an even number of terms; in this case the sum of the four middle coefficients and the next one at either end is taken. The rationale behind the index is clear from para. 13.57; the smaller its value, the better the wave-cutting properties of the formula.

13.59 Systematic inaccuracies in demographic and actuarial statistics do not usually produce distortions in the form of waves. (An exception is mentioned in paras 16.1–16.20, where a special graduation technique is described for dealing with the problem.) The wave-cutting properties of a summation formula are therefore of only minor importance.

Table 13.4 *A method for calculating the smoothing index of Spencer's 21-term formula*

The central coefficient in the formula is indicated by an asterisk, and the first repeated term in column (6) is indicated by a dagger

(1)	(2)	(3)	(4)	(5)	(6)
-1				-1	1
-3	3			0	0
-5	9	-3		1	1
-5	15	-9	1	2	4
-2	15	-15	3	1	1
6	6	-15	5	2	4
18	-18	-6	5	-1	1
33	-54	18	2	-1	1
47	-99	54	-6	-4	16
57	-141	99	-18	-3	9
60*	-171	141	-33	-3	9
57	-180	171	-47	1	1
47	-171	180	-57	-1	1†
.	.	.	.	.	.
.	.	.	.	.	.
.	.	.	.	.	.
					96

Well-known summation formulae

13.60 In Table 13.5 we summarize a selection of well-known summation formulae. The advantages and disadvantages of each of these formulae should be evident from the table. Hardy's wave-cutting formula, for example, has excellent wave-cutting and good error-reducing properties, but poor smoothing properties. The error-reducing, smoothing and wave-cutting properties of the Kenchington formula, on the other hand, are all quite good, but the range of the formula is somewhat too wide for mortality graduation purposes.

13.61 Spencer's 21-term formula is probably the best-known and generally satisfactory of all summation formulae. It was used, for example, to graduate the ultimate section of the A1924–29 (assured lives) mortality table, and has been used in recent years to produce the Australian national life tables.

13.62 Hardy's friendly society formula is the only formula in Table 13.5 to have non-zero second-difference distortion. The second and

Name	Formula	Range	δ^2	δ^4	reducing index	Smoothing index	cutting index	Central coefficient
Spencer 13	$\dfrac{[2][3][4][5]}{1440}\{87[1]-25[3]\}$;	13	0	$-2\cdot7$	·457	·0217	·975	364/1440
Spencer 15	$\dfrac{[5][4][4]}{320}\{[1]+6[3]-3[5]\}$;	15	0	$-3\cdot9$	·439	·0167	·938	74/320
Woolhouse	$\dfrac{[5]^3}{125}\{10[1]-3[3]\}$;	15	0	$-5\cdot4$	·423	·0655	·920	25/125
Higham	$\dfrac{[5]^3}{125}\{2[3]-[5]\}$;	17	0	$-6\cdot0$	·416	·0111	·878	25/125
Hardy friendly society	$\dfrac{[4][5][6]}{120}\{2[3]-[5]\}$;	17	1/12	$-6\cdot5$	·406	·0105	·850	24/120
Larus 19	$\dfrac{[3][5][7]}{945}\{-6[1]+5[3]+7[5]-5[7]\}$;	19	0	$-10\cdot0$	·388	·0070	·790	169/945
Spencer 21	$\dfrac{[5]^2[7]}{350}\{[1]+[3]+[5]-[7]\}$;	21	0	$-12\cdot6$	·378	·0063	·766	60/350
Hardy wave-cutting	$\dfrac{[5][13]}{65}\{[3]+[5]-[7]\}$;	23	0	$-48\cdot8$	·333	·0146	·415	5/65
Vaughan G	$\dfrac{[5][6][8]}{2880}\{12[3]+5[5]-7[7]\}$;	23	0	$-19\cdot1$	·359	·0040	·701	444/2880
Larus 25	$\dfrac{[5][7][9]}{945}\{4[3]+[5]-2[7]\}$;	25	0	$-28\cdot2$	·341	·0032	·644	133/945
Larus 27	$\dfrac{[3][5][7][9]}{2835}\{-7[1]+[3]+7[5]-4[7]\}$;	27	0	$-33\cdot1$	·335	·0026	·629	385/2835
Kenchington	$\dfrac{[5][7][11]}{385}\{[3]+[5]-[7]\}$;	27	0	$-44\cdot8$	·320	·0031	·559	45/385

fourth differences of the mortality functions q_x, m_x and μ_x are usually positive in the adult section of a life table. So the small positive second-difference distortion term in Hardy's friendly society formula may be an advantage, because it will tend to compensate for the negative fourth-difference term.

13.63 The result of a summation of an even number of terms is to produce a value located midway between the two central terms. A second even summation brings the resulting values back into alignment, and hence a formula using, say, the operators [4] [5] [6] produces values for integral arguments. One important disadvantage of even summations in general is that in order to eliminate second-difference distortion, the linear compound operator usually needs to be rather complicated (e.g. Vaughan's G formula in Table 13.5). Hardy's friendly society formula avoids a complicated linear compound operator by allowing a small second-difference error.

13.64 The error-reducing, smoothing and wave-cutting indices in Table 13.5 allow comparisons to be made of alternative formulae. Without absolute scales for these indices, however, we cannot really decide which of the formulae are absolutely satisfactory. Absolute scales for the error-reducing and smoothing indices are provided in paras 13.69 and 13.73 respectively.

Adjusted-average graduation formulae with optimal error-reducing power

13.65 We noted in para. 13.29 that there are an infinite number of formulae of the expanded type which cannot be derived from summation formulae. Let us now consider a graduation formula of the expanded type having range $(2r+1)$:

$$K_0 v_x + K_1(v_{x+1} + v_{x-1}) + \ldots K_r(v_{x+r} + v_{x-r}) \tag{13.8}$$

where
$$K_0 + 2 \sum_{j=1}^{r} K_j = 1 \tag{13.9}$$

We note from para. 13.36 that for the formula to have zero second-difference distortion

$$\sum_{j=1}^{r} j^2 K_j = 0 \tag{13.10}$$

The error-reducing index of the formula is

$$\phi_E = (K_0^2 + 2 \sum_{j=1}^{r} K_j^2)^{\frac{1}{2}} \tag{13.11}$$

13.66   To optimize the error-reducing power of the formula, we need to minimize ϕ_E^2, subject to the constraints (13.9) and (13.10). After some straightforward but slightly tedious algebra we find that the coefficient curve has the shape of a parabola and

$$K_i = \frac{3(3r^2 + 3r - 1)}{(2r-1)(2r+1)(2r+3)} - \frac{15i^2}{(2r-1)(2r+1)(2r+3)}. \quad (13.12)$$

13.67   The error-reducing, smoothing and wave-cutting indices of this optimal error-reducing formula turn out to be

$$\phi_E = \left(\frac{3(3r^2 + 3r - 1)}{(2r-1)(2r+1)(2r+3)} \right)^{\frac{1}{2}} = \sqrt{K_0} \quad (13.13)$$

$$\phi_S = \frac{3\sqrt{(12r^4 + 24r^3 + 39r^2 + 27r + 23)}}{(2r-1)(2r+1)(2r+3)\sqrt{5}} \quad (13.14)$$

$$\phi_W = \frac{15(3r^2 + 3r - 11)}{(2r-1)(2r+1)(2r+3)} = 10K_1 - 5K_0 \quad (13.15)$$

13.68   Values of ϕ_E, ϕ_S, ϕ_W and K_0 for formulae with ranges 5 to 27 and 225 are exhibited in Table 13.6, and it will be noted that a 225-term formula is needed to reduce errors to an average of one-tenth of their original value.

Table 13.6   *The characteristics of optimal error-reducing formulae*

Range of formula	Error-reducing index ϕ_E	Smoothing index ϕ_S	Wave-cutting index ϕ_W	Central coefficient K_0
5	·6969	·3174	1·0000	·4857
7	·5773	·1940	1·1905	·3333
9	·5054	·1418	1·0606	·2554
11	·4555	·1124	·9207	·2075
13	·4181	·0935	·8042	·1748
15	·3888	·0801	·7014	·1511
17	·3649	·0702	·6347	·1331
19	·3449	·0624	·5728	·1190
21	·3280	·0563	·5214	·1076
23	·3133	·0512	·4783	·0981
25	·3004	·0470	·4258	·0902
27	·2890	·0435	·4100	·0835
225	·1000	·0163	·0500	·0100

13.69 The error-reducing efficiency of a summation or adjusted-average formula can be calculated by dividing the optimal error-reducing index for a formula of that range by the error-reducing index of the formula. Spencer's 21-term formula, for example, has an error-reducing efficiency of 0·3280/0·3784 or 87 per cent.

13.70 Sheppard (1914) has shown that the single graduated value obtained by applying the optimal n-term error-reducing formula with no first-, second- or third-difference distortion to observations at n successive ages is the same as the value which would be obtained by fitting an unweighted least squares cubic to the n ungraduated values.

Adjusted-average graduation formulae with optimal smoothing power

13.71 To optimize the smoothing power of a formula, we need to minimize ϕ_S^2, subject to the constraints (13.9) and (13.10). The coefficient curve turns out to be a polynomial of degree 8. In fact, for a formula of range $2r - 3$,

$$K_i = \frac{315\{(r-1)^2 - i^2\}\{r^2 - i^2\}\{(r+1)^2 - i^2\}\{(3r^2 - 16) - 11i^2\}}{8r(r^2 - 1)(4r^2 - 1)(4r^2 - 9)(4r^2 - 25)} \quad (13.16)$$

13.72 The coefficients, and error-reducing, smoothing and wave-cutting indices for the optimal-smoothing adjusted-average formulae with ranges 5 to 23, are shown in Table 13.7.

13.73 The smoothing efficiency of a summation or adjusted-average graduation formula can be calculated by dividing the optimal smoothing index for a formula of that range by the smoothing index of the formula. Spencer's 21-term formula, for example, has a smoothing efficiency of 0·004812/0·00625 or 77 per cent.

13.74 It will be noted that the optimal 21-term smoothing formula is 90 per cent efficient as an error-reducer. The optimal 21-term error-reducing formula, on the other hand, is only 8·5 per cent efficient as a smoothing formula. Similar results are true for the optimal formulae of other ranges. We conclude therefore that an optimal smoothing adjusted-average formula is much more suitable for graduation purposes than an optimal error-reducing formula.

13.75 Spencer's 21-term formula has already been mentioned as perhaps the most popular and successful summation graduation formula. The error-reducing, smoothing and wave-cutting indices of this formula are more or less the same as those of the optimal 19-term smoothing formula.

Table 13.7 Optimal smoothing formulae with ranges 5 to 23

	Range									
	5	7	9	11	13	15	17	19	21	23
K_0	·559441	·412587	·331140	·277945	·240057	·211541	·189231	·171266	·156469	·144060
K_1	·293706	·293706	·266557	·238693	·214337	·193742	·176390	·161691	·149136	·138318
K_2	−·073427	−·058741	·118470	·141267	·147356	·145904	·141112	·134965	·128423	·121949
K_3		−·058741	−·009873	−·035723	·065492	·082918	·092293	·096658	·097956	·097395
K_4			−·040724	−·026792	·000000	·024027	·042093	·054685	·063038	·068303
K_5				−·027864	−·027864	−·014134	−·002467	·017475	·029628	·038933
K_6					−·019350	−·024499	−·018640	−·008155	·003119	·013430
K_7						−·013730	−·020370	−·018972	−·012896	−·004948
K_8							−·009960	−·016601	−·017614	−·014527
K_9								−·007378	−·013455	−·015687
K_{10}									−·005570	−·010918
K_{11}										−·004278
Error-reducing index ϕ_E	·704474	·597124	·532297	·486473	·451460	·423415	·400219	·380580	·363650	·348845
Smoothing index ϕ_s	·263542	·114660	·058078	·033066	·020415	·013384	·009192	·006551	·004812	·003626
Wave-cutting index ϕ_w	1·000000	1·117481	1·101194	1·037865	·963443	·890833	·824235	·764578	·711587	·664594

The ends of the table

13.76 Although summation and adjusted-average formulae provide graduated rates for the main body of a table, the ends of the table always need to be completed by some other method.

13.77 Gompertz and Makeham-type curves are often used to graduate mortality rates at the high ages. This approach has been used, for example, in the construction of the Australian national life tables. The two sections of the graduation then need to be blended (paras 14.57–14.68).

13.78 Extrapolation methods are sometimes used. Although such procedures tend to be rather hazardous, they can be successful if great care is exercised. The ends of the A1924–29 ultimate table, for example, were completed by third-difference extrapolation.

13.79 In the case of a graduation formula of range $2r+1$, r graduated values need to be calculated at either end of the table. Graduated values at the first r ages can be obtained by fitting an unweighted least-squares cubic (para. 14.36) near the first $2r+1$ unadjusted values, and values for the final r ages can be obtained in a similar manner using the final $2r+1$ unadjusted values. The graduated values obtained by means of this approach are identical with those obtained by means of the non-symmetric adjusted-average formulae with maximum error-reducing power proposed by Greville (1947, 1948). Greville also devised non-symmetric optimal-smoothing formulae for completing the ends of a table. These produce smooth results, but the smooth values tend to drift away from the true underlying curve. The least squares approach is preferable.

13.80 When the methods of para. 13.79 are used, no values are lost from the ends of the table, and improved smoothness can be obtained by repeated graduation. It should be noted, however, that two applications of the optimal smoothing formula of range 21 are equivalent to a single application of a non-optimal formula of range 41, and because of the wide effective range, the danger of distortion is considerable. Matrix theory tells us that repeated graduation by summation or adjusted-average formula, and using one of the methods of para. 13.79 for the tails, will result in a cubic curve being fitted to the data asymptotically.

Advantages of summation and adjusted-average methods of graduation

13.81 Summation graduation formulae were developed, chiefly by

British actuaries, at a time when available calculating equipment was very limited—even multiplications were basically additions (as in the earlier arithmometers), and consequently it was computationally very advantageous to employ more additions and fewer multiplications. Modern electronic calculators have eliminated any difficulty about multiplication, but the summation method is still very convenient for hand computation. The process is purely mechanical and does not require a highly skilled operator, as does the graphic method.

13.82 The expanded form of a summation formula will usually be employed when the graduation is to be done by computer, and any computational advantage of the summation formula as such disappears. Graduation by optimal-smoothing adjusted-average formula is then preferable.

13.83 Summation and adjusted-average methods are suitable for standard tables based on large experiences, and can be relied upon to give adequate smoothness, provided that the unadjusted rates themselves progress fairly smoothly. Results are produced quickly.

13.84 Perhaps the greatest merit of these methods is the preservation in the graduated rates of additive relationships existing among the ungraduated rates for functions like sickness rates. Suppose that

$$f(x) = a_1 f_1(x) + a_2 f_2(x) + \ldots + a_p f_p(x)$$

where the a's are constants and x is variable. If the functions $f, f_1, f_2, \ldots,$ f_p are graduated separately by the same summation formula, it will be seen that the same equation will connect the graduated rates.

Disadvantages of summation and adjusted-average methods of graduation

13.85 Although skill is needed in choosing a suitable formula, once the choice has been made, there is no scope for individual judgement. As a result it is impossible to retain any special feature of the experience (such as a discontinuity in withdrawal rates) which the operator might feel to be an essential feature. It is certain to be greatly modified in the graduation and might even disappear altogether.

13.86 The ends of the table always need to be completed by some other method.

13.87 The summation or adjusted-average method cannot be used satisfactorily for select rates, and since it assumes that the function operated on has negligible fourth differences over the range of the

formula, its use is in practice restricted to ratios such as q_x, μ_x, etc.
13.88 In the development of the formulae, the assumption was made that the variances of the random errors $\{e_x\}$ were approximately constant (para. 13.44). It is impossible, therefore, with the summation or adjusted-average method to take into account the weight of the exposed to risk at each age.

13.89 Unless the crude rates progress fairly smoothly, the results will be unsatisfactory. This means in effect that the experience must be large. The following example demonstrates a simple method for determining whether or not the progression of the ungraduated rates is smooth enough for the summation or adjusted-average method to produce satisfactory results.

Example 13.4

The average absolute third difference of the crude mortality rates in Table 12.1 is 0·01135. The smoothing index for Spencer's 21-term formula is 0·0063. If we were to use Spencer's formula to graduate these data, we would expect the average absolute third difference of the graduated rates to be approximately

$$0·01135 \times 0·0063 = 0·00007$$

Graduated mortality rates are usually recorded correct to five decimal places, and a smooth graduation has most of its absolute third differences less than about 0·00003 at the ages in question. It is clear, therefore, that Spencer's formula is unlikely to produce a smooth graduation of these data. Spencer's formula was in fact used to graduate these data in Table 13.2, and the average absolute third difference turned out to be 0·00007. The graduation lacks smoothness.

Statistical tests

13.90 Although we have concentrated our attention on error-reduction and smoothness, it should be borne in mind that all the usual tests of adherence to data should be applied to the results of any graduation.

13.91 When the chi-square goodness-of-fit test is applied to a summation or adjusted-average mortality graduation, the null hypothesis actually being tested is that each section of the underlying mortality curve can be represented satisfactorily by a curve of degree three or less and that the errors $\{e_x\}$ have equal variances. A significant value of the test statistic leads to the rejection of this null hypothesis and the conclusion that the use of the summation or adjusted-average graduation formula is inappropriate.

13.92 J. H. Pollard (1971) has shown that when the chi-square test is applied to mortality data graduated by summation or adjusted-average formula with central coefficient K_0 and error-reducing index ϕ_E, the expected value of the test statistic under the null hypothesis is approximately

$$v = n(1 - 2K_0 + \phi_E^2) \qquad (13.17)$$

where n denotes the number of separate ages included in the chi-square calculation. Since the expected value of a χ_v^2 random variable is v, formula (13.17) implies a reduction of

$$n(2K_0 - \phi_E^2) \qquad (13.18)$$

in the number of degrees of freedom, to allow for the fitting of the mortality rates.

13.93 In an earlier simulation study with Spencer's 21-term formula and a chi-square test based on thirty distinct ages, Seal (1943) came to the conclusion that 'about 5 degrees of freedom' were lost. Formula (13.18) predicts a reduction of six.

13.94 Although (13.17) provides a reasonably accurate value for the expectation of the 'chi-square' statistic, no formal proof has been given that the actual distribution is chi-square when the mortality data are graduated by summation or adjusted-average formula. The process of reduction of degrees of freedom is founded on an analogy with curve-fitting. Recent unpublished computer simulations do seem to indicate, however, that the chi-square distribution is appropriate, at least approximately.

Historical notes

13.95 John Finlaison, first President of the Institute of Actuaries, is recorded as having used a weighted running average for graduation purposes as early as 1823, and the technique was probably known to others at that time. Woolhouse (1866) drew attention to the distortion inherent in simple running averages, and developed (1870) a 'summation' method which was correct to third differences. He outlined a simpler arithmetic procedure for this graduation method in 1878, and the discussion of that paper indicates that his graduation method had already been adopted by other actuaries. Woolhouse's method was further developed by J. A. Higham (1882, 1883) and Ackland (1882).

13.96　The summation n notation seems to have been introduced by G. F. Hardy (1896). We also find the error-reducing index and smoothing index defined in this paper, although an earlier account of the error-reducing index was given by Woolhouse (1878).

13.97　Spencer's powerful 21-term formula was developed in connection with the graduation of the Manchester Unity sickness experience and published in the *Journal of the Institute of Actuaries* in 1904.

13.98　Adjusted-average graduation formulae, which have been popular in North America, were developed by an American mathematician Erastus L. De Forest (1834–88) and published in obscure places. They were little noticed or used until attention was drawn to them in 1925 by Wolfenden. The De Forest formulae seem to have been rediscovered by the British mathematician Sheppard (1914), but they received little attention from British actuaries.

It is perhaps interesting to note that a letter to the Editor from De Forest appears in *J. Inst. Actu.* (1880), **22**, 231, claiming priority in the derivation of the well-known mortality formula

$$\mu_x = \{8(l_{x-1} - l_{x+1}) - (l_{x-2} - l_{x+2})\}/(12l_x)$$

REFERENCES

Ackland, T. G. (1882). On the graduation of mortality tables. *J. Inst. Actu.* **23**, 352–9.

Greville, T. N. E. (1947). Actuarial note: adjusted average graduation formulas of maximum smoothness. *The Record, Amer. Inst. Actu.* **36**, 249–64.

Greville, T. N. E. (1948). Actuarial note; tables of coefficients in adjusted average formulas of maximum smoothness. *The Record, Amer. Inst. Actu.* **37**, 11–30.

Hardy, G. F. (1896). Graduation formulas. *J. Inst. Actu.* **32**, 371–8.

Higham, J. A. (1882). On the adjustment of mortality tables. *J. Inst. Actu.*, **23**, 335–52.

Higham, J. A. (1883). On the adjustment of mortality tables. *J. Inst. Actu.*, **24**, 44–51.

Kendall, M. G. and Stuart, A. (1968). *The Advanced Theory of Statistics*, Vol. 3, second edition, Griffin, London, 371.

Pollard, J. H. (1971). The application of the chi-square test of goodness-of-fit to mortality data graduated by summation formulae. *J. Inst. Actu.*, **97**, 325–30.

Seal, H. L. (1943). Tests of a mortality table graduation. *J. Inst. Actu.*, **71**, 5–47.

Sheppard, W. F. (1914). Graduation by reduction in mean square of error I.*J. Inst. Actu.*, **48**, 171–85.

Sheppard, W. F. (1914). Graduation by reduction in mean square of error II. *J. Inst. Actu.*, **48**, 390–412.

Spencer, J. (1904). On the graduation of the rates of sickness and mortality presented by the experience of the Manchester Unity of Oddfellows during the period 1893–97. *J. Inst. Actu.*, **38**, 334–43.

Vaughan, H. (1933). Summation formulae of graduation with a special type of operator. *J. Inst. Actu.*, **64**, 428–48.

Vaughan, H. (1935). Further enquiries into the summation method of graduation. *J. Inst. Actu.*, **66**, 463–98.

Woolhouse, W. S. B. (1866). On the construction of tables of mortality.*J.Inst. Actu.*, **13**, 75–102.

Woolhouse, W. S. B. (1870). Explanation of a new method of adjusting mortality tables with some observations on Mr Makeham's modification of Gompertz's theory. *J. Inst. Actu.*, **15**, 389–410.

Woolhouse, W. S. B. (1878). On the adjustment of mortality tables. *J. Inst. Actu.*, **21**, 37–66.

Wolfenden, H. H. (1925). On the development of formulae for graduation by linear compounding, with special reference to the work of Erastus L. De Forest, *T.A.S.A.*, **26**, 81–121.

EXERCISES FOR CHAPTER THIRTEEEN

1   What are the advantages and disadvantages of a summation or adjusted-average formula with a wide range?

2   Analyse fully Hardy's friendly society formula:

$$V_x = \frac{[4][5][6]}{120}\{2[3] - [5]\}v_x$$

Compare your results with those in Table 13.5.

3   What are the merits and demerits of the following graduation formula?

$$V_x = \frac{1}{27}(7v_0 + 15v_{\pm 1} - 6v_{\pm 2} + v_{\pm 3})$$

4   Write a computer program to graduate the data in Table 12.1 by Spencer's 21-term formula. Compare your graduated rates with those in Table 13.2.

5   Write a computer program to graduate the data in Table 12.1 by the optimal smoothing 21-term adjusted-average formula. Compare the smoothness of the graduated rates with the smoothness of the rates obtained by Spencer's formula. Test the graduation for adherence to data.

6   Write a general computer program which will graduate mortality data by the optimal smoothing 21-term formula. The program should include the

least-squares method of para. 13.79 for completing the ends of the table, and tests for smoothness and adherence to data. Output should include l_x, p_x, q_x and μ_x.

7　The summation graduation formula

$$\frac{[3]^4}{729}\{145[1] - 62[3] + 10[5]\}$$

has been proposed by a student. Analyse the formula fully, and comment upon its merits and demerits.

CHAPTER FOURTEEN

GRADUATION BY MATHEMATICAL FORMULA

14.1 We now come to the third method referred to in Chapter 11, namely, the fitting of a mathematical curve. Most reasonable curves produce a suitable regular shape, so that the question which arises is not whether sufficient smoothness has been attained but whether the chosen 'shape' of the curve is justified by the data (i.e. whether the curve adheres sufficiently to the data). As indicated in Chapter 11, successful use of this method requires some prior knowledge or a reasonable hypothesis about the general shape and trend of the set of observed values to be graduated.

Makeham and Gompertz curves

14.2 The first important contribution towards finding a 'law of mortality' (as it was then called) was made by Benjamin Gompertz (1825), who argued on physiological grounds that the intensity of mortality gained equal proportions in equal intervals of age (para. 1.48). The force of mortality μ_x would then be represented by the formula Bc^x.

14.3 A development of Gompertz's law was subsequently made by Makeham (1860), who adopted the formula

$$\mu_x = A + Bc^x \tag{14.1}$$

Makeham introduced the constant A as well as the exponentially increasing component of the force of mortality to reflect the division of causes of death into two kinds, those due to chance and those due to deterioration (para. 1.48). With its three constants A, B and c this formula was found to give satisfactory adherence to data for a number of experiences in the late nineteenth and early twentieth centuries, and several standard tables were graduated by its use. A mass of literature, mathematical and otherwise, has grown up around the formula, and the student of the subject of life contingencies will be familiar with the ways in which joint-life functions and problems of complicated multiple-life statuses can be more easily manipulated if the table used has been graduated by Makeham's formula. So convenient is it for the calculation of monetary functions that its adoption has been justified at the expense of some departure from the degree of adherence to data that would otherwise be required.

14.4 It has been found increasingly difficult, however, to obtain satisfactory graduations by this simple formula and more complicated formulae have therefore been developed. We discuss some of these formulae later in paras 14.11–14.26.

• Preliminary tests for a Gompertz or Makeham graduation

14.5 When Gompertz's 'law' holds,

$$-\log(-\log p_x) = \log\left[\frac{\log c}{B(c-1)}\right] - x\log c \qquad (14.2)$$

The graph of this function is a straight line. It is possible therefore to form an opinion as to whether a Gompertz graduation is likely to prove successful by plotting the values

$$-\log[-\log(1-\mathring{q}_x)]$$

14.6 If the points suggest a straight line fit, estimates of c and B can be obtained by sketching the line and noting its slope and y-intercept:

$$\hat{c} = \exp(-\text{slope})$$

$$\hat{B} = \frac{\log\hat{c}}{(\hat{c}-1)}\exp(-\text{intercept})$$

Graduated survival rates can then be calculated by means of the formula

$$\hat{p}_x = \exp\left[-\frac{\hat{B}(\hat{c}-1)}{\log\hat{c}}\hat{c}^x\right] \qquad (14.3)$$

14.7 It is helpful to include confidence limits in the diagram. If we denote the approximate 95 per cent upper and lower limits of q_x (paras 12.4–12.5) by q_x^U and q_x^L, the limits of $-\log(-\log p_x)$ for inclusion in the diagram are

$$-\log[-\log(1-q_x^U)] \quad \text{and} \quad -\log[-\log(1-q_x^L)]$$

14.8 The constant A in a Makeham graduation is always small and positive. At the higher ages it is swamped by the exponential term Bc^x,

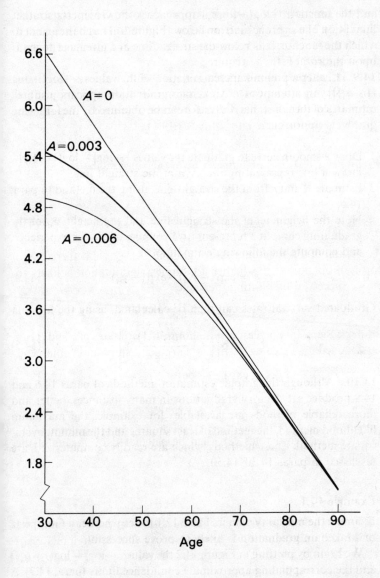

FIGURE 14.1   Graphs of the function $-\log(-\log p_x)$ when the underlying mortality follows Makeham's 'law' with $B = 0.0001$ and $c = 1.09$. The three curves correspond to $A = 0$, $A = 0.003$ and $A = 0.006$

and the function $-\log(-\log p_x)$ approaches the Gompertz straight line (14.2). The approach is from below (Figure 14.1), and the extent to which the function falls below the straight line at a given age depends upon the size of A.

14.9 If, after a preliminary examination of the values $\{-\log[-\log(1 - \mathring{q}_x)]\}$, an attempt at a Makeham graduation appears justified, estimates of the constants A, B and c can be obtained by the following graphical approach:

1 Draw a smooth curve to graduate the values $\{-\log[-\log(1 - \mathring{q}_x)]\}$.
2 Draw a line representing the asymptotic straight line.
3 Estimate B and c from the straight line, using the method of para. 14.6.
4 Note the height y_G of the straight line and the height y_M of the graduating curve at a representative younger age in the experience, and compute the following estimate of A:

$$\hat{A} = \exp(-y_M) - \exp(-y_G) \tag{14.4}$$

Graduated survival rates can then be calculated, using the formula

$$\hat{p}_x = \exp\left[-\hat{A} - \frac{\hat{B}(\hat{c}-1)}{\log \hat{c}} \hat{c}^x\right] \tag{14.5}$$

14.10 Although the graphic estimation methods of paras 14.6 and 14.9 produce satsifactory graduations in many instances, better and more reliable methods are available: for example, the maximum likelihood method, the method of least squares and the minimum chi-square method. These methods, which are readily computerized, are discussed in paras 14.30–14.50.

Example 14.1

Examine the mortality data in Table 12.1 to see whether a Gompertz or Makeham graduation is likely to prove successful.

We begin by plotting in Figure 14.2 the values $-\log[-\log(1 - \mathring{q}_x)]$ and the corresponding approximate confidence limits (para. 14.7). A series of straight lines is drawn connecting consecutive pairs of upper limit points and another series is drawn connecting the lower limit points. A straight line fit appears very reasonable.

The line shown in figure 14.2 was drawn by eye. Its slope is

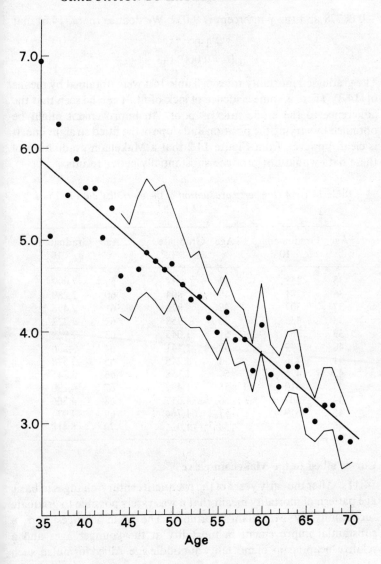

FIGURE 14.2   The values $-\log[-\log(1-\mathring{q}_x)]$ obtained from the mortality experience in Table 12.1. Approximate 95 per cent confidence limits for $-\log(-\log p_x)$ are also shown on the diagram. The straight line was drawn by eye

-0.08778 and the y-intercept is 9.032. We deduce (para. 14.6) that

$$\hat{c} = 1.09175$$
$$\hat{B} = 0.0001143$$

The graduated mortality rates in Table 14.1 were obtained by means of (14.3). There is some evidence of lack-of-fit. It can be seen that the adherence to the crude rates is poor. An improvement might be obtained by varying the position and slope of the fitted straight line. It is clear, however, from Figure 14.2 that a Makeham graduation of these data would not produce substantially better results.

Table 14.1   *A Gompertz graduation of the mortality data in Table 12.1*

Age x	Graduated $q_x \times 10^5$	Age x	Graduated $q_x \times 10^5$	Age x	Graduated $q_x \times 10^5$
35	258	47	737	59	2,099
36	281	48	804	60	2,289
37	307	49	878	61	2,496
38	335	50	958	62	2,722
39	366	51	1,045	63	2,968
40	399	52	1,141	64	3,236
41	436	53	1,245	65	3,528
42	476	54	1,358	66	3,845
43	519	55	1,482	67	4,190
44	567	56	1,617	68	4,566
45	619	57	1,764	69	4,974
46	675	58	1,924	70	5,418

Curves allied to the Makeham curve

14.11   After the early years of the twentieth century, changes in basic age pattern of mortality meant that it was rarely possible to graduate successfully by Makeham's formula. The main changes were a substantial improvement in mortality at the younger ages and a relative 'heaping up' of mortality at middle age. Allied formulae, such as

$$\mu_x = A + Hx + Bc^x \tag{14.6}$$

$$\mu_x = ma^x + nb^x \tag{14.7}$$

and

$$-\log p_x = ma^x + nb^x = me^{\alpha x} + ne^{\beta x} \tag{14.8}$$

were tried without any very great success. The real difficulty, arising from the fact that the observed mortality experience is heterogeneous and mixes generations, is that a single curve will not fit the whole range of the table.

Perks' formulae

14.12   Perks (1932) proposed some new formulae which represented, at the time, the most promising attempt to fit a single curve to the whole range of the table (para 1.49). The principal formulae were

$$\mu_x(\text{or } q_x) = \frac{A + Bc^x}{1 + Dc^x} \qquad (14.9)$$

and

$$\mu_x = \frac{A + Bc^x}{Kc^{-x} + 1 + Dc^x} \qquad (14.10)$$

14.13   Perks' formulae have had considerable influence on subsequent formulae, and his paper should be read carefully by anyone interested in the development of the subject.

English Life Table nos 11 and 12

14.14   Unlike English Life Tables 7–10, which were graduated by King's method (Chapter 16), E.L.T. 11, based on the deaths in England and Wales in 1950–2 and the population census of 1951, was graduated by a mathematical formula. The main reason for this change was that there was no longer any justification for graduating the population and deaths separately. In breaking away from this traditional approach of dealing with population and deaths separately, it was decided to take a new look at the method of graduation itself. Mathematical formulae were currently favoured in mortality work because (1) unlike summation formulae they did not leave the rates for terminal ages to be dealt with by other and somewhat arbitrary means, and (2) they enabled prior experience of the 'natural' shape of the μ_x or q_x curve to be taken into account. In particular it was desired to make provision for the fact that the mortality of young men had been declining more rapidly than that of men in middle life. This had produced a pronounced secondary hump in the curve of the ratio m_{x+5}/m_x which had previously been non-existent or very slight. The curve finally adopted was (for both sexes):

$$m_x = a + \frac{b}{1 + \exp\{-\alpha(x - x_1)\}} + c \exp\{-\beta(x - x_2)^2\} \quad (14.11)$$

14.15 The same form of curve was used to produce E.L.T. 12.

14.16 It will be seen that equation (14.11) is a combination of a logistic curve with a symmetrical normal curve. Seven parameters are required for each curve, so that, while this is an interesting experiment in building an empirical model of mortality progression with age, it is a rather complicated method of graduation. It should be borne in mind that in a large experience such as this, covering many millions of lives, random sampling errors are insignificant, and the graduation is concerned only with irregularities arising from misstatements of age which themselves have become of much diminished importance. Graduation is barely required at all. A simple method producing only a very light degree of smoothing would be adequate, and any method designed to be light would be likely to produce as good a graduation as another. King's method was no longer appropriate, but a curve fitting necessitating the calculation of seven parameters may be an overelaborate alternative. In the case of E.L.T. 12 the formula was only applicable from the age of 27 upwards, so that quite a large range of ages still needed to be graduated by other methods.

Assured lives mortality 1949–52

14.17 In 1955, the Continuous Mortality Investigation Committee of the Institute of Actuaries and the Faculty of Actuaries produced a new standard table of mortality based on the pooled experience of the contributing offices for the years 1949–52. A two-year period of selection was adopted. The aggregate table was not in the first instance sub-divided by class of business, but it was decided to give increasing weight at the older ages to the experience in the whole-life with-profit (medical) class. These decisions to accept a degree of heterogeneity and some selection of data necessarily modified the approach to the problem of graduation. The construction of a smooth series of rates was considered more important than the achievement of a degree of fidelity to the data which would satisfy significance tests. The Committee 'hoped, therefore, that a mathematical formula could be found which would give a satisfactory representation of current assured lives' mortality and so provide a good working instrument for life office calculations'. It was not a graduation in the ordinary sense but a search for a suitable shape for the q_x curve for males, the main features of which had to be: (i) an almost flat level of q_x at young ages, (ii) a sharp upward turn between 40 and 55, and (iii) a flattening off in the upper part of the q_x curve.

14.18 The following formula derived by R. E. Beard and clearly related to the Perks family of curves, was used:

$$q_x = A + Bc^x/[Ec^{-2x} + 1 + Dc^x]$$

The parameters were found by trial and error after numerous experiments. The formula made no attempt to reproduce mortality rates decreasing with increasing age at the youngest ages, an effect reflecting deaths from accidents. As a result, the formula gave rates of mortality which were lower than the experience up to nearest age 24, and these were counter-balanced by rates higher than the experience in the age-group 31–5.

Assured lives mortality 1967–70

14.19 When it came to the problem of choosing an appropriate formula for graduating the assured lives mortality experience for 1967–70, the Continuous Mortality Investigation Committee of the Institute and Faculty of Actuaries decided to take a completely fresh look at the problem. The Committee wanted to avoid using a Beard-type shape again for several reasons, but particularly because its use would result in either substantially too low mortality around age 20, or substantially too high mortality around age 30, or something of both.

14.20 At Barnett's suggestion the formula

$$q_x/p_x = A - Hx + Bc^x \qquad (14.12)$$

was tried, and was found to give a satisfactory fit to the experience both for select and ultimate rates. The formula $q_x/p_x = f(x)$ transforms to

$$q_x = f(x)/[1 + f(x)]$$

so that Barnett's formula is equivalent to

$$q_x = \frac{A - Hx + Bc^x}{1 + A - Hx + Bc^x} \qquad (14.13)$$

Clearly this formula could be generalized by introducing different terms in the numerator and denominator. Such elaboration, however, proved unnecessary, and the simpler form was used to graduate the A1967–70 table.

1421 The new formula allowed mortality to decrease at the younger adult ages and produced a very satisfactory graduation. Nevertheless it was criticized on the grounds that it does not readily allow comparison of its parameters with those of other tables at different times (such as the A1949–52) or in other countries. See, for example, Buus (1960) and Wilkie (1976). The use of an *ad hoc* formula for each graduation is not very satisfying, but the single simple mathematical formula applicable to all types of mortality experience and at all times is rather elusive.

Pensioners' and annuitants' mortality 1967–70

14.22 Experiments with the pensioners' experience (1967–70) indicated that

$$q_x = \frac{\exp(F(x))}{1 + \exp(F(x))} \tag{14.14}$$

would be an appropriate formula, where $F(x)$ is a polynomial in x. Clearly

$$p_x = \frac{1}{1 + \exp(F(x))}$$

and the formula may be expressed as

$$\log(q_x/p_x) = F(x) \tag{14.15}$$

The range of $\log(q_x/p_x)$ is potentially from $-\infty$ to ∞, and the function can be represented much more appropriately by a polynomial than q_x, which is constrained to lie between 0 and 1.

14.23 Formula (14.15) was used for all the graduations of the pensioners' and annuitants' experiences in the Second *Report* of the Continuous Mortality Investigation Committee.

A law applicable to the whole life span

14.24 The above 'laws' are only really applicable to the adult ages, and, even then, most of them fail to represent the accident hump at the young adult ages. L. Heligman and J. H. Pollard have obtained promising results over the *entire* life span with the 'law':

$$q_x/p_x = A^{(x+B)^c} + D \exp\left\{-E(\log x - \log F)^2\right\} + GH^x \tag{14.16}$$

Their representation of the Australian national mortality in 1960–62, for example, is shown in Figure 14.3 (males) and Figure 14.4 (females), and in Table 14.2.

14.25 The number of parameters at first sight appears excessive.

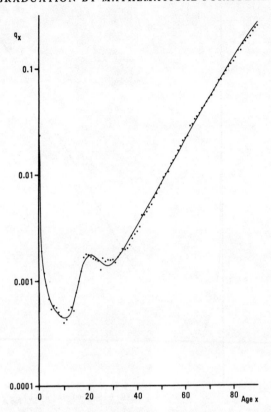

FIGURE 14.3 Graduation of Australian National Mortality Data (Males) 1960–62 by Heligman and Pollard. The observed rates are indicated by dots

However, when it is recalled that the curve reproduces three distinct features—the mortality of a child adapting to its new environment, the mortality associated with the ageing of the body and the superimposed accident mortality—and the 'law' is applicable throughout the life span of more than 100 ages, the number of parameters seems very reasonable. Most of the parameters are also readily interpreted. A, for example, is almost the same as q_1. C measures the rate of decline in mortality in early life (the rate at which a child adapts to his environment). G indicates the level of senescent mortality, while H measures the rate of increase of that mortality. D represents the intensity of the accident hump, while F indicates the location of the hump and E its spread.

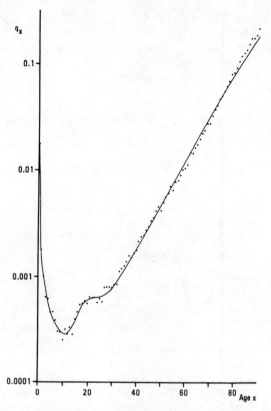

FIGURE 14.4 Graduation of Australian National Mortality Data (Females) 1960–62 by Heligman and Pollard. The observed rates are indicated by dots

Table 14.2 *Graduation parameters for the Australian national mortality experience 1960–62*

Parameter	Males	Females
A	0·00184	0·00177
B	0·0189	0·0303
C	0·1189	0·1309
D	0·001096	0·000254
E	13·552	8·8321
F	20·43	20·37
G	0·0000711	0·0000353
H	1·0992	1·1022

14.26 If the law turns out to be widely applicable, it will allow mortality comparisons to be made between different countries as well as comparisons over time within a particular country.

Estimation of parameters

14.27 The earlier sections of this chapter were devoted to a discussion of mathematical formulae which have been used to graduate mortality data. Little was said, however, about how the parameters in the formulae were estimated. We now direct our attention to that problem.

14.28 In the days before the advent of large-scale computer systems trial and error methods were commonly used (e.g. the A1949–52 table). The trial and error method is still very useful, particularly if the user can work an interactive computer terminal.

14.29 The modern computer has, however, made it possible to estimate the parameters in a graduation formula by statistical methods which have certain optimal properties but were previously computationally prohibitive. The three main methods we shall discuss are:

   (i)   the method of maximum likelihood;
  (ii)   the method of least squares;
 (iii)   the minimum chi-square method.

Maximum likelihood

14.30 Maximum likelihood estimators have a number of desirable features, and for this reason they are widely used by statisticians. The method has also been used by the Continuous Mortality Investigation Committee of the Institute and Faculty of Actuaries to graduate all recent tables. The *principle of maximum likelihood* tells us that we should use, as our estimate of a parameter, that value which maximizes the likelihood of the observed event. (The distinction between *likelihood* and *probability* is explained in a footnote on page 8 of Kendall and Stuart, Vol. 2, 1967.)

14.31 If the exposed to risk at age x is E_x, and the mortality rate at that age is q_x, the number of deaths θ_x has the binomial distribution with parameters E_x and q_x. Furthermore deaths at the various ages in the experience are assumed to be mutually independent.

14.32 The *likelihood* of a particular outcome is

$$L = \prod_x \binom{E_x}{\theta_x} q_x^{\theta_x} p_x^{E_x - \theta_x} \tag{14.17}$$

E_x and θ_x are known. The mortality and survival rates, on the other hand, are unknown. If the underlying mortality is assumed to follow a particular mathematical formula (e.g. Gompertz's 'law'), q_x and p_x will be functions of the unknown parameters in that formula (B and c in the Gompertz case).

14.33 The maximum likelihood estimates of the unknown parameters are the values which maximize (14.17). Those values also maximize

$$\log L = \sum_x \left[\log \binom{E_x}{\theta_x} + \theta_x \log q_x + (E_x - \theta_x) \log p_x \right]$$

and because the first term on the right-hand side of this formula is known and fixed, we deduce that the maximum likelihood estimates of the parameters are those values which maximize

$$\Lambda = \sum_x \left[\theta_x \log q_x + (E_x - \theta_x) \log p_x \right] \tag{14.18}$$

14.34 Simultaneous equations for the maximum likelihood estimates of the unknown parameters can be obtained by equating to zero the first partial derivatives of Λ with respect to the parameters. The resulting equations, however, are usually far too complicated to be of any practical use, and alternative numerical methods must be employed to optimize Λ.

14.35 Computer algorithms are available for this purpose. All of them require the user to provide a sub-routine to calculate the function for given values of the parameters, and many require first partial derivatives as well. Some even require second partial derivatives. An algorithm which does not require the evaluation of any derivatives is that of Nelder and Mead (1965), and a FORTRAN program for this simplex method has been given by O'Neill (1971).

Example 14.2

The mortality data in Table 12.1 were graduated by A. D. Wilkie by means of the mathematical formula

$$\log (q_x/p_x) = a + b(x - 70) \tag{14.19}$$

and the method of maximum likelihood. The exposed to risk and deaths at each age from 35 to 70 were input to the computer, as well as initial trial values $a = -3\cdot0$ and $b = 0\cdot08$, and a sub-routine was written to evaluate Λ.

The maximum likelihood solution obtained was

$$\log (q_x/p_x) = -2\cdot8023721 + 0\cdot085626528(x - 70)$$

and the resulting graduated rates are shown in Table 14.3. Tests on the graduation reveal very good adherence to data. The chi-square value on 34 degrees of freedom (para. 14.56), for example, is $34\cdot6$.

The time required to obtain the graduation was 15 minutes at a computer terminal, and three 5-minute attempts at getting the system right, plus 6 seconds' computer time.

The method of least squares

14.36 The maximum likelihood method for fitting a mathematical formula to mortality data was described in paras 14.32–14.35. An alternative approach is to use 'least squares'.

14.37 Let us imagine that we wish to graduate some mortality data, using the mathematical formula

$$q_x = F(x) \qquad (14.20)$$

$F(x)$ is a given function of x involving unknown parameters $a, b, c, \ldots$

Table 14.3 *Graduation of the mortality data in Table 12.1, using (14.19) and maximum likelihood*

Age x	Graduated $q_x \times 10^5$	Age x	Graduated $q_x \times 10^5$	Age x	Graduated $q_x \times 10^5$
35	302	47	839	59	2,311
36	329	48	914	60	2,512
37	358	49	995	61	2,730
38	390	50	1,083	62	2,967
39	425	51	1,178	63	3,224
40	463	52	1,282	64	3,502
41	504	53	1,395	65	3,803
42	549	54	1,518	66	4,129
43	597	55	1,652	67	4,482
44	650	56	1,797	68	4,863
45	708	57	1,954	69	5,275
46	771	58	2,125	70	5,720

14.38 The observed mortality rate at age x is $\mathring{q}_x$. The value we are attempting to fit at that age is $F(x)$, and the parameters $a, b, c, \ldots$ must be chosen so that the fitted curve $F(x)$ passes as close as possible to the observed $\{\mathring{q}_x\}$.

14.39 A good fit will have been obtained if all the distances between the observed values and the corresponding fitted values are small. The least-squares curve minimizes the sum of the squares of these distances

$$\sum_x [\mathring{q}_x - F(x)]^2 \tag{14.21}$$

and provides a unique solution to the problem.

14.40 The unweighted least-squares approach described above works well when the observed mortality rates are equally reliable (i.e. they have equal variance). This is rarely true in practice, however.

14.41 The observation at age x, for example, might be known to have a very small variance, whereas the variance of the observation at y might be relatively large. In this situation it is desirable that the fitted curve pass very close to $(x, \mathring{q}_x)$ and possibly not as close to $(y, \mathring{q}_y)$. We need a curve-fitting method which will place greater weight on the observation $\mathring{q}_x$ than on $\mathring{q}_y$. The unweighted least-squares method can be readily modified to do this.

14.42 If the variance of the observation at age x is proportional to w_x^{-1}, the appropriate *weighted least-squares* curve is obtained by minimizing

$$\sum_x w_x [\mathring{q}_x - F(x)]^2$$

This criterion should be compared with (14.21). The $\{w_x\}$ are called 'weights'. A large weight at a particular point (corresponding to a small variance) will result in the fitted curve passing very close to that point.

14.43 The variance of $\mathring{q}_x$ is approximately q_x/E_x. The underlying mortality rate q_x is unknown, and we approximate to it in the variance by q_x^s (the mortality rate in a suitable standard table) or by $\mathring{q}_x$. The weighted least-squares criterion which we minimize then becomes

$$\sum_x (E_x/q_x^s)[\mathring{q}_x - F(x)]^2 \tag{14.22}$$

or

$$\sum_x (E_x/\mathring{q}_x)[\mathring{q}_x - F(x)]^2 \tag{14.23}$$

14.44 Simultaneous equations for the weighted least-squares estimates of the unknown parameters can be obtained by equating to zero the first partial derivatives with respect to those parameters of (14.22), or (14.23). Simultaneous linear equations will be obtained when $F(x)$ is linear in the unknown parameters. Otherwise, simultaneous non-linear equations are obtained, and these are usually too complicated to be of any practical use.

14.45 All large-scale computer systems, however, have sophisticated software packages for fitting curves by weighted least squares. The method for formulating the problem in the computer will vary from system to system. It is always necessary, of course, to provide the machine with the data values and the weights. When $F(x)$ is linear in the unknown parameters, a linear least-squares regression routine should be used.

14.46 Non-linear least-squares problems need to be solved iteratively, and the computer routine usually requires starting values for the parameters. In the case of Makeham's formula, for example, we know that c lies between about $1 \cdot 05$ and $1 \cdot 13$, and A and B are both small and positive. Starting values like $A = 0 \cdot 0003$, $B = 0 \cdot 0003$ and $c = 1 \cdot 08$ are usually quite adequate.

14.47 The weights $E_x/\mathring{q}_x$ and E_x/q_x^s suggested in para 14.43 are only approximations to the correct weight E_x/q_x (q_x is the unknown underlying mortality rate). Occasions may arise when it is useful to perform the graduation in two steps: first the calculation of initial graduated rates $\{\mathring{q}_x^{(1)}\}$, using either of the above approximate weights, and then the actual graduation with weights $\{E_x/\mathring{q}_x^{(1)}\}$. Further iteration is unlikely to produce substantial changes in the graduated rates. It is worth noting, however, that if such an iterative approach were adopted, and it converged, the resulting graduation would be the minimum chi-square solution to the estimation problem (para. 14.49).

14.48 The method of weighted least squares can be used to fit formulae to mortality functions other than q_x. The principles are the same, and we now give an example.

Example 14.3

Makeham's 'law' may be expressed in the form

$$-\log p_x = a + \beta e^{\gamma x} \tag{14.24}$$

Graduate the data in Table 12.1 by the method of weighted least squares using this formula.

We note that $-\log \mathring{p}_x \doteq \mathring{q}_x$, so that Var $(-\log \mathring{p}_x) \doteq$ Var $(\mathring{q}_x) \doteq \mathring{q}_x/E_x$. Weights $\{E_x/\mathring{q}_x\}$ can therefore be used. The data supplied to the computer include

(a) the individual ages (x values),
(b) the observed values $-\log \mathring{p}_x$ (y values), and
(c) the weights $E_x/\mathring{q}_x$.

The particular computer package used by the authors to fit (14.24) makes use of the multi-dimensional Newton–Raphson method for solving non-linear equations, and it is necessary to write a small sub-routine to evaluate the function (14.24) and its partial derivatives with respect to α, β and γ.

Starting values $\alpha = 0 \cdot 001$, $\beta = 0 \cdot 001$ and $\gamma = 0 \cdot 09$ were used, and fitted parameter values $\alpha = 0 \cdot 00000$, $\beta = 0 \cdot 00012124$ and $\gamma = 0 \cdot 088604$ were obtained. The graduated mortality rates are shown in Table 14.4. The chi-square goodness-of-fit statistic on 33 degrees of freedom (para. 14.56) is $37 \cdot 7$, which is not significant. Other tests of adherence to data are set as exercise 8.

The usual Makeham parameters are A, B and c (para. 14.3), and

$$\alpha = A$$
$$\beta = B(c-1)/\log c$$
$$\gamma = \log c$$

The weighted least-squares estimates of the A, B and c are therefore

$$\hat{A} = 0 \cdot 000000$$
$$\hat{B} = 0 \cdot 000118$$
$$\hat{c} = 1 \cdot 092648$$

These values should be compared with the values obtained graphically in example 14.1.

14.49 The use of a non-linear least-squares package can sometimes be avoided by linearizing the function which is to be fitted. Makeham's 'law', for example, can be written in the form (14.24). If a trial value of γ is inserted, the formula becomes linear in α and β, and a linear least-squares computer package can be used to estimate α and β. If a series of trial values of the parameter γ are used, a weighted linear least-squares program can be used to evaluate the

Table 14.4 *Graduation of the mortality data in Table 12.1 by Makeham's formula using weighted least squares*

Age x	Crude $\hat{q}_x$	Graduated q_x	Age x	Crude $\hat{q}_x$	Graduated q_x	Age x	Crude $\hat{q}_x$	Graduated q_x
35	·00095	·00269	47	·00779	·00777	59	·02827	·02234
36	·00638	·00294	48	·00862	·00849	60	·01722	·02439
37	·00191	·00321	49	·00951	·00928	61	·02942	·02661
38	·00419	·00350	50	·00866	·01013	62	·03374	·02904
39	·00278	·00383	51	·01109	·01106	63	·02735	·03169
40	·00381	·00419	52	·01291	·01208	64	·02731	·03458
41	·00384	·00458	53	·01274	·01319	65	·04323	·03772
42	·00665	·00500	54	·01579	·01441	66	·04926	·04114
43	·00477	·00546	55	·01873	·01573	67	·04114	·04486
44	·01015	·00596	56	·01482	·01717	68	·04099	·04892
45	·01093	·00652	57	·02002	·01874	69	·05835	·05333
46	·00860	·00711	58	·02011	·02047	70	·06103	·05812

corresponding pairs of values of α and β. The combination of α, β and γ yielding the smallest residual sum of squares provides the least-squares solution to the problem of fitting (14.24) to the data. Although this approach to the problem causes the user more work, it does avoid the use of sometimes troublesome non-linear least-squares programs.

Example 14.4

The graduated rates in Table 14.5 were derived from the data in Table 12.1, using (14.8) as a graduating curve, weights $\{E_x/\mathring{q}_x\}$ and a weighted least-squares program. Starting values $m = 1 \times 10^{-5}$, $\alpha = 0.06$, $n = 1.1 \times 10^{-5}$ and $\beta = 0.10$, were used, and fitted parameter values $m = 0.000022682$, $\alpha = 0.093094$, $n = 0.000077029$, and $\beta = 0.091847$ were obtained. The chi-square goodness-of-fit statistic on 32 degrees of freedom (para. 14.56) is 39·8, which is not significant.

The Makeham formula (14.24) is a special case of (14.8), and at first sight it is a little surprising that the Makeham chi-square value is less than the value just obtained. There are two main reasons for this:

1 The curve-fitting technique used is a least-squares method rather than a minimum chi-square method, and while a reduction in squared standardized deviations will tend to reduce chi-square, the final least-squares graduated rates will not in general coincide with the minimum chi-square rates. (Note, however, that the fully iterative method outlined in para. 14.47 should, if it converges, yield the minimum chi-square solution.)

2 The underlying mortality appears to be Gompertz rather than Makeham (example 14.1). Infinitely many solutions are possible to the problem of fitting (14.8) to a set of (smooth) mortality rates following Gompertz's law, and numerical procedures for fitting (14.8) to mortality data closely approximating Gompertz's law are accordingly rather unstable.

Minimum chi-square

14.50 This is yet another method which can be used to estimate the parameters in a mathematical formula. As the name suggests, the method minimizes the chi-square value for the experience by suitable choice of the parameters. A computer routine is normally required to obtain a numerical solution, and one of the optimization algorithms

Table 14.5 *Graduation of the mortality data in Table 12.1 using (14.8) and the method of weighted least squares*

Age x	Crude $\hat{q}_x$	Graduated q_x	Age x	Crude $\hat{q}_x$	Graduated q_x	Age x	Crude $\hat{q}_x$	Graduated q_x
35	·00095	·00251	47	·00779	·00755	59	·02827	·02263
36	·00638	·00275	48	·00862	·00828	60	·01722	·02479
37	·00191	·00301	49	·00951	·00906	61	·02942	·02714
38	·00419	·00330	50	·00866	·00994	62	·03374	·02973
39	·00278	·00361	51	·01109	·01089	63	·02735	·03255
40	·00381	·00396	52	·01291	·01194	64	·02731	·03564
41	·00384	·00434	53	·01274	·01308	65	·04323	·03901
42	·00665	·00477	54	·01579	·01434	66	·04926	·04269
43	·00477	·00523	55	·01873	·01571	67	·04114	·04671
44	·01015	·00572	56	·01482	·01721	68	·04099	·05111
45	·01093	·00628	57	·02002	·01886	69	·05835	·05590
46	·00860	·00689	58	·02011	·02066	70	·06103	·06113

outlined in para. 14.35 can be used. Alternatively, the iterative method of para. 14.47 might be tried.

Maximum likelihood, least-squares or minimum chi-square?

14.51 The choice between maximum likelihood, least-squares and minimum chi-square is largely a matter of personal preference. Sometimes, however, for a particular formula one of the methods will have a distinct computational advantage. All give approximately the same answer.

14.52 When the exposed-to-risk values $\{E_x\}$ are large at all ages, the normal approximation to the binomial can be used, and the likelihood function for the experience becomes

$$L = \prod_x \frac{1}{\sqrt{(2\pi)}\sqrt{(E_x p_x q_x)}} \exp\left[-\tfrac{1}{2} \frac{(\theta_x - E_x q_x)^2}{E_x p_x q_x} \right]$$

14.53 An approximate maximum likelihood solution can be obtained by replacing the variance of the number of deaths by $E_x q_x^s$ (q_x^s is the mortality rate in a similar standard table). We then maximize

$$L^* = \prod_x \frac{1}{\sqrt{(2\pi)}\sqrt{(E_x q_x^s)}} \exp\left[-\tfrac{1}{2} \frac{(\theta_x - E_x q_x)^2}{E_x q_x^s} \right]$$

which is equivalent to minimizing

$$\Lambda^* = \sum_x E_x (\mathring{q}_x - q_x)^2 / q_x^s$$

and the least-squares solution is obtained.

14.54 Alternatively, we might replace the standard deviation $\sqrt{(E_x p_x q_x)}$ by $\sqrt{\theta_x}$. We then maximize

$$L^{**} = \prod_x \frac{1}{\sqrt{(2\pi)}\sqrt{\theta_x}} \exp\left[-\tfrac{1}{2} \frac{(\theta_x - E_x q_x)^2}{E_x p_x q_x} \right]$$

which is equivalent to minimizing

$$\Lambda^{**} = \sum_x \frac{(\theta_x - E_x q_x)^2}{E_x p_x q_x}$$

and the minimum chi-square solution is obtained.

Tests of adherence to data

14.55 The method of graduation by mathematical formula always produces smooth results. So the question as to whether sufficient smoothness has been attained does not arise. The statistical tests of adherence to data, on the other hand, should always be performed.

14.56 The application of the χ^2 test to a graduation by curve-fitting presents no special features, except that each constant in the equation found from the given data results in the loss of one degree of freedom. (Strictly speaking, one degree of freedom is lost for each *linear* constraint. It should also be noted that if the form of the curve is chosen after a study of the data, a further [unknown] reduction in the number of degrees of freedom should really be made.) The Makeham curve, for example, involves three parameters A, B and c which need to be estimated from the data, and in applying the χ^2 test n-3 degrees of freedom should be used (n denotes the number of separate age-groups used in the χ^2 calculation).

The use of two curves. Blending

14.57 It is often impossible to fit a single curve to the whole of the data, although one curve may be satisfactory at the younger ages and a second curve at the older ages. A satisfactory graduation over the whole age range might be obtained by using the graduated rates from the first table at the younger ages and the graduated rates from the second table at the older ages. The chief difficulty is in passing from one curve to the other and this brings us to the question of *blending* and *blending functions*.

14.58 Suppose that a curve has been fitted to the data at the younger ages, giving graduated values

$$u_0^a, u_1^a, \ldots u_r^a, \overline{u_{r+1}^a, \ldots, u_{s-1}^a}$$

and a second curve at the higher ages, giving graduated values

$$\overline{u_{r+1}^b, u_{r+2}^b, \ldots u_{s-1}^b}\, u_s^b, u_{s+1}^b, \ldots$$

The two curves overlap, and the overlapping values are indicated by brackets.

14.59 The problem is to combine or fuse the overlapping values in such a way that the final values pass smoothly from the first curve, which gives values up to and including age r, to the second curve, which gives values from age s onwards. Let us assume that a typical blended function u_{r+t} is given by

$$u_{r+t} = \kappa_{r+t} u_{r+t}^a + \lambda_{r+t} u_{r+t}^b$$

where

$$\kappa_{r+t} + \lambda_{r+t} = 1$$
$$\kappa_r = 1$$
$$\kappa_s = 0$$
$$\lambda_r = 0$$
$$\lambda_s = 1$$

It is usual (though not essential) to make the symmetry assumption $\kappa_{r+t} = \lambda_{s-t}$.

14.60 κ_{r+t} and λ_{r+t} can be thought of as continuous functions of t which are evaluated at $t = 0, 1, 2, \ldots$ For a smooth transition from the first graduation curve to the second, it is essential that the derivative of κ_{r+t} with respect to t be zero at $t = 0$, and the second and third derivatives be close to zero, so that the blending function has little curvature at either end.

14.61 The range of values over which blending is carried out needs to be fairly large to produce a smooth transition. Much will depend on the differences between the pairs of overlapping values and also on the differences in gradient and curvature of the two main curves at the ends of the blending range. We return to these problems in paras 14.67–14.68.

The curve of sines

14.62 The sine curve moves smoothly from $+1$ and zero gradient at $\pi/2$ to -1 and zero gradient at $3\pi/2$. It follows that a reasonable blending curve is given by

$$\kappa_{r+t} = \tfrac{1}{2}\left\{1 + \sin\left(\frac{\pi}{2} + \frac{t\pi}{s-r}\right)\right\} = \tfrac{1}{2}\left(1 + \cos\frac{t\pi}{s-r}\right) \quad (14.25)$$

which is one at $t = 0$ and zero at $t = s - r$, and has zero slope at both these points. The absolute value of the second derivative at either end is $\tfrac{1}{2}\pi^2/(s-r)^2$ or about $5/(s-r)^2$. We note that $\lambda_{s-t} = \kappa_{r+t}$.

14.63 The curvature of the blending function will be small at both ends of the range, provided $s - r$ is fairly large (say 10 or over).

The curve of squares

14.64 Another popular blending function is obtained by combining two parabolas, and is known as the 'curve of squares':

$$\kappa_{r+t} = \begin{cases} 1 - 2\left(\dfrac{t}{s-r}\right)^2, & t \le \dfrac{s-r}{2} \\ 2\left(1 - \dfrac{t}{s-r}\right)^2, & t \ge \dfrac{s-r}{2} \end{cases}$$

14.65 The slope at either end of the range is zero, and the absolute value of the second derivative is $4/(s-r)^2$. A reasonable value of $s-r$ (say 10 or more) will make the curvature quite small at both ends of the range. It will be noticed that, as before, $\lambda_{s-t} = \kappa_{r+t}$.

14.66 Although the curve of squares has a slightly smaller curvature at the ends of the range than the curve of sines, the more natural curve of sines is to be preferred to the rather artificial curve of squares. In practice the use of either method is likely to give similar results.

Limitations of blending—alternative methods

14.67 Blending can be relied upon to give good results if the two main curves do not intersect (Figure 14.5) or they intersect twice (Figure 14.6). When the two curves to be blended intersect only once, the methods of paras 14.57–14.66 are unlikely to give the best results, because the blended curve is dragged out of its natural course, and constrained to pass through the point of intersection (Figure 14.7).

14.68 Generally speaking, therefore, when the two main curves intersect only once near the point where blending is to be effected, it is preferable to pass from one curve to the other by a process of

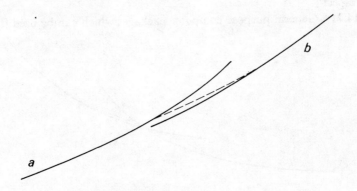

FIGURE 14.5 The blending of two non-intersecting curves

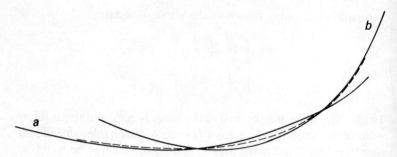

FIGURE 14.6   The blending of two curves which intersect twice

osculatory interpolation (para. 16.7). A third degree polynomial is convenient for this purpose because it involves four constants. We can arrange for the interpolating curve to pass through u_r^a and have the same gradient as the a-curve at that point, and to pass through u_s^b with the same gradient as the b-curve at that point (exercise 7).

Advantages of graduation by mathematical formulae

14.69   The greatest advantage is that the results are ideally smooth. If the same form of curve is fitted to mortality data at different epochs, a study of the changes in the parameters at the curve may throw light on the way mortality is changing and assist in the projection of future mortality. See, for example, A. H. Pollard (1949).

14.70   The fitting procedure itself will often cause the total deviation (actual deaths – expected deaths) and the accumulated deviation to be zero or very close to zero. So the fit should be satisfactory in this respect.

14.71   General purpose computer packages which can be used for

FIGURE 14.7   The blending of two curves which intersect only once

fitting purposes are available. These routines take account of the weight of data at each age.

14.72 The use of Makeham's and closely allied curves enables the calculation of complicated functions to be simplified greatly.

Disadvantages of curve-fitting

14.73 It may be difficult to find a suitable curve; but families of curves, (e.g. $\log q_x$ = polynomial) allow for many possibilities; these possibilities have not yet been fully explored. Once an appropriate curve has been found, the subsequent work can usually be automated. In practice many attempts have to be made, and quick results can be produced only if one of the earlier experiments proves successful. Access to an interactive computer terminal is an advantage during the trial period.

14.74 It is doubtful whether a simple single curve can ever be fitted successfully to heterogeneous data.

REFERENCES

Buus, H. (1960). Investigation of mortality variations. *Trans. 16th International Congress of Actuaries*, **3**, 364.

Continuous Mortality Investigation Committee (1974). Considerations affecting the preparation of standard tables of mortality. *J. Inst. Actu.*, **101**, 135–216; and *T.F.A.*, **34**, 135.

Continuous Mortality Investigation *Reports*, No. 2 (1976), Institute of Actuaries and Faculty of Actuaries.

Gompertz, B. (1825). On the nature of the function of the law of human mortality and on a new mode of determining the value of life contingencies. *Phil. Trans. of Royal Society*, **115**, 513–85.

Heligman, L. and Pollard, J. H. (1980) The age pattern of mortality. *J. Inst. Actu.*, **107**, (in press).

Kendall, M. G. and Stuart, A. (1967) *The Advanced Theory of Statistics*, Vol. 2, *Inference and Relationship*, second edition, Griffin, London.

Makeham, W. M. (1860). On the law of mortality. *J. Inst. Actu.*, **13**, 325–58.

Nelder, J. A. and Mead, R. (1965). A simplex method for function minimisation. *Computer J.*, **7**, 308–13.

O'Neill, R. (1971). Algorithm AF47. Function minimisation using a simplex procedure. *J.R.S.S.*, Series C, **20**, 338–45.

Perks, W. F. (1932). On some experiments in the graduation of mortality statistics. *J. Inst. Actu.* **63**, 12–40.

Pollard, A. H. (1949) Methods of forecasting mortality using Australian data. *J. Inst. Actu.*, **75**, 151–70.

Wilkie, A. D. (1976) An international comparison of recent trends in population mortality. *Trans. of 20th International Congress of Actuaries*, **3**, 761.

EXERCISES FOR CHAPTER FOURTEEN

1 Use the method of paras 14.5–14.10 to fit a Makeham curve to the data in Table 14.6.

Table 14.6

Age-group	Initial exposed to risk	Deaths
40–44	15,518	65
45–49	19,428	144
50–54	21,594	219
55–59	21,890	378
60–64	19,174	465
65–69	15,775	557
70–74	11,414	683
75–79	6,993	644
80–84	3,276	471
85–89	1,096	217
90–94	201	67

2 Use a trial value of c and a weighted simple linear regression package to perform a Makeham graduation of the data in question 1.

3 Use a weighted non-linear least-squares program to fit a Makeham curve to the mortality data in question 1.

4 Graduate the data in Table 12.1 by the maximum likelihood method, using the formula

$$\log (q_x/p_x) = a + bx + cx^2$$

5 The following blending function has been proposed by a student:

$$\kappa_{r+t} = \tfrac{1}{2} + \tfrac{1}{2}\left\{1 - \frac{4t^2}{(s-r)^2}\right\}^{\frac{1}{2}}, \quad 0 \le t \le \frac{s-r}{2};$$

$$\kappa_{r+t} = \tfrac{1}{2} - \tfrac{1}{2}\left\{1 - \frac{4(s-r-t)^2}{(s-r)^2}\right\}^{\frac{1}{2}}, \quad \frac{s-r}{2} \le t \le s-r$$

(i) Sketch the blending curve.
(ii) Comment on its suitability.
(iii) Mention any difficulties which you foresee in the use of this particular function.

6 The polynomial

$$\kappa_{r+t} = a + bt + ct^2 + dt^3$$

can be used as a blending function if the values of $a, b, c,$ and d are chosen in such a way that

$$[\kappa_{r+t}]_{t=0} = 1 \qquad \left[\frac{d}{dt}\kappa_{r+t}\right]_{t=0} = 0$$

$$[\kappa_{r+t}]_{t=s-r} = 0 \qquad \left[\frac{d}{dt}\kappa_{r+t}\right]_{t=s-r} = 0$$

Find a, b, c and d, and prove that the absolute value of the second derivative at either end of the range is $6/(s-r)^2$.

7   Table 14.7 shows certain values of q_x extracted from two different life tables (A and B).

Table 14.7

Age	q_x^A	q_x^B	Age	q_x^A	q_x^B
39	·00531	·00635	46	·00861	·00832
40	·00562	·00658	47	·00925	·00869
41	·00598	·00683	48	·00990	·00910
42	·00639	·00710	49	·01057	·00957
43	·00687	·00738	50	·01128	·01010
44	·00741	·00768	51	·01206	·01070
45	·00799	·00799			

(i)   Blend the two series to obtain values of q_x passing from the table A values at ages 42 and under to the table B values at ages 48 and over.

(ii)   Criticize the junction effected and state reasons for any unsatisfactory feature.

(iii)   Use the method of osculatory interpolation outlined in para. 14.68 to obtain a more suitable series fulfilling the same conditions.

8   Examine thoroughly the adherence to data of the graduation in Table 14.4.

CHAPTER FIFTEEN

GRADUATION BY REFERENCE TO A STANDARD TABLE

15.1 When the data are scanty but are known or suspected to come from an experience similar to that for which a standard (graduated) table already exists, it may be possible to use this standard table as a 'base curve' for graduating the new data. There are many ways in which this can be done. One of the simplest is to calculate the ratios of the q's derived from the data to the corresponding q's of the standard table and to graduate these ratios. Any one of the standard graduation methods can be used for this purpose.

15.2 The ratios suggested in para. 15.1 are successive values of $\mathring{q}_x/q_x^s$. Since the standard table is believed to be similar to that underlying the experience, no value of the ratio should vary too much from unity. It may therefore be feasible to graduate the ratios graphically on one diagram and hence produce a set of graduated rates of mortality from what appeared to be inadequate data.

15.3 The choice of the standard table is important, since any special feature in its graduation will be reproduced, even exaggerated, in the graduation of the new data.

Lidstone's transformation

15.4 Lidstone (1892) improved on this method by dealing not with the ratio $\mathring{q}_x/q_x^s$ but with $\log(p_x^s/\mathring{p}_x)$. This function produces values which are not only smaller than $\mathring{q}_x/q_x^s$ but usually progress more smoothly, and are more readily drawn.

15.5 It is worth noting that if the unknown underlying force of mortality μ_x and the standard table force of mortality μ_x^s are connected by the linear relation

$$\mu_x = \mu_x^s + c$$

where c is a constant, all the values of p_x will bear a constant ratio to the corresponding values of p_x^s, and the function $\log(p_x^s/p_x)$ will be a straight line parallel to the x-axis.

15.6 Lidstone graduated $\log(p_x^s/\hat{p}_x)$ graphically. In the following example we graduate Lidstone's function by a mathematical formula.

Example 15.1

Graduate the mortality data in Table 12.1, using Lidstone's transformation and English Life Table 12 (Males) as standard.

The observed mortality rates are listed in column (4) of Table 15.1, and the standard mortality rates are shown in column (5). The graduated survival rate at age x will be denoted by $\hat{p}_x$.

The values of $\log(p_x^s/\hat{p}_x)$ are small and vary considerably. Some of this variation can be removed by taking a running average of seven terms—column (6). The averaged values appear to increase initially with age, then drop away, and possibly increase again at the older ages. Let us therefore fit a cubic relationship of the form

$$\log(p_x^s/\hat{p}_x) = b_0 + b_1 x + b_2 x^2 + b_3 x^3 \qquad (15.1)$$

$$var \log \frac{p_x^s}{\hat{p}_x} = var[\log \hat{p}_x] = var[-(\log(1-\hat{q}_x))]$$
$$\doteq var[-(-\hat{q}_x \hat{p}_x^s)]$$

by the method of weighted least squares. The variance of $\log(p_x^s/\hat{p}_x)$ is approximately the same as the variance of $\mathring{q}_x$, which is q_x/E_x. The underlying mortality rate q_x is unknown, and we approximate to it in the variance by using the E.L.T. 12 rate q_x^s. The approximate weight at age x is therefore E_x/q_x^s—column (7) in Table 15.1. A weighted least-squares computer package was used to fit the cubic (15.1), and the resulting graduated mortality rates are listed in column (8) of Table 15.1. The graduated rates are also depicted in Figure 15.1.

Adherence to data appears to be satisfactory. The chi-square value, for example, on 32 degrees of freedom (para. 15.18) is 33·2, and seventeen of the thirty-six deviations between the observed and fitted deaths are positive. There are twenty-one changes of sign, and the number of positive groups, 11, exceeds the expected number of 9.4. Other tests of adherence to data (particularly tests on the cumulative deviations) should also be applied.

English Life Table 12 was graduated by mathematical formula, and is therefore ideally smooth. Furthermore a mathematical relationship was fitted between the experience mortality and that of E.L.T. 12. It is not necessary, therefore, to examine the smoothness of the graduated rates.

Other formulae

15.7 Although Lidstone's transformation was originally used in

Table 15.1   *Graduation of the mortality data in Table 12.1 by reference to English Life Table 12 (Males), using Lidstone's transformation and the method of least squares*

Age	Exposed	Deaths	Observed	Standard	$\dfrac{[7]}{7}\log(p^s_x/\hat{p}_x)$	Weight	Graduated
x	E_x	θ_x	$\mathring{q}_x \times 10^5$	$q^s_x \times 10^5$	$\times 10^4$	$(E_x/q^s_x) \times 10^{-2}$	$\hat{q}_x \times 10^5$
(1)	(2)	(3)	(4)	(5)	(6)	(7)	(8)
35	1,051	1	95	155	—	6,781	194
36	940	6	638	167	—	5,629	269
37	1,048	2	191	181	—	5,790	337
38	716	3	419	196	14	3,653	399
39	719	2	278	214	20	3,360	458
40	1,051	4	381	235	16	4,472	513
41	1,042	4	384	259	25	4,023	564
42	1,804	12	665	287	32	6,286	614
43	1,468	7	477	319	37	4,602	663
44	1,576	16	1,015	356	39	4,427	712
45	1,647	18	1,093	399	41	4,128	762
46	1,861	16	860	448	40	4,154	814
47	1,669	13	779	505	40	3,305	871
48	1,624	14	862	570	35	2,849	932
49	1,157	11	951	644	30	1,797	999
50	2,193	19	866	728	27	3,012	1,074
51	1,803	20	1,109	823	29	2,191	1,158
52	2,402	31	1,291	930	33	2,583	1,251
53	2,120	27	1,274	1,051	28	2,017	1,358
54	2,406	38	1,579	1,184	31	2,032	1,476
55	1,975	37	1,873	1,331	29	1,484	1,607
56	2,564	38	1,482	1,492	35	1,718	1,753
57	1,798	36	2,002	1,668	23	1,078	1,913
58	2,536	51	2,011	1,859	24	1,364	2,089
59	2,511	71	2,828	2,065	25	1,216	2,282
60	1,858	32	1,722	2,287	20	812	2,492
61	1,835	54	2,943	2,525	6	727	2,719
62	1,393	47	3,374	2,778	14	501	2,965
63	1,462	40	2,736	3,049	17	480	3,230
64	1,245	34	2,731	3,339	22	373	3,518
65	1,064	46	4,323	3,648	7	292	3,828
66	1,502	74	4,927	3,978	9	378	4,163
67	875	36	4,114	4,332	22	202	4,526
68	927	38	4,099	4,712	—	197	4,919
69	497	29	5,835	5,122	—	97	5,347
70	983	60	6,104	5,566	—	177	5,814

conjunction with the graphic method of graduation, we saw in example 15.1 that the transformation can also be useful before graduation by mathematical formula. The mathematical formula

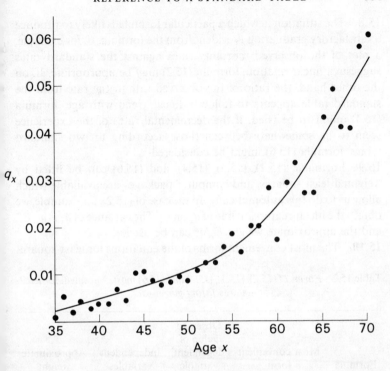

FIGURE 15.1 Graphical representation of the graduated mortality rates in Table 15.1. The observed mortality rates are indicated by dots. The graduation was by reference to English Life Table 12 (Males), using Lidstone's transformation and the weighted least-squares fitting of a mathematical formula (example 15.1)

used in the example is given as (15.1). Other formulae for graduation by reference to a standard table have also been suggested, for example,

$$q_x = aq_x^s + b \tag{15.2}$$

$$\mu_x = a\mu_x^s + b \tag{15.3}$$

$$q_x = q_x^s(ax + b) \tag{15.4}$$

$$\mu_x = \mu_{x+n}^s + K \tag{15.5}$$

$$q_x = aq_x^{(1)} + bq_x^{(2)} \tag{15.6}$$

In these equations a, b, K and n are constants; $q_x^{(1)}$ refers to one standard table and $q_x^{(2)}$ to a second.

15.8 The situation in which a particular formula is likely to produce a satisfactory graduation is evident from the formula. If, for example, a plot of the observed mortality rates against the standard rates suggests a linear relation, formula (15.2) may be appropriate. If, on the other hand, the ratio of the observed rate to the rate from the standard table appears to follow a linear trend with age, formula (15.4) ought to be tried. If the decremental rates of the experience seem to lie somewhere between those according to two standard tables, formula (15.6) might be considered.

15.9 Formulae (15.2), (15.3), (15.4), and (15.6) can be fitted by weighted least squares, and computer packages are available which allow us to do this automatically. In the case of (15.2), for example, we obtain the linear regression line of q_x on q_x^s. The variance of $\mathring{q}_x$ is q_x/E_x, and the approximate weight E_x/q_x^s can be used.

15.10 The most convenient forms of the equations for least-squares

Table 15.2 *Forms of (15.2), (15.3), (15.4) and (15.6) most convenient for least-squares fitting purposes*

Formula	Most convenient form	Observed value of 'dependent' variable	'Independent' variables		Approximate weight
(15.2)	$q_x = aq_x^s + b$	$\mathring{q}_x$	q_x^s	1	E_x/q_x^s
(15.3)	$\log p_x = a \log p_x^s - b$	$\log \mathring{p}_x$	$\log p_x^s$	-1	E_x/q_x^s
(15.4)	$q_x/q_x^s = ax + b$	$\mathring{q}_x/q_x^s$	x	1	E_x/q_x^s
(15.6)	$q_x = aq_x^{(1)} + bq_x^{(2)}$	$\mathring{q}_x$	$q_x^{(1)}$	$q_x^{(2)}$	$2E_x/(q_x^{(1)}+q_x^{(2)})$

fitting purposes are shown in Table 15.2. The observed values of the 'dependent' variables, the 'independent' variables and the weights, all of which need to be supplied to the least-squares computer package, are also shown in this table.

15.11 Formula (15.5) cannot be fitted by weighted least squares in a straightforward manner. Indeed, except when Makeham's law applies, it is not possible to find n other than by trial and error. It should be noted, however, that the formula implies the following relation:

$$\log(p_{x+n}^s/p_x) = K. \tag{15.7}$$

The variance of $\log(p_{x+n}^s/p_x)$ is approximately the same as the variance of $\mathring{q}_x$, which is close to q^s_{x+n}/E_x. For a given trial value of n, therefore, a weighted estimate of K is provided by

$$\left\{\sum_x W_x \log(p^s_{x+n}/\mathring{p}_x)\right\}/\left\{\sum_x W_x\right\} \tag{15.8}$$

where
$$W_x = E_x/q^s_{x+n} \tag{15.9}$$

Graduated mortality rates can be calculated by means of the formula

$$\hat{q}_x = 1 - p^s_{x+n}e^{-K}. \tag{15.10}$$

15.12   The complete graduation process, in respect of formula (15.5), may be summarized as follows:

1   A trial value of n is chosen.
2   K is estimated, using (15.8).
3   Graduated mortality rates are obtained via (15.10).
4   The chi-square goodness-of-fit statistic is computed.
5   Steps 1 to 4 are repeated for different values of n.
6   The graduation with the smallest chi-square value is chosen.
7   This graduation is examined for adherence to data.

Iteration

15.13   The weights suggested in example 15.1 and Table 15.2 are only approximations to the correct but unknown weights. Occasions may arise when it is useful to perform a weighted least-squares graduation in two steps: first, the calculation of initial graduated rates $\{\hat{q}^{(1)}_x\}$, using the suggested approximate weights; then the actual graduation with weights based on the $\{\hat{q}^{(1)}_x\}$. Further iteration is unlikely to produce substantial changes in the graduated rates. If iteration is attempted, however, and the rate at each age converges to a limit, the solution obtained approximates to the minimum chi-square fit.

Hand-computational methods

15.14   Simple hand-computational methods are available for fitting formulae (15.2), (15.3), (15.4) and (15.6). Although these methods are not optimal in the weighted least-squares sense or the minimum chi-square sense, they usually produce reasonable results. In the case of (15.2), for example, it is easy to see that

$$\begin{aligned}\Sigma E_x q_x &= a\Sigma E_x q^s_x + b\Sigma E_x\\ \Sigma\Sigma E_x q_x &= a\Sigma\Sigma E_x q^s_x + b\Sigma\Sigma E_x\end{aligned}\quad\left.\right\} \tag{15.11}$$

the program 'sum'

$E_x q_x^s$ is the expected deaths at age x according to the standard table, and $E_x q_x$ is the expected number of deaths according to the unknown mortality table we are trying to estimate. Values for the constants a and b can be estimated by replacing the expected deaths $\{E_x q_x\}$ by the observed deaths $\{\theta_x\}$ and solving the simultaneous equations

$$\left.\begin{array}{l} a\Sigma E_x q_x^s + b\Sigma E_x = \Sigma \theta_x \\ a\Sigma\Sigma E_x q_x^s + b\Sigma\Sigma E_x = \Sigma\Sigma \theta_x \end{array}\right\} \quad (15.12)$$

The first of these equations is formed by summing all the available expected deaths, exposed to risk and observed deaths. The second equation is obtained by summing the cumulative sums. Different double sums will be obtained, depending upon whether the accumulation is from the bottom or top of the table. The solutions for a and b, however, are unaffected.

15.15 The most convenient forms of formulae (15.2), (15.3), (15.4) and (15.6) for hand-fitting purposes are shown in Table 15.3 Formula (15.5) can be fitted by hand, using the method of paras 15.11–15.12.

15.16 When the data are grouped and E_x is not available for individual ages, the expected deaths are usually calculated by using q_x for the central age of the group: e.g. for a group of five ages 30–34, q_{32} would be used, while for a group of four ages 30–33, $q_{31\frac{1}{2}}$ would be used. This is not strictly correct, but the slight error introduced is not usually a serious matter when the data are scanty and sampling errors are considerable.

Example 15.2

In this example we demonstrate the hand-computational method for fitting formula (15.2) to the mortality data in Table 15.4. We shall use as our standard table English Life Table 12 (Males).

Table 15.3 *Equations summed and double-summed to fit formulae (15.2), (15.3), (15.4) and (15.6) by hand*

Formula	Equation
(15.2)	$(E_x q_x^s)a + (E_x)b = \theta_x$
(15.3)	$(\log p_x^s)a - b = \log \hat{p}_x$
(15.4)	$(xE_x q_x^s)a + (E_x q_x^s)b = \theta_x$
(15.6)	$(E_x q_x^{(1)})a + (E_x q_x^{(2)})b = \theta_x$

Table 15.4 *A mortality experience*

Age-group	Exposed	Deaths	Observed mortality rate $\times 10^5$	Central age
35–44	1,053	4	380	40
45–49	1,663	13	782	47
50–54	2,397	30	1,252	52
55–59	1,803	35	1,941	57
60–64	1,400	47	3,357	62

The sums and double sums needed to compute a and b are calculated in Table 15.5. When we solve the simultaneous equations

$$102 \cdot 2a + 8,316b = 129$$
$$212 \cdot 1a + 24,114b = 279$$

we obtain $a = 1 \cdot 12834$, $b = 0 \cdot 001646$.

The graduated mortality rates at the individual years of age can then be calculated by means of the formula

$$\hat{q}_x = aq_x^s + b$$

The graduated rates at the central ages, for example, are listed in the final column of Table 15.5.

English life Table 12 was graduated by mathematical formula, and we have used a mathematical formula to derive the graduated rates in this example from the English Life Table rates. We do not, therefore, need to examine the smoothness of our rates. It is *essential*, however, that the rates be tested for adherence to data.

Statistical tests of adherence to data

15.17 The standard table will normally be smooth. If, therefore, the graduation method used to connect the experience and standard mortalities is one which always produces smooth results, the graduated mortality rates will be smooth, and there is no need to examine smoothness. It is *always* necessary to check adherence to data, however, and the tests of Chapter 11 should be applied.

15.18 Each constant estimated from the data results in the loss of one degree of freedom in the chi-square test. Two degrees of freedom should therefore be subtracted for each of the formulae in para. 15.7. The choice of standard table(s) also imposes constraints on the

Table 15.5 Work sheet for example 15.2

Age-group (1)	Central age x (2)	Exposed E_x (3)	ΣE_x (4)	Standard $q_x^s \times 10^5$ (5)	$E_x q_x^s$ (6)	$\Sigma E_x q_x^s$ (7)	Deaths θ_x (8)	$\Sigma \theta_x$ (9)	Graduated $\hat{q}_x \times 10^5$ (10)
35–44	40	1,053	1,053	235	2·5	2·5	4	4	430
45–49	47	1,663	2,716	505	8·4	10·9	13	17	734
50–54	52	2,397	5,113	930	22·3	33·2	30	47	1,214
55–59	57	1,803	6,916	1,668	30·1	63·3	35	82	2,047
60–64	62	1,400	8,316	2,778	38·9	102·2	47	129	3,299
Total	—	8,316	24,114	—	102·2	212·1	129	279	—

system, and an unknown further reduction in degrees of freedom should be made to take this into account. The reduction depends upon the extent to which the choice of standard table was based on the data. Although it is impossible to quantify the reduction, the graduator must be aware of the additional constraints imposed.

Advantages of the method

15.19 The method of graduation by reference to a standard table is not generally used for standard tables, and is therefore seldom discussed in the actuarial literature. The method, however, is particularly valuable when the data are scanty, so that most other methods are out of the question. In such cases even a graphic graduation would be largely guesswork.

15.20 If the standard table is smooth (as it certainly should be) and a mathematical formula has been fitted connecting the experience and the standard table mortality rates, the graduated rates will be satisfactory as far as smoothness is concerned, and it is possible to concentrate on tests for adherence to data. Knowledge of other tables based on similar experiences is automatically brought into use in the process of graduation. The method can be adapted to select tables, but with scanty data the select rates themselves are suspect, as the sampling errors are so great. The ends of the table cause little difficulty, but the reliability of the results may of course be doubtful.

Disadvantages of the method

15.21 It is not always possible to find a suitable standard table, so that even if the constants in the graduation formula are chosen properly, the adherence of the results to the rough data is not satisfactory.

REFERENCE

Lidstone, G. J. (1892). On an application of the graphic method to obtain a graduated mortality table. *J. Inst. Actu.*, **30**, 212; Reprints, 1935.

EXERCISES FOR CHAPTER FIFTEEN

1 (a) Prove that the variance of $\log(p_x^s/\mathring{p}_x)$ is approximately the same as the variance of $\mathring{q}_x$.

   (b) Deduce that var $\{\log(p_x^s/\mathring{p}_x)\} \doteqdot q_x^s/E_x$.

2 Prove that var $(\mathring{q}_x/q_x^s) \doteqdot 1/(E_x q_x^s)$.

3 Graduate the data in Table 11.4 by reference to a standard table using formula (15.3).

4　Graduate the data in Table 11.4 by reference to two standard tables using formula (15.6).

5　Use the iterative method of para. 15.13, formula (15.2) of para. 15.7, and English Life Table 12 (Males) as standard to graduate the mortality data in Table 12.1.

6　Describe a weighted least-squares method for graduating mortality data by reference to standard tables, using the formula

$$q_x = (ax + b)q_x^{(1)} + cq_x^{(2)}$$

(a, b and c are unknown constants; $q_x^{(1)}$ refers to one standard table and $q_x^{(2)}$ to a second).

7　Show that the hand-computational method of summation and double summation (paras 15.14–15.16) is equivalent to the statistical estimation procedure known as the 'method of moments' when the age-groups of the experience are equal in width.

CHAPTER SIXTEEN

OSCULATORY INTERPOLATION AND SPLINE GRADUATION: ABRIDGED AND MODEL LIFE TABLES

16.1 Before 1911 five-year age-groups were used in the censuses of England and Wales instead of individual ages. To produce an English Life Table, it was therefore necessary to adopt a graduation method applicable to quinquennially grouped data. Individual ages were used from 1911 onwards but local misstatements of age (preferences for even ages or multiples of five) continued to be a problem for some time. The effects of these local misstatements were usually reduced by grouping the data in quinquennial age groups.

16.2 Local misstatement of age is still a problem in a number of countries. The extent of the problem in the 1965 census of Turkey for example, is indicated in Figure 16.1. Age 33 is unpopular, because it is odd. The even age 32 on the other hand is a little more popular. Age 31 is very unpopular because it is odd and alongside the very popular age 30. Age 34 would be more popular as an even number but for the fact that it lies alongside 35. This basic pattern is repeated again and again in Figure 16.1.

King's method

16.3 Because of the size of national populations, random variations in the observed death rates are very small. It follows that provided the effects of local misstatements of age are overcome, the graduating power of the method adopted does not need to be very great.

16.4 The method of pivotal values and osculatory interpolation was devised by George King to reduce the effects of age misstatement and provide mild graduation, and was used to produce English Life Tables 7 to 10. It is perhaps the method of least general application.

16.5 The exposed to risk at the various ages in a national population tend to follow a regular pattern. Misstatement of age is usually more pronounced in census data than in deaths, and King's

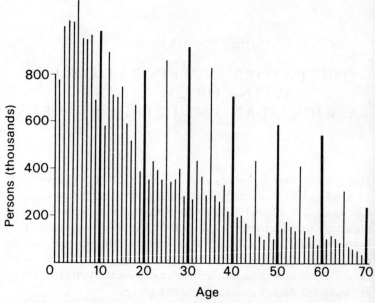

FIGURE 16.1 The population of Turkey by age (1965 census)

method was used to graduate separately the exposed to risk and deaths and so reduce the effects of age misstatement. Graduated mortality rates were obtained by division.

16.6 The method may be summarized as follows:

1 The exposed to risk are grouped into quinquennial age-groups.
2 A pivotal exposed to risk value is calculated for the central age of each group, using (16.3) below.
3 Graduated exposed to risk values at the remaining ages are found by osculatory interpolation, using (16.4).
4 Graduated deaths are obtained by applying steps 1 to 3 to the observed deaths.
5 Graduated mortality rates are found by division.

16.7 When ordinary interpolation is applied along sections of a curve one by one, a continuous curve is obtained, but the derivatives of the interpolating arcs are discontinuous at the pivots. The curve lacks smoothness. Osculatory interpolation helps overcome this difficulty by ensuring that the more important derivatives are also continuous at the joins of the sections. The curves join smoothly or 'kiss'—hence the name 'osculatory interpolation'.

16.8 King's pivotal value formula is derived in paras 16.10–16.13 and the osculatory interpolation formula in paras 16.14–16.19. A numerical example follows para. 16.20.

16.9 Although the method of pivotal values and osculatory interpolation was originally devised so that it could be applied separately to the exposed to risk and deaths, it can also be applied directly to the crude mortality rates, provided age misstatement is not serious. This approach was in fact tried with English Life Table 9 (1921) and the rates obtained were very similar to those produced by operating on populations and deaths separately. The method is now largely of historical interest, although it does provide a useful introduction to spline graduation and the formation of abridged life tables.

King's pivotal value formula

Know method but not all details of proof.

16.10 King's pivotal value formula gives the value of a single central ordinate in terms of sums of equally spaced ordinates. To derive it, we consider a third degree polynomial u_x and define

$$w_{-1} = [n]u_{-n}; \; w_0 = [n]u_0; \; w_1 = [n]u_n$$

16.11 In the usual case $n = 5$ and

$$w_{-1} = u_{-7} + u_{-6} + u_{-5} + u_{-4} + u_{-3}$$

$$w_0 = u_{-2} + u_{-1} + u_0 + u_1 + u_2$$

$$w_1 = u_3 + u_4 + u_5 + u_6 + u_7$$

16.12 We require a formula for u_0 in terms of w_{-1}, w_0 and w_1. According to (13.1),

$$w_0 = [n]u_0 = nu_0 + \frac{n(n^2-1)}{24}\Delta^2 u_{-1} \tag{16.1}$$

$$w_{-1} + w_0 + w_1 = [3n]u_0 = 3nu_0 + \frac{3n(9n^2-1)}{24}\Delta^2 u_{-1} \tag{16.2}$$

Subtracting three times (16.1) from (16.2), we obtain

$$\Delta^2 w_{-1} = n^3 \Delta^2 u_{-1}$$

Substituting $(\Delta^2 w_{-1})/n^3$ for $\Delta^2 u_{-1}$ in (16.1) and rearranging we obtain King's pivotal value formula:

$$u_0 = \frac{1}{n}\left\{w_0 - \frac{(n^2-1)}{24n^2}\Delta^2 w_{-1}\right\} \tag{16.3}$$

16.13 The smoothing effect of a sum was noted in para. 13.4. By forming the sums $\{w_j\}$ we reduce the effects of age misstatements and graduate the data slightly.

King's osculatory interpolation formula

16.14 Let us imagine that we wish to interpolate between the pivotal points B and C in Figure 16.2, by means of a polynomial of degree three. The fact that the curve must pass through B and C imposes two constraints. If we impose two further constraints by insisting that the slope of the curve at B be the same as the slope of the AB section of the curve at B, and the slope of the curve at C be the same as the slope of the CD section of the curve at C, the cubic interpolation curve is fully determined.

16.15 The interpolating cubic may be obtained in the following manner:

1   Fit a quadratic through A, B, C (three constants; three points). Calculate the gradient at B.
2   Fit a quadratic through B, C, D (three constants; three points): Calculate the gradient at C.
3   Fit a cubic through B, C (4 constants; 2 points and 2 gradients). The two gradients are those calculated in 1 and 2 above.

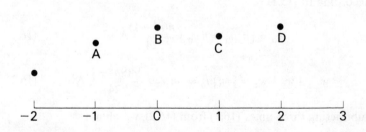

FIGURE 16.2   Development of King's osculatory interpolation formula

The resulting interpolation curve is continuous and has continuous first derivative at the pivotal points.

16.16 The quadratic through A, B and C is given by

$$u_x = (1+\Delta)^{x+1}u_{-1} = u_{-1} + (x+1)\Delta u_{-1} + \tfrac{1}{2}x(x+1)\Delta^2 u_{-1}$$

The slope of this quadratic at the point B is given by

$$\left[\frac{d}{dx}u_x\right]_{x=0} = \Delta u_{-1} + \tfrac{1}{2}\Delta^2 u_{-1}$$

16.17 The quadratic through B, C and D is given by

$$u_x = (1+\Delta)^x u_0 = u_0 + x\Delta u_0 + \tfrac{1}{2}x(x-1)\Delta^2 u_0$$

and the slope of this quadratic at the point C is given by

$$\left[\frac{d}{dx}u_x\right]_{x=1} = \Delta u_0 + \tfrac{1}{2}\Delta^2 u_0$$

$$= \Delta u_{-1} + \tfrac{3}{2}\Delta^2 u_{-1} + \tfrac{1}{2}\Delta^3 u_{-1}$$

since $\Delta u_0 = \Delta(1+\Delta)u_{-1}$ and $\Delta^2 u_0 = \Delta^2(1+\Delta)u_{-1}$

16.18 Let the interpolating cubic between B and C be

$$ax^3 + bx^2 + cx + d$$

with gradient

$$3ax^2 + 2bx + c$$

16.19 Equating the ordinates and gradients at $B(x=0)$ and $C(x=1)$ to the values calculated above, we obtain

$$d = u_0 \qquad \text{(ordinate at } B)$$

$$c = \Delta u_{-1} + \tfrac{1}{2}\Delta^2 u_{-1} \qquad \text{(gradient at } B)$$

$$a + b + c + d = u_1 \qquad \text{(ordinate at } C)$$

$$3a + 2b + c = \Delta u_{-1} + \tfrac{3}{2}\Delta^2 u_{-1} + \tfrac{1}{2}\Delta^3 u_{-1} \qquad \text{(gradient at } C)$$

We then solve for a, b, c and d, and deduce that

$$u_x = u_0 + x\Delta u_{-1} + \frac{x+x^2}{2}\Delta^2 u_{-1} - \frac{x^2 - x^3}{2}\Delta^3 u_{-1} \qquad (16.4)$$

16.20 This formula is the same as the well-known Gauss backward formula as far as second differences. The osculatory effect is obtained by changing the third difference term.

Example 16.1

Use King's method of pivotal values and osculatory interpolation to graduate the data in Table 12.1.

King's formulae assume that the underlying curve can be represented adequately by a cubic, at least over sections of its length. An examination of the data soon reveals that the exposed to risk do not follow a very regular pattern, and it would be wrong therefore to apply King's method to the exposed to risk and deaths separately. Instead we shall apply the method directly to the crude mortality rates.

Pivotal values are calculated in columns (2)–(5) of Table 16.1. The graduated rates at the intermediary ages are then calculated by means of the osculatory interpolation formula (16.4). For example,

$$q_{49} = 0.00909 + 0.4 \times 0.00327 + 0.28$$
$$\times (-0.00032) - 0.048 \times 0.00576$$
$$= 0.01003$$

A complete list of graduated rates is given in Table 16.2. The rates are not very smooth, owing to the variation in the crude rates (the exposed

Table 16.1   *Calculation of pivotal values for the mortality data in Table 12.1*

Age x (1)	$\sum\limits_{y=x}^{x+4} \hat{q}_y$ (2)	Δ (3)	Δ^2 (4)	$\frac{1}{5}(w_0 - \frac{1}{25}\Delta^2 w_{-1})$ (5)	Δ (6)	Δ^2 (7)	Δ^3 (8)	Pivotal age (9)
35	·01621							37
		·01301		$\frac{1}{5}(0.01922 - \frac{1}{25}0,00322)$				
40	·02922		·00322	·00582				42
		·01623			·00327			
45	·04545		−·00049	·00909 = q_{47}		−·00032		47
		·01574			·00295		·00576	
50	·06119		·02502	·01204 = q_{52}		·00546		52
		·04076			·00841		−·00783	
55	·10195		−·00767	·02045		−·00237		57
		·03309			·00604			
60	·13504		·06484	·02649				62
		·09793						
65	·23297							67

(column header annotation: $(16.3 \text{ with } n=5)$)

$q_{53} = 0,01204 + 0,2 \times 0,00295 + \frac{0,2 + 0,2^2}{2} \times 0,00546 - \frac{0,2^2 - 0,2^3}{2}(-0,0078$

$q_{56} = 0,01204 + 0,5 \times 0,00295 + \frac{0,5 + 0,5^2}{2} \times 0,00546 - \frac{0,5^2 - 0,5^3}{2}(-0,007$

Table 16.2 *Graduated mortality rates*

Age x	Graduated $\hat{q}_x \times 10^5$	Age x	Graduated $\hat{q}_x \times 10^5$
47	909	53	1338
48	961	54	1512
49	1003	55	1699
50	1048	56	1883
51	1111	57	2045
52	1204		

to risk are not very large) and the limited graduating power of the method. Note that graduated rates are obtained for only eleven ages, and that another method is needed for the ten ages each side for which the method does not provide rates.

Spline functions

16.21 Although osculatory interpolation formulae were known last century, increasing interest has been shown in them in recent years. Attention has been focussed on a particular set of osculatory polynomials, known as *spline functions* (the word 'spline' refers to a device used by draughtsmen to draw a smooth curve, and consisting of a strip of some flexible material, to which weights can be attached at certain points in order to constrain the curve to pass through or close to certain given data points).

16.22 The name 'spline function' is given to a function obtained by joining together a sequence of polynomial arcs, the polynomials being chosen in such a way that derivatives up to and including the order one less than the degree of the polynomial used are continuous everywhere. The pivotal values where the polynomial arcs meet are usually called *knots*. For purposes of interpolation the use of such functions offers substantial advantages. One can often avoid the marked undulatory behaviour commonly encountered when a single polynomial is fitted exactly through a large number of data points, and at the same time greater smoothness is obtained than with traditional interpolation procedures, which give rise to discontinuities in the first derivative of the interpolating function. A spline function provides continuity of the greatest possible number of derivatives of the interpolating function consistent with the use of polynomials of lower degree than would be required to fit all data points exactly by a single polynomial.

Example 16.2

Fit a cubic spline through the points $(x, \log x)$ for $x = 1, 2, 3, ..., 7$.

This can be done in a number of ways. Let us proceed in the following manner:

1 Fit a quadratic through the first three points.
2 Calculate the first and second derivative of this quadratic at the third point.
3 Fit a cubic through the points $(3, \log 3)$ and $(4, \log 4)$, having the same first and second derivatives at $x = 3$ as the previous quadratic.
4 Calculate the first and second derivatives of this cubic at the point $x = 4$.
5 Fit a cubic through the points $(4, \log 4)$ and $(5, \log 5)$, having the same first and second derivatives at $x = 4$ as the previous cubic.
6 Continue in the same manner until the point $(7, \log 7)$ is reached.

The resulting curve is shown in Figure 16.3. Although the curve is smooth in a local sense (it is continuous and the first two derivatives are continuous), it displays a marked undulatory behaviour. It is quite

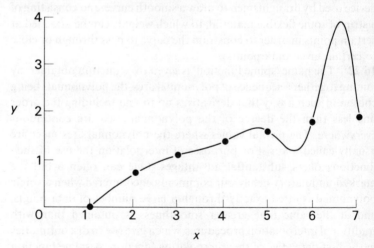

FIGURE 16.3   A cubic spline curve through the values of $\log x$ at the integer points $x = 1, 2, ..., 7$

unsatisfactory for interpolation, and in the absence of a justification for further conditions will not lead to a satisfactory result.

Note that the spline curve through a set of points is not unique. We might have started the curve-fitting process using, for example, a straight line through the first two points, or a cubic through the first four points. The resulting spline functions would have been different. Alternatively, we could have started the fitting process using the last few points and worked backwards, or even started in the middle.

16.23 The choice of possible spline curves through a given set of data points is infinite. It is clear from example 16.2 that a particular spline function chosen arbitrarily is unlikely to produce a satisfactory interpolation. A constraint must be introduced to eliminate the undulation problem. Greville has shown that the determination of the smoothest interpolating spline for given data points takes a particularly simple form in the case of a cubic.

16.24 Before describing Greville's solution to the problem, however, we need to introduce the concept of a _natural spline_. A spline of odd degree $2k - 1$ with knots at $x_1, x_2, ..., x_n$ is called a natural spline if it is given in each of the two intervals $(-\infty, x_1)$ and (x_n, ∞) by a polynomial of degree $k - 1$ or less. The polynomials of degree $k - 1$ in the two tails are not in general the same.

16.25 The smoothest interpolating cubic spline through a given set of data points is the natural cubic spline. It is linear before the first data point and linear after the final point (para. 16.24).

Example 16.3

The natural cubic spline through the points $(x, \log x)$ for $x = 1, 2, 3, ..., 7$ is shown as Figure 16.4. We see immediately that the undulatory behaviour of example 16.2 has disappeared. The method used to fit the natural spline is described in the following sections.

Natural spline interpolation

16.26 Let us imagine that we wish to fit a natural cubic spline through the points $(x_1, y_1), (x_2, y_2), ..., (x_n, y_n)$, where

$$x_1 < x_2 ... < x_n$$

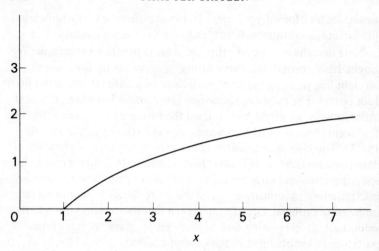

FIGURE 16.4 The natural cubic spline through the points $\log x$ for $x = 1,2,3,...,7$

16.27 Over the range $(-\infty, x_1)$ the natural cubic spline is a straight line (para. 16.25) and may be written in the form

$$y = a_0 + a_1 x \qquad (x < x_1) \qquad (16.5)$$

At the point (x_1, y_1) the curve becomes a cubic with the same first and second derivatives as the initial straight line. A suitable cubic can be obtained by adding to (16.5) a cubic term of the form $b_1(x - x_1)^3$. We then have

$$y = a_0 + a_1 x + b_1(x - x_1)^3 \quad (x_1 \leq x < x_2) \qquad (16.6)$$

The first two derivatives of (16.6) are the same as those of (16.5) at the point (x_1, y_1) because the first two derivatives of $b_1(x - x_1)^3$ are zero at that point.

16.28 If we define

$$\phi_1(x) = \begin{cases} 0 & (x < x_1) \\ (x - x_1)^3 & (x \geq x_1) \end{cases} \qquad (16.7)$$

formulae (16.5) and (16.6) can be combined into a single simple form

$$y = a_0 + a_1 x + b_1 \phi_1(x) \qquad (16.8)$$

The shape of $\phi_1(x)$ in Figure 16.5 should be noted.

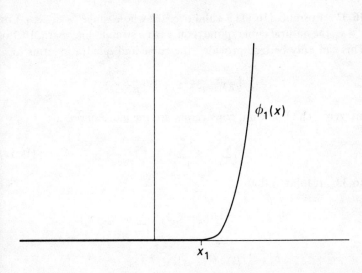

FIGURE 16.5   The spline function $\phi_1(x)$ defined in para. 16.28

16.29   The cubic spline over the range $x_2 \leq x < x_3$ will be different from the cubic over the interval $x_1 \leq x < x_2$, although the two must have the same first and second derivatives at x_2. The cubic over $x_2 \leq x < x_3$ can be obtained from the earlier one by adding $b_2(x - x_2)^3$ to (16.8). Both cubics have the same first two derivatives at x_2 because the first two derivatives of $b_2(x - x_2)^3$ are zero at that point.

16.30   If we define

$$\phi_2(x) = \begin{cases} 0 & (x < x_2) \\ (x - x_2)^3 & (x \geq x_2) \end{cases} \tag{16.9}$$

the natural spline for $x < x_3$ can be written in the single simple form

$$y = a_0 + a_1 x + b_1 \phi_1(x) + b_2 \phi_2(x) \tag{16.10}$$

16.31   It is apparent that the complete natural cubic spline passing through the n data points can be written in the form

$$y = a_0 + a_1 x + \sum_{j=1}^{n} b_j \phi_j(x) \tag{16.11}$$

where

$$\phi_j(x) = \begin{cases} 0 & (x < x_j) \\ (x - x_j)^3 & (x \geq x_j) \end{cases} \tag{16.12}$$

16.32 Formula (16.11) is valid over the whole range $(-\infty, \infty)$. For $x \geq x_n$, the natural cubic spline reduces to a straight line (para. 16.25). This can only be true provided the cubic and quadratic terms in

$$\sum_{j=1}^{n} b_j(x^3 - 3x^2x_j + 3xx_j^2 - x_j^3)$$

are zero. The following constraints are therefore imposed:

$$\sum_{j=1}^{n} b_j = \sum_{j=1}^{n} b_jx_j = 0 \tag{16.13}$$

16.33 It follows that

$$b_{n-1} = -\{1/(x_n - x_{n-1})\}\sum_{j=1}^{n-2} b_j(x_n - x_j)$$

$$b_n = \{1/(x_n - x_{n-1})\}\sum_{j=1}^{n-2} b_j(x_{n-1} - x_j)$$

and we deduce the following form for the natural cubic spline over the entire interval $(-\infty, \infty)$:

$$y = a_0 + a_1x + \sum_{j=1}^{n-2} b_j\Phi_j(x) \tag{16.14}$$

where

$$\Phi_j(x) = \phi_j(x) - \{(x_n - x_j)/(x_n - x_{n-1})\}\phi_{n-1}(x)$$
$$+ \{(x_{n-1} - x_j)/(x_n - x_{n-1})\}\phi_n(x) \tag{16.15}$$

16.34 The functions $\{\Phi_j(x)\}$ are straightforward to evaluate and (16.14) can be fitted using a standard multiple linear regression computer package. The number of fitted constants is equal to the number of data points; the natural spline will therefore pass through all the data points and the residual sum of squares will be zero. The curve in example 16.3 was obtained in this manner.

Natural spline graduation

16.35 The natural cubic spline is very useful for graduation purposes. The numerical procedure may be summarized as follows:

1   Choose a small number of knots or pivotal ages. The age or x-value at each of these knots is specified, but not the ordinate.

2 The functions $\{\Phi_j(x)\}$ are calculated.
3 A curve of the form (16.14) is fitted, using a weighted multiple linear regression package. If observed mortality rates $\{\mathring{q}_x\}$ are being graduated, weights $\{E_x/q_x^s\}$ should be used; q_x^s is the mortality rate at age x in a similar standard table.

16.36 The use of k knots requires the estimation of k regression coefficients $(a_0, a_1, b_1, b_2, ..., b_{k-2})$. If k exceeds the number of data points, n, the system will be over-determined; k must therefore be less than or equal to n. If $k = n$ and the knot ages coincide with the data ages, the spline function will pass through all the original data points and a perfect fit will be obtained; there will be no graduation.

16.37 The use of a small number of knots will usually result in a bold smooth graduation, and the effect of increasing the number is to improve adherence to data (possibly at the expense of smoothness). In the following example we use four equally spaced knots. It is not necessary for the knots in a spline graduation to be equally spaced, although equal spacing does make the computation of the $\{\Phi_i(x)\}$ simpler. There may, in fact, be an advantage in placing a knot near a point where a marked change in curvature is anticipated (e.g. the young adult accident hump in the male mortality curve).

Example 16.4

Graduate the mortality data in Table 12.1 by means of a natural cubic spline.

The observed mortality rates are available for thirty-six consecutive ages (35 to 70 inclusive). Let us use four equally spaced knots at ages 35, 47, 59 and 71. The spline functions $\{\phi_i(x)\}$ and $\{\Phi_i(x)\}$ are calculated as in Table 16.3.

Let us base our weights $\{E_x/q_x^s\}$ on the English Life Table 12 rates $\{q_x^s\}$ in Table 15.1. These weights, together with the crude mortality rates, the ages, and the $\Phi_1(x)$ and $\Phi_2(x)$ values for $35 \le x \le 70$ are supplied to a multiple linear regression program which calculates a_0, a_1, b_1 and b_2, and outputs the graduated rates. These are shown in Table 16.4 and Figure 16.6. The smoothness is good, and the chi-square value of 33·5 is quite satisfactory (para. 16.39).

Tests on a cubic spline graduation

16.38 Provided a small number of pivotal ages are used and these are well chosen (para. 16.37), a smooth graduation should result.

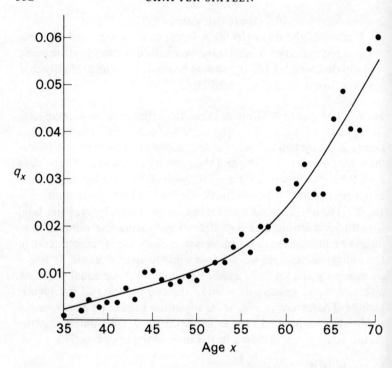

FIGURE 16.6   Natural cubic spline graduation of the data in Table 12.1. The observed mortality rates are indicated by dots

Nevertheless it is advisable to examine the first three orders of differences in the usual manner.

16.39   All the usual tests of adherence to data should be performed. The application of the χ^2 test to a cubic spline graduation presents no special features, except that each fitted constant estimated from the data results in the loss of one degree of freedom. If the pivotal ages are chosen after an examination of the crude data, a further unknown reduction should theoretically be made. The total reduction in example 16.4 is four.

Advantages of cubic spline graduation

16.40   Provided a small number of pivotal ages are used and these are well chosen, a smooth graduation will usually emerge, and the entire process is readily automated. The graduation method is in fact a special case of graduation by mathematical formula. Alternative

Table 16.3   *Spline functions $\{\phi_i(x)\}$ and $\{\Phi_i(x)\}$ for example 16.4*

Age x	$\phi_1(x)$	$\phi_2(x)$	$\phi_3(x)$	$\phi_4(x)$	$\Phi_1(x)$	$\Phi_2(x)$
35*	0	0	0	0	0	0
36	1	0	0	0	1	0
37	8	0	0	0	8	0
38	27	0	0	0	27	0
39	64	0	0	0	64	0
40	125	0	0	0	125	0
41	216	0	0	0	216	0
42	343	0	0	0	343	0
43	512	0	0	0	512	0
44	729	0	0	0	729	0
45	1,000	0	0	0	1,000	0
46	1,331	0	0	0	1,331	0
47*	1,728	0	0	0	1,728	0
48	2,197	1	0	0	2,197	1
49	2,744	8	0	0	2,744	8
50	3,375	27	0	0	3,375	27
51	4,096	64	0	0	4,096	64
52	4,913	125	0	0	4,913	125
53	5,832	216	0	0	5,832	216
54	6,859	343	0	0	6,859	343
55	8,000	512	0	0	8,000	512
56	9,261	729	0	0	9,261	729
57	10,648	1,000	0	0	10,648	1,000
58	12,167	1,331	0	0	12,167	1,331
59*	13,824	1,728	0	0	13,824	1,728
60	15,625	2,197	1	0	15,622	2,195
61	17,576	2,744	8	0	17,552	2,728
62	19,683	3,375	27	0	19,602	3,321
63	21,952	4,096	64	0	21,760	3,968
64	24,389	4,913	125	0	24,014	4,663
65	27,000	5,832	216	0	26,352	5,400
66	29,791	6,859	343	0	28,762	6,173
67	32,768	8,000	512	0	31,232	6,976
68	35,937	9,261	729	0	33,750	7,803
69	39,304	10,648	1,000	0	36,304	8,648
70	42,875	12,167	1,331	0	38,882	9,505
71*	46,656	13,824	1,728	0	41,472	10,368
72	50,653	15,625	2,197	1	44,064	11,232
73	54,872	17,576	2,744	8	46,656	12,096
.	.	.	.	.	.	.
.	.	.	.	.	.	.
.	.	.	.	.	.	.

* The four pivotal ages.

Table 16.4 *Natural cubic spline graduation of the mortality data in Table* 12.1

Age x	Crude $\mathring{q}_x \times 10^5$	Graduated $\hat{q}_x \times 10^5$
35	95	215
36	638	270
37	191	325
38	419	381
39	278	437
40	381	492
41	384	549
42	665	605
43	477	663
44	1,015	720
45	1,093	779
46	860	838
47	779	897
48	862	958
49	951	1,022
50	866	1,091
51	1,109	1,166
52	1,291	1,250
53	1,274	1,345
54	1,579	1,453
55	1,873	1,575
56	1,482	1,715
57	2,002	1,873
58	2,011	2,051
59	2,828	2,253
60	1,722	2,479
61	2,943	2,727
62	3,374	2,996
63	2,736	3,284
64	2,731	3,588
65	4,323	3,906
66	4,927	4,237
67	4,114	4,579
68	4,099	4,928
69	5,835	5,284
70	6,104	5,643

graduations are easily obtained by varying the number and position of the knots, and computer programs can be devised to optimize the choice of knots (McCutcheon and Eilbeck, 1977, 1978). The method can be used for quite small experiences as well as large.

Disadvantages of cubic spline graduation

16.41 The choice of pivotal ages calls for some skill, and the method is not readily applicable to very sparse experiences.

English Life Table 13

16.42 The spline method is being used to graduate English Life Table 13.

Abridged life tables

16.43 It may sometimes be desired to use a set of pivotal values of q_x to provide values of l_x and $\mathring{e}_x$ of the corresponding life table at every fifth age. Methods have been specially devised for passing directly from quinary pivotal values of q_x to an abridged life table without going through the tedious process of interpolating individual values of q_x.

16.44 George King in 1914, for example, assumed that the function $\log p_x$ could be approximated sufficiently accurately by a polynomial of degree 3, at least over sections of its length, and deduced the following results:

$$_5p_x = p_x^3 \, p_{x+5}^2 \left(\frac{p_x \, p_{x+5}}{p_{x-5} \, p_{x+10}} \right)^{1/5} \tag{16.16}$$

$$_5p_x = p_x^2 \, p_{x+5}^3 \, (p_x^2 \, p_{x+5}^2 \, p_{x+15})^{1/5} / p_{x+10} \tag{16.17}$$

Formula (16.17) is used to calculate $_5p_x$ over the first quinquennial age step, and (16.16) is employed over the remainder of the table.

16.45 Once the quinquennial survival rates $\{_5p_x\}$ are known, values of l_x can be calculated for every fifth age, using the recurrence relation

$$l_{x+5} = l_x \times {}_5p_x$$

The complete expectations of life $\mathring{e}_x$ is defined by

$$\mathring{e}_x = \frac{1}{l_x} \int_0^\infty l_{x+t} \, dt$$

and values of $\mathring{e}_x$ for every fifth year of age can be calculated, using the quinquennial l_x-values and a suitable numerical integration formula.

If, for example, Simpson's rule is adopted, the calculation formula becomes

$$\mathring{e}_x = \frac{5}{3l_x}(l_x + 4l_{x+5} + 2l_{x+10} + 4l_{x+15} + \ldots) \qquad (16.18)$$

16.46 In connection with the construction of a service table for use in pension-fund work, Freeman (1930) suggested a simple process that can be adapted to the purpose of constructing an abridged life table. The principle of the method is to assume that $p_{x+1}p_{x+4} \doteqdot p_x p_{x+5}$ (i.e. one age down and one up) and that $p_{x+2}p_{x+3} = p_x p_{x+5}$ (i.e. two ages down and two up). Then

$$_5p_x = p_x^3 p_{x+5}^2 \qquad (16.19)$$

This formula can be used over the initial quinquennial age step and throughout the table, and should be compared with King's formula (16.16). Freeman's method is probably not as accurate as King's, but it is simpler to apply, and it usually produces results which are quite adequate. Values of l_x and $\mathring{e}_x$ at quinquennial ages can be calculated, using the methods of para. 16.45.

16.47 Now that computers can be programmed to produce extended life tables as easily as shorter tables, abridged tables are of diminished interest, but the need to produce such a table rapidly and with ordinary desk machines does arise from time to time. Either of the above methods can be used. Other methods for constructing abridged life tables have also been devised by Snow (1914), Greville (1943), Greville (1945), Reed and Merrell (1939), the Institute of Actuaries (1914) and the General Register Office. References are given at the end of this chapter.

Model life tables

16.48 Systems of model life tables have been developed by a number of authors. These are particularly useful for estimating complete life tables or abridged life tables from limited mortality data. Knowing only a few details about the mortality of a population (e.g. $\mathring{e}_0$, q_0, q_{60}), it is possible to choose a suitable life table with these characteristics and hence estimate any required mortality function (e.g. $_{10}p_{60}$, $\mathring{e}_{30}$).

16.49 The first set of model life tables was computed by the United Nations in the early 1950s under the direction of V. Valaoras. They were not life tables for any particular country but hypothetical life tables based on 158 life tables from a wide selection of countries and representing different periods of time.

16.50 A further set of model life tables was published by Coale and Demeny in 1966, based on over 300 life tables, each for males and females separately and reflecting actual recorded mortality in various countries. The basic set of data was divided into four subsets (i.e. families), within each of which the mortality pattern was found to be homogeneous. These sets are now referred to familiarly by the names 'West', 'North', 'South' and 'East'. The 'West' tables covering twenty countries showed a mortality experience which did not deviate in general pattern from the world average. The 'East' tables covered mainly Central European countries, and the 'North' and 'South' tables were derived mainly from life tables from Scandinavia and Southern Europe respectively. These three groups were separated out because they revealed age patterns with substantial and significant deviations from world average. Within each of the four sets there are twenty-four tables, for males and females separately at different mortality levels with values of $\overset{\circ}{e}_0$ equally spaced from 20·0 years (level 1) to 77·5 years (level 24). The number of tables published is sufficiently large to justify linear interpolation between tables, should this be necessary.

16.51 The Coale–Demeny tables also include stable population figures for various rates of population growth from − 1 per cent per annum to 5 per cent per annum by $\frac{1}{2}$ per cent steps, and these can be used by the actuary to deduce annuity values at rates of interest equal to the population growth rates.

16.52 Model life tables have also been developed by Ledermann (1969) and Brass (1971).

REFERENCES

Brass, W. (1971) (ed.). 'On the scale of mortality', in *Biological Aspects of Demography*, Taylor and Francis, London.

Coale, A. J. and Demeny, P. (1966). *Regional Model Life Tables and Stable Populations*, Princeton University Press, Princeton.

Freeman, H. (1930). Notes on a short method of valuation of pension funds. *J. Inst. Actu.*, **61**, 9.

Freeman, H. (1960). *Mathematics for Actuarial Students*, Vol. 2, *Finite Differences*, Cambridge University Press, 147.

Greville, T. N. E. (1943). *Record of Am. Inst. Act.*, **32**, 29.

Greville, T. N. E. (1945). *Vitd. Stat. Spec. Reports*, **23**, 241.

Greville, T. N. E. (1967). Data fitting by spline functions. *Trans. of Twelfth*

Conference of Army Mathematicians, Report 67–1, U.S. Army Research Office, Durham, North Carolina.

Greville, T. N. E. (1967). Spline functions, interpolation and numerical quadrature. *Mathematical Methods for Digital Computers*, Vol. 2, A. Raltson and H. S. Wilf (eds), Wiley, New York.

Greville, T. N. E. (1969) (ed.). *Theory and Applications of Spline Functions*, Academic Press, New York.

Institute of Actuaries (1914). An editorial note on a paper by G. King, 'A short method of constructing an abridged mortality table'. *J.Inst. Actu.*, **48**, 301.

King, G. (1914). A short method of constructing an abridged mortality table. *J. Inst. Actu.*, **48**, 294.

Ledermann, S. (1969). *Nouvelles tables—types de mortalité*, Institut National d'Études Démographiques (INED).

Lidstone, G. J. (1908). Alternative demonstration of the formula for osculatory interpolation. *J. Inst. Actu.*, **42**, 394.

McCutcheon, J. J. (1971) Actuarial Notes: Some remarks on basic mortality functions. A method for constructing an abridged life table. *T.F.A.* **32**, 395–411.

McCutcheon, J. J. and Eilbeck, J. C. (1977). Experiments in graduation of the English Life Tables (No. 13) data *T.F.A.*, **35**, 281–96.

McCutcheon, J. J. and Eilbeck, J. C. (1978). Graduations of the data for the Scottish Life Tables (1970–72). *T.F.A.*, **36**, 42–52.

Reed, L. J. and Merrell, M. (1939) A short method for constructing an abridged table. *Am. J. Hygiene*, **30**, 33.

Snow, E. C. (1914). *Supplement to the 75th Annual Report of the Registrar General, Part 2: Abridged Life Tables*, HMSO.

United Nations (1955). *Age and Sex patterns of mortality. Model life tables for underdeveloped countries*, UNO.

United Nations (1965).*The concept of a stable population. Applications to the study of populations of countries with incomplete demographic statistics*, UNO.

EXERCISES FOR CHAPTER SIXTEEN

1 Apply King's graduation method of pivotal values and osculatory interpolation to the data of exercise 7 in Chapter 11.

2 Confirm (16.14) and (16.15).

3 Use a least-squares multiple regression program to fit a natural cubic spline through the data points $(x, \log x)$ for $x = 1, 2,..., 7$ and confirm the results of example 16.3.

4 Graduate the data in Table 12.1, using a natural cubic spline and a multiple linear regression program. Base your weights on the graduated mortality rates in Table 16.4.

5 Graduate the mortality data of question 8 in Chapter 11, using a natural cubic spline and a multiple linear regression program. Base your weights on the graduated rates listed in that question.

6 Confirm (16.16) and (16.17).

7   Form an abridged life table from the data in exercise 7 of Chapter 11,
using Freeman's method. Compare your results with those which would be
obtained by King's method.

8   The experience in Table 12.1 has been graduated in the text in example
12.1, Table 13.2, examples 14.1, 14.2, 14.3, 14.4, 15.1 and 16.4 and possibly
by the student in exercises 14.4, 15.5 and 16.4, and has been compared with
E.L.T.10 (Males) in Table 11.1. Compare the resulting values of q_x in a
table. Using graph paper with a vertical log scale, plot the crude values of $\mathring{q}_x$,
the 95 per cent confidence limits, and each of the graduated curves (or as
many as can be included while retaining clarity). (Alternatively, calculate
$\log q_x$ and plot these on ordinary graph paper). Have you any reason to
prefer one graduation to another? What criteria might you use to choose
between them?

Hint: calculate (or extract from the text) the value of χ^2 and the number
of degrees of freedom for each graduation, and also the value of

$$\Lambda = \sum_x \{\theta_x \log q_x + (E_x - \theta_x) \log p_x\}$$

Do these help?

Omit

CHAPTER SEVENTEEN

STOCHASTIC PROCESSES

17.1 The life table values obtained from a graduation are *estimates* of the true underlying values in the population, based on the finite amount of data available. They depend upon the particular outcome observed in the mortality experience, and are therefore random variables.

17.2 The graduated mortality rates $\{\hat{q}_x\}$ will normally be used to compute *estimates* of more complicated functions like $_tp_x$, e_x, a_x, A_x, etc. The exact values of these functions are unknown, because, although the interest rate might be specified, the true underlying mortality is unknown. The estimators of these functions are random variables, and though in most experiences the data are numerous and sampling errors small, it is still advisable to examine their reliability and also the possibility of bias.

17.3 In particular we ought to check whether the estimators $_t\hat{p}_x$, $\hat{e}_x$, $\hat{a}_x$, $\hat{A}_x$, etc. based on the graduated rates $\{\hat{q}_x\}$ are unbiased (i.e. whether their expected values are equal to the corresponding population values) and we should examine their variability. Such investigations enable us to assess the accuracy with which we can pinpoint the numerical values of $_tp_x$, e_x, a_x, A_x, etc., and the major part of this chapter will be devoted to this problem.

Other sources of stochastic variation

17.4 The life table and other actuarial functions we estimate will be used for a variety of purposes: to project populations, to compute life-assurance premium rates, to determine pension fund contribution rates, etc. Such calculations lead invariably to further stochastic uncertainty.

17.5 Let us imagine, for example, that a mortality experience and graduation method allow us to estimate the annuity function a_x very accurately. The accurate estimate might be used to calculate the discounted value of an annuity of one per annum on a single life aged x. It is likely, however, that the discounted value of the payments actually made to the life aged x will be very different from the calculated value. The life may die almost immediately, for example, in which case the actual discounted value is very small, or he may live to become a nonagenarian. Furthermore the appropriate interest rate for discounting purposes may vary.

17.6 It is clearly desirable that a life office selling only a small number of such contracts include a reasonably large contingency loading in the annuity purchase price. A considerable amount of time and effort might be spent improving the estimate of a_x. That time and effort will be largely wasted, however, if the additional refinement is completely swamped by the contingency loading the office is compelled to make.

17.7 It is important to keep a sense of proportion, and to achieve this a basic understanding of age at death as a stochastic variable is required, as well as an appreciation of the problems inherent in a stochastically varying interest rate. The effect of variation in the age at death on actuarial functions is discussed in paras 17.38–17.42, and a brief introduction to the problem of stochastically varying interest rates is given in paras 17.43–17.48. Before turning to these problems, however, we discuss first the accuracy and reliability of the estimators of the various life table and other actuarial functions.

Life table functions calculated directly from observed mortality rates

17.8 The number of deaths for a given exposed to risk at a particular age is a random variable. The observed mortality rate, obtained by dividing the observed number of deaths by the corresponding exposed to risk is also a random variable, and it estimates q_x.

17.9 Let us imagine that an estimate $_t\mathring{p}_x$ of the life table function $_tp_x$ will be calculated directly from the observed mortality rates $\{\mathring{q}_x\}$ as follows:

$$_t\mathring{p}_x = \mathring{p}_x\mathring{p}_{x+1} \cdots \mathring{p}_{x+t-1} \tag{17.1}$$

where

$$\mathring{p}_x = 1 - \mathring{q}_x$$

17.10 Given the exposed to risk at the various ages, the observed mortality rates $\{\mathring{q}_x\}$ are usually independent unbiased estimators of the underlying $\{q_x\}$. The observed survival rates $\{\mathring{p}_x\}$ are then independent and unbiased, and

$$\mathcal{E}\,{}_t\mathring{p}_x = \mathcal{E}\prod_{j=0}^{t-1}\mathring{p}_{x+j}$$

$$= \prod_{j=0}^{t-1}\mathcal{E}\,\mathring{p}_{x+j}$$

$$= \prod_{j=0}^{t-1}p_{x+j}$$

$$= {}_tp_x$$

We conclude that the observed survival rate (17.1) provides an unbiased estimate of true underlying survival rate.

17.11 The variance of ${}_t\mathring{p}_x$ is readily determined. We recall that the expected value of the square of a random variable is equal to the sum of the variance of the random variable and the square of the expected value of the variable. The expected value of $\mathring{p}_x^2$ is therefore $(p_xq_x/E_x) + p_x^2$. Then

$$\mathcal{E}\,({}_t\mathring{p}_x)^2 = \mathcal{E}\prod_{j=0}^{t-1}\mathring{p}_{x+j}^2$$

$$= \prod_{j=0}^{t-1}\mathcal{E}\,\mathring{p}_{x+j}^2$$

$$= \prod_{j=0}^{t-1}\{(p_{x+j}q_{x+j}/E_{x+j}) + p_{x+j}^2\}$$

$$= ({}_tp_x)^2\prod_{j=0}^{t-1}\{1+q_{x+j}/(p_{x+j}E_{x+j})\}$$

17.12 To obtain the variance of ${}_t\mathring{p}_x$ we subtract $({}_tp_x)^2$ from this formula. When the exposed-to-risk values are reasonably large, second-order terms can be ignored in the above product, and

$$\text{Var }{}_t\mathring{p}_x \doteqdot ({}_tp_x)^2\sum_{j=0}^{t-1}q_{x+j}/(p_{x+j}E_{x+j}) \qquad (17.2)$$

(M. Greenwood, 1926).

17.13 The covariance of ${}_t\mathring{p}_x$ and ${}_s\mathring{p}_x$ can be calculated in a similar manner. For $s>t$,

$$\text{Cov}\,({}_t\mathring{p}_x, {}_s\mathring{p}_x) \doteqdot {}_tp_x\,{}_sp_x\sum_{j=0}^{t-1}q_{x+j}/(p_{x+j}E_{x+j}) \qquad (17.3)$$

17.14 An estimate of the curtate expectation of life at age x can be calculated directly from the observed survival rates by means of the formula

$$e_x(\text{obs.}) = \sum_{t=1}^{\infty} {}_t\overset{\circ}{p}_x \tag{17.4}$$

17.15 It is easy to deduce from para. 17.10 that the above estimate of e_x is unbiased. To obtain the variance of e_x (obs.), we note that

$$\text{Var } e_x(\text{obs.}) = \sum_{t=1}^{\infty} \text{Var } {}_t\overset{\circ}{p}_x + 2 \sum_{t=1}^{\infty} \sum_{s>t} \text{Cov} ({}_t\overset{\circ}{p}_x, {}_s\overset{\circ}{p}_x)$$

17.16 When (17.2) and (17.3) are substituted into this formula and the order of summation of the t and j variables is reversed, we find that

$$\text{Var } e_x(\text{obs.}) = \sum_{j=0}^{\infty} \{q_{x+j}/(p_{x+j}E_{x+j})\} \left\{ \sum_{t=j+1}^{\infty} ({}_tp_x)^2 \right.$$

$$\left. + 2 \sum_{t=j+1}^{\infty} \sum_{s>t} {}_tp_x \, {}_sp_x \right\}$$

$$= \sum_{j=0}^{\infty} \{q_{x+j}/(p_{x+j}E_{x+j})\} ({}_jp_x \, e_{x+j})^2 \tag{17.5}$$

(See, for example, C. L. Chiang, 1968, 237–9.)

17.17 The quantities q_{x+j}, p_{x+j}, ${}_jp_x$ and e_{x+j} in (17.5) are population values and therefore unknown. An estimate of the variance of e_x (obs.) can be obtained, however, by substituting observed or graduated values of these quantities into (17.5). Alternatively, values from a suitable standard table might be used.

Example 17.1

The initial exposed to risk and deaths for Australian males aged 80 and over (1970–2) are shown in Table 17.1. Calculate a 95 per cent confidence interval for e_{80}, the curtate expectation of life at age 80.

An unbiased estimate of e_{80} is provided by

$$e_{80}(\text{obs.}) = \sum_{t=1}^{\infty} {}_t\overset{\circ}{p}_{80} = 4.99$$

The total of column (5) in table 17.1 has been rounded up to compensate for the truncation at age 100.

The variance of e_{80} (obs.) is given by (17.5). The mortality functions

Table 17.1 *Estimation of* e_{80} *for Australian Males 1970–2*

Age	Initial exposed	Deaths	Observed		Australian Males Mortality 1960–2		
x (1)	E_x (2)	θ_x (3)	$\mathring{q}_x$ (4)	$_{x-80}\mathring{p}_{80}$ (5)	q_x (6)	l_x (7)	e_x (8)
80	36,028	4,303	·1194	1·0000	·11617	24,669	5·1
81	31,535	3,945	·1251	·8806	·12607	21,803	4·7
82	27,466	4,035	·1469	·7704	·13679	19,054	4·4
83	23,596	3,693	·1565	·6573	·14836	16,448	4·1
84	19,747	3,212	·1627	·5544	·16062	14,008	3·9
85	15,962	2,806	·1758	·4642	·17363	11,758	3·6
86	13,491	2,520	·1868	·3826	·18726	9,716	3·3
87	10,383	2,045	·1970	·3111	·20151	7,897	3·1
88	7,747	1,741	·2247	·2498	·21620	6,306	2·9
89	6,194	1,450	·2341	·1937	·23133	4,943	2·7
90	4,739	1,113	·2349	·1484	·24675	3,800	2·5
91	3,295	919	·2789	·1135	·26241	2,862	2·4
92	2,266	697	·3077	·0818	·27821	2,111	2·2
93	1,755	510	·2906	·0567	·29415	1,524	2·1
94	1,198	361	·3015	·0402	·31023	1,076	1·9
95	850	265	·3119	·0281	·32649	742	1·8
96	619	218	·3522	·0193	·34294	500	1·7
97	351	108	·3077	·0125	·35963	329	1·6
98	266	70	·2632	·0087	·37654	211	1·5
99	169	55	·3264	·0064	·39364	132	1·4
100	193	50	·2591	·0043	·41087	80	1·2
Total	–	–	–	5·9840	–	–	–

subtract $1 = {}_0\mathring{p}_{80}$

on the right-hand side of this formula are unknown, and need to be estimated. Let us use the Australian Life Table (1960–2) for this purpose (The relevant figures are also given in Table 17.1). We find that

$$\text{var } e_{80} \text{ (obs.)} \doteqdot 5·04 \times 10^{-4}$$

The standard deviation of e_{80} (obs.) is therefore 0·022, and the required 95 per cent confidence interval is approximately $4·99 \pm 0·04$.

Life table functions calculated from graduated mortality rates

17.18 Estimates of the curtate expectation of life and other life table functions will not normally be based on crude death rates, but on graduated rates, which tend to be closer to the true underlying mortality rates than the crude rates.

17.19 The probability that a life age x survives t years may be estimated from the graduated mortality rates $\{\hat{q}_x\}$ as follows:

$$
\begin{aligned}
_t\hat{p}_x &= \prod_{j=0}^{t-1} (1 - \hat{q}_{x+j}) \\
&= {}_t p_x \prod_{j=0}^{t-1} \{1 - (\hat{q}_{x+j} - q_{x+j})/p_{x+j}\} \\
&= {}_t p_x \left\{ 1 - \sum_j \left(\frac{\hat{q}_{x+j} - q_{x+j}}{p_{x+j}} \right) \right. \\
&\quad \left. + \sum\sum_{j \neq k} \left(\frac{\hat{q}_{x+j} - q_{x+j}}{p_{x+j}} \right) \left(\frac{\hat{q}_{x+k} - q_{x+k}}{p_{x+k}} \right) - \ldots \right\}
\end{aligned} \tag{17.6}
$$

17.20 Graduation procedures are usually designed to produce unbiased values for the graduated rates of decrement. We shall assume therefore that

$$
\mathscr{E}\, \hat{q}_{x+j} = q_{x+j}
$$

Formula (17.6) then tells us that

$$
\mathscr{E}\, {}_t\hat{p}_x \doteq {}_t p_x \left\{ 1 + \sum\sum_{j \neq k} \frac{\operatorname{cov}(\hat{q}_{x+j}, \hat{q}_{x+k})}{p_{x+j} p_{x+k}} \right\} \tag{17.7}
$$

Table 17.2 *Correlation between neighbouring rates graduated by Spencer's 21-term formula (assuming a constant variance for the observed rates)*

Age difference	Correlation	Age difference	Correlation
0	1·0000	11	−0·0530
1	0·9569	12	−0·0300
2	0·8361	13	−0·0122
3	0·6604	14	−0·0005
4	0·4609	15	0·0029
5	0·2694	16	0·0034
6	0·1112	17	0·0023
7	0·0003	18	0·0011
8	−0·0612	19	0·0003
9	−0·0815	20	0·0001
10	−0·0740	≥21	0·0000

17.21 Graduated mortality rates at successive ages are *not* independent. They are usually positively correlated (the high correlation between neighbouring rates graduated by Spencer's 21-term formula, for example, is indicated in Table 17.2). The covariances in (17.7) are therefore predominantly positive, and we deduce that the survival probability estimator $_t\hat{p}_x$ has a positive bias. The estimator of the curtate expectation of life

$$\hat{e}_x = \sum_{t=1}^{\infty} {}_t\hat{p}_x$$

will also be positively biased (i.e. overestimate e_x on average).

17.22 The following expressions for the variance and covariance of the survival function calculated from graduated mortality rates may be deduced from (17.6):

$$\text{var } {}_t\hat{p}_x \doteqdot {}_tp_x^2 \text{var}\left(\sum_{j=0}^{t-1} \hat{z}_j \right) \tag{17.8}$$

$$\text{cov}\left({}_t\hat{p}_{x'}\, {}_s\hat{p}_x \right) \doteqdot {}_tp_x\, {}_sp_x \text{cov}\left(\sum_{j=0}^{t-1} \hat{z}_{j'} \sum_{k=0}^{s-1} \hat{z}_k \right) \tag{17.9}$$

where

$$\hat{z}_j = \hat{q}_{x+j}/p_{x+j} \tag{17.10}$$

17.23 Equivalent formulae for the survival rate calculated directly from the observed mortality rates can be written down by simply replacing the circumflex in (17.8), (17.9) and (17.10) by a small circle.

17.24 The variance of each $\hat{z}_j$ will be considerably less than the variance of the corresponding $\mathring{z}_j$. In the case of a graduation by Spencer's 21-term formula, for example, the ratio of var $\hat{z}_j$ to var $\mathring{z}_j$ will be approximately $\phi_E^2 = 0\cdot143$. At first sight it would appear therefore that var $_t\hat{p}_x$ is considerably smaller than var $_t\mathring{p}_x$. This is *not* true, however, Neighbouring $\hat{z}_j$ have high positive correlation, and var $(\Sigma\, \hat{z}_j)$ turns out to be close to var $(\Sigma\, \mathring{z}_j)$.

17.25 Indeed, for any graduation showing reasonable adherence to data, observed and expected deaths in a given wide age range should be almost equal, and we deduce (with a slightly different weighting of the crude and graduated q-values) that

$$\sum_{j=0}^{t-1} \hat{z}_j \doteqdot \sum_{j=0}^{t-1} \mathring{z}_j$$

Except for very small t, therefore,

$$\text{var } {}_t\hat{p}_x \doteq \text{var } {}_t\mathring{p}_x \tag{17.11}$$

and

$$\text{cov } ({}_t\hat{p}_{x'}\text{ }_s\hat{p}_x) \doteq \text{cov } ({}_t\mathring{p}_{x'}\text{ }_s\mathring{p}_x) \tag{17.12}$$

Formulae (17.2), (17.3) and (17.5) can thus be used to calculate approximate moments for ${}_t\hat{p}_x$ and $\hat{e}_x$.

Example 17.2

The mortality data of Table 12.1 were graduated by Spencer's 21-term formula in Table 13.2. Calculate the bias in the estimator ${}_5\hat{p}_{50}$ when applied to these data.

We begin by noting that

$$\text{cov}(\hat{q}_{50}, \hat{q}_{51}) = \text{cov}\left(\sum_{j=-10}^{10} K_j \mathring{q}_{50+j}, \sum_{J=-10}^{10} K_J \mathring{q}_{51+J} \right)$$

$$= \sum_{j=-9}^{10} K_j K_{j-1} \text{ var } \mathring{q}_{50+j}$$

$$= \sum_{j=-9}^{10} K_j K_{j-1} \text{ } q_{50+j}/E_{50+j}$$

The underlying mortality rates $\{q_{50+j}\}$ are unknown. If we estimate them, using the graduated rates in Table 13.2, we find that

$$\text{cov}(\hat{q}_{50}, \hat{q}_{51}) = 8\cdot 8 \times 10^{-7}$$

The covariances of all the other possible pairs of $\hat{q}_{50}, \hat{q}_{51}, \hat{q}_{52}, \hat{q}_{53}$ and $\hat{q}_{54}$ are worked out similarly and substituted into (17.7); the unknown $\{p_x\}$ are again estimated by the graduated rates. We find the bias in ${}_5\hat{p}_{50}$ to be about eight parts per million, which is negligible.

Example 17.3

Obtain approximate 95 per cent confidence limits for ${}_5p_{50}$ for the population underlying the data in Table 12.1, using the graduated mortality rates in Table 13.2.

The estimate of ${}_5p_{50}$ based on these graduated rates is

$${}_5\hat{p}_{50} = (1 - 0\cdot 01021)(1 - 0\cdot 01109)\ldots(1 - 0\cdot 01490) = 0\cdot 93964.$$

According to para. 17.25, the variance of ${}_5\hat{p}_x$ is given approximately by (17.2). The underlying mortality rates in this formula are unknown, but they can be estimated by means of the graduated rates. We find that

$$\text{var } _5\hat{p}_{50} \doteqdot (0.93964)^3 \left\{ \frac{0.01021}{0.98979 \times 2193} + \cdots + \frac{0.01490}{0.98510 \times 2406} \right\}$$

$$= 2.7 \times 10^{-5}$$

The standard deviation of $_5\hat{p}_{50}$ is therefore about 0.0052, and we deduce the following 95 per cent ($2 \times$ standard deviation) confidence interval for $_5\hat{p}_{50}$:

$$0.93964 \pm 0.0104$$

Actuarial functions

17.26 Let us imagine that the rate of interest is constant and known. An estimate of the average present value of an annuity on a life aged x can be calculated, using either the observed survival rates $\{_t\mathring{p}_x\}$ or the graduated rates $\{_t\hat{p}_x\}$. That is, we can use either

$$a_x(\text{obs.}) = \sum_{t=1}^{\infty} {}_t\mathring{p}_x v^t \qquad (17.13)$$

or

$$\hat{a}_x = \sum_{t=1}^{\infty} {}_t\hat{p}_x v^t \qquad (17.14)$$

17.27 It is evident from paras. 17.10 and 17.21 that (17.13) provides an unbiased estimate of a_x, whereas (17.14) contains a slight positive bias. We also deduce from para. 17.16, (17.2) and (17.3) that

$$\text{var } \hat{a}_x \doteqdot \text{var } a_x(\text{obs.}) \doteqdot \sum_{j=0}^{\infty} \{ q_{x+j} / (p_{x+j} E_{x+j}) \} ({}_j p_x v^j a_{x+j})^2 \qquad (17.15)$$

17.28 Table 17.3 shows the standard deviation of the estimator $a_x(\text{obs.})$ at 5 per cent interest for various ages, based on an equal exposure of 100 at all ages up to and including 65 and a stationary population at the higher ages. The assumed underlying mortality is that of the A1949–52 ultimate table, although the results are relatively insensitive to the mortality table adopted. If the experience were ten times as large (but with the same age distribution) the entries in the table would be reduced by the factor $\sqrt{10}$.

17.29 Formula (17.15) can be used to compute approximate 95 per cent confidence limits for a_x, the average present value of an annuity on a life aged x, based on an observed mortality experience.

17.30 An estimate of the assurance function A_x can be obtained from either (17.13) or (17.14), using the premium conversion formula

$$A_x = 1 - d(1 + a_x) \tag{17.16}$$

It is clear that an unbiased estimate will be obtained via (17.13), whereas a slight negative bias will result from (17.14). The variance of the estimator is

$$\text{var } \hat{A}_x \doteqdot \text{var } A_x(\text{obs.}) = d^2 \text{ var } a_x(\text{obs.}) \tag{17.17}$$

Random mortality fluctuations and the binomial model

17.31 In the earlier chapters and preceding sections of this chapter the assumption has been made that all lives of a particular age are subject to the same fixed probability of death q_x, and this leads immediately to the binomial distribution as the natural model for the observed number of deaths at that age. There are in fact sound practical reasons to doubt the validity of some of the assumptions underlying the binomial model. The heterogeneity of many populations with respect to mortality has already been noted in paras. 11.45–11.48.

17.32 We also have reason to suspect that the probability q_x may not be fixed, but may itself be subject to random fluctuations. It is a

Table 17.3 *The standard deviation of the estimator a_x (obs.) at 5 per cent interest*

Based on an equal exposure of 100 at all ages up to and including 65 and a stationary population at the higher ages. The assumed underlying mortality is according to the A1949–52 ultimate table.

Age x	Standard deviation of a_x(obs.)
20	0·20
30	0·23
40	0·29
50	0·35
60	0·37

well-known fact, for example, that human mortality rates depend upon weather conditions: a severe winter will cause mortality rates, especially at the older ages and at the very young ages, to rise: conversely, a mild winter will mean that the mortality rates experienced are lighter than usual.

17.33 A. H. Pollard (1970) has shown that when the mortality probability q_x itself is a random variable which varies stochastically with mean Q and variance $\text{Var}(q_x)$, the variance of the number of deaths among N lives all aged x is

$$NPQ + N(N-1)\,\text{Var}\,(q_x) \tag{17.18}$$

The first term is the usual binomial variance and the second takes account of the variability of q_x.

17.34 $\text{Var}\,(q_x)$ is usually very much smaller than Q, and the second term in (17.18) only becomes important when the exposure N is very large (e.g. in a national population). Let us imagine, for example, that the mean and standard deviation of q_x are 0·002 and 0·0001 respectively. If the exposure N were 1,000,000, the second-term contribution to the variance of the number of deaths would be 10,000, which is more than five times the binomial variance (1,996). If, on the other hand, the exposure were only 100,000, the second-term contribution to the variance would be 100, or half the corresponding binomial variance.

17.35 The reader needs to be aware of this source of additional variation. There is a danger, for example, of undergraduation if it is overlooked in connection with the graduation of a very large experience. (x' make longer than true value)

Annuities and assurances on individual lives

17.36 We now turn to the other sources of stochastic variation outlined in paras. 17.4–17.7.

17.37 The present value of an annuity of one per annum to a life now aged x is a random variable for two main reasons. First, because the age at death of the life is a random variable and, secondly, because the future earnings of the fund will vary in a stochastic manner. Most actuarial functions in fact are really random variables. To distinguish actuarial functions treated as random variables from the ordinary deterministic functions, we shall print the stochastic variables in heavy type.

Stochastic variation in the age at death

17.38 Let us for the moment assume a known constant interest rate i and concentrate on the effect of variation in the age at death on the present values of annuities and assurances. We shall consider a life aged x from a population with known mortality. The probability that the life will die aged $x+n$ last birthday is d_{x+n}/l_x, and it follows that the first two moments of the life annuity $\ddot{a}_x$ are given by

$$\mathscr{E}\ddot{a}_x = \sum_{n=0}^{\infty} \ddot{a}_{\overline{n+1}|}d_{x+n}/l_x = \ddot{a}_x \qquad (17.19)$$

$$\mathrm{Var}\,\ddot{a}_x = \sum_{n=0}^{\infty} (\ddot{a}_{\overline{n+1}|})^2 d_{x+n}/l_x - (\ddot{a}_x)^2. \qquad (17.20)$$

17.39 Similar formulae can also be written down for $\mathscr{E}A_x$, $\mathrm{Var}\,A_x$ and $\mathrm{cov}\,(\ddot{a}_x, A_x)$. The correlation of $\ddot{a}_x$ and A_x in fact turns out to be minus one in this situation and

$$A_x = 1 - d\ddot{a}_x \qquad (17.21)$$

(A. H. Pollard and J. H. Pollard, 1969). Sample values of the moments of $\ddot{a}_x$ and A_x based on the A1949–52 ultimate mortality table and 5 per cent interest are shown in Table 17.4.

17.40 A simple example of the use of these results is the assessment of mortality contingency loadings in non-participating whole-life assurance premiums. Consider a new whole-life policy of one on a life aged exactly x written by an office which always earns exactly 5 per cent per annum interest. The pure premium is $P_x = A_x/\ddot{a}_x$, but an office premium $P_x(1+L)$ will be charged to allow for the effects of

Table 17.4 *Moments of $\ddot{a}_x$ and A_x based on A1949–52 ultimate mortality and 5 per cent interest**

Age	Expectations		Standard deviations	
x	$\ddot{a}_x$	A_x	$\ddot{a}_x$	A_x
20	18·970	0·0967	2·11	0·100
30	17·954	0·1450	2·40	0·114
40	16.325	0·2226	3·03	0·144
50	13·978	0·3344	3·74	0·178
60	11·074	0·4727	4·04	0·192

*Source: A. H. Pollard and J. H. Pollard (1969).

adverse statistical fluctuations in the age at death. (We shall ignore expense loadings.) The present value of the office's profit from the contract is given by

$$\mathbf{Z} = P_x(1+L)\ddot{\mathbf{a}}_x - \mathbf{A}_x \tag{17.22}$$

17.41 Let us now imagine that the office writes N such contracts on independent lives all aged x. The expectation and variance of the present value of the profit to the office from this block of new business are respectively $N\mathscr{E}\mathbf{Z}$ and $N\operatorname{Var}\mathbf{Z}$. If the office is to avoid loss from this block of new business with a high probability, the loading factor L must be chosen so that

$$N\mathscr{E}\mathbf{Z} \geq 3(N\operatorname{Var}\mathbf{Z})^{\frac{1}{2}} \tag{17.23}$$

17.42 The moments of $\mathbf{Z}$ are readily determined from those of $\ddot{\mathbf{a}}_x$ and $\mathbf{A}_x$, and we deduce that

$$L \doteqdot 3C/(\mathbf{A}_x\sqrt{N}) \tag{17.24}$$

where C is the coefficient of variation of $\ddot{\mathbf{a}}_x$ (standard deviation divided by expectation). Some sample mortality loading factors are shown in Table 17.5. The figures can be used to supplement professional judgement in the area of premium loadings for non-participating business even when the policies are not all the same size or on lives the same age.

Example 17.4

A life office writes 1,500 non-participating whole-life policies on independent lives all aged 40. Each policy is for £10,000 and the annual office premium is £168.

Find the probability that the office will make a loss on this block of new business, given the following:

1 All the policies stay in force until maturity.
2 The office earns exactly 5 per cent interest per annum.
3 Initial expenses amount to £200 per policy.
4 Renewal expenses comprise 10 per cent of each renewal premium.
5 Mortality is according to the A1949–52 ultimate table.

The office's profit in respect of a particular contract
$$= 151{\cdot}2\ddot{\mathbf{a}}_{40} + 16{\cdot}8 - 200 - 10{,}000\mathbf{A}_{40}$$

$$= 627{\cdot}391\ddot{\mathbf{a}}_{40} - 10{,}183{\cdot}2 \text{ using } (17.21)$$

Table 17.5 *Whole-life premiums calculated at 5 per cent interest: the loading required to cover adverse mortality fluctuations**

Age x	Mortality loading (per cent)		
	100 new contracts	1,000 new contracts	10,000 new contracts
20	35	11	4
30	28	9	3
40	25	8	3
50	24	8	2
60	23	7	2

*Source: J. H. Pollard (1976).

The expected profit from this contract is $627 \cdot 391 \times 16 \cdot 325 - 10,183 \cdot 2 = 58 \cdot 96$.

and the variance is

$$(627 \cdot 391)^2 \times (3 \cdot 03)^2 = 3.61 \times 10^6$$

The expected profit from the block of new business is therefore

$$58 \cdot 96 \times 1,500 = 88,440$$

and the variance is

$$(3 \cdot 61 \times 10^6) \times 1,500 = (73,600)^2$$

According to the central limit theorem, the distribution of company's profit from this block of new business will be approximately normal, with mean 88,440 and standard deviation 73,600. The probability that the office will make a loss on the business is therefore

$$\frac{1}{\sqrt{(2\pi)}} \int_{-\infty}^{-\frac{88,440}{73,600}} e^{-\frac{1}{2}x^2} dx = 0 \cdot 115$$

Fluctuating interest rates

17.43 The effects of fluctuating interest rates were ignored in paras 17.38–17.42. We now take them into account. Whereas an adequate stochastic model of mortality is immediately available, there is no obvious simple stochastic model for the investment earnings of a fund, and we need to develop one.

17.44 Let us assume that the fund has an earnings rate of i_t in the year preceding time t. The corresponding force of interest is δ_t and the discounted value of one discounted to the beginning of the year is v_t.

17.45 The force of interest in year t will be related to the force of interest earned by the fund in the preceding years. If it has been rising steadily for some years, we might expect the trend upwards to continue. Conversely, if it has been falling steadily, the downward trend might be expected to continue. J. H. Pollard (1971) has proposed the following stochastic model (a second-order autoregressive process) for the force of interest:

$$\mathbf{u}_t = 2k\mathbf{u}_{t-1} - k\mathbf{u}_{t-2} + \mathbf{e}_t \qquad (17.25)$$

where

$$\mathbf{u}_t = \delta_t - \bar{\delta}$$

is the difference between the force of interest δ_t at time t and the assumed long-term average force of interest $\bar{\delta}$, and the $\{\mathbf{e}_t\}$ are independent normal random variables with zero means and common variance σ^2. The constant k, which needs to be determined, is positive and strictly less than one.

17.46 If we define

$$S_n = \sum_{t=1}^{n} \mathbf{u}_t \qquad (17.26)$$

we see that the $\{S_n\}$ are correlated normal random variables, and the present value of one due n years in the future is

$$\mathbf{v}_1\mathbf{v}_2 \ldots \mathbf{v}_n = e^{-n\bar{\delta}}\exp(-S_n) \qquad (17.27)$$

This random variable has the log-normal distribution.

17.47 Pollard has used this model to calculate the moments of $\ddot{a}_x$ and A_x when both the age at death and interest earnings are allowed to vary stochastically. He also devised a simple formula for calculating the appropriate premium loading to cover adverse statistical fluctuations in mortality and interest (J. H. Pollard, 1976). The special case $k = 0$ has been investigated by P. P. Boyle (1974), P. D. Praetz (1976), A. D. Wilkie (1976) and H. R. Waters (1978).

17.48 It is interesting to note that by far the greater proportion of the variance of $\ddot{a}_x$ (or A_x) is due to variations in the age at death. Paradoxically, the small additional variability due to fluctuations in the interest rate may be of far greater importance to a life office than the mortality variability. The office will usually write a large number of independent contracts, and the Law of Large Numbers will ensure that the total mortality effect will be relatively small. The interest effect, on the other hand, is not reduced by increasing the number of independent contracts.

Concluding remarks

17.49 The major part of this chapter has been devoted to the problem of assessing the accuracy with which estimates of the various life table and other actuarial functions can be made. Estimates calculated directly from the ungraduated observed rates were found to be unbiased, whereas those based on the graduated rates are usually biased. The bias, however, is negligible, except perhaps in the case of a very small experience. Formulae were derived for the variances of the various functions, and these can be used for calculating approximate confidence limits for these functions:

17.50 In assessing the reliability of the estimates the purpose for which they are required needs to be borne in mind, because further sources of stochastic uncertainty are usually introduced when the estimates are actually used. It is important to keep a sense of proportion, and for this reason the latter part of the chapter was devoted to variability in actuarial calculations arising from variation in the age at death of a life and stochastic variation in investment earnings.

17.51 The actual present value of an annuity on a life aged x may differ from the estimated present value for three main reasons:

(1) because the estimate of the underlying mortality in the population, based on a finite sample, was incorrect;
(2) because of stochastic variation in the age at death of the life;
(3) because of stochastic variation in the discount rate of interest

The second source of variation is usually by far the largest (para. 17.48, and Tables 17.3 and 17.4). In the case of a life office selling a large number of such contracts, however, it is probably the least important. The contracts will normally be on independent lives, and the law of large numbers ensures that the total mortality effect will be relatively unimportant. The other two sources of variation, however, are not reduced by increasing the number of independent contracts. Similar considerations apply to other actuarial functions.

17.52 In a single chapter it is only possible to outline some of the stochastic methods directly related to mortality. The models we have sketched are discussed fully in the following references, and the interested reader should study them closely.

REFERENCES

Benjamin, B. (1972). Stochastic processes as applied to life tables. *Bull. Inst. of Mathematics and its Applications*, **8**, No. 1, 12–16.

Boyle, P. P. (1974). Rates of return as random variables (unpublished manuscript).

Chiang, C. L. (1968). *Introduction to Stochastic Processes in Biostatistics*, Wiley, London, pp. 189–241.

Greenwood, M. (1926). The natural duration of cancer. *Reports on Public Health and Medical Subjects*, No. 33, 1–26.

Pollard, A. H. (1970). Random mortality fluctuations and the binomial hypothesis. *J. Inst. Actu.* **96**, 251–64.

Pollard, A. H. and Pollard, J. H. (1969). A stochastic approach to actuarial functions. *J. Inst. Actu.*, **95**, 79–113.

Pollard, J. H. (1971). On fluctuating interest rates. *Bull. de l'Assoc. Roy. des Actuaires Belges*, **66**, 68–97.

Pollard, J. H. (1976). Premium loadings for non-participating business. *J. Inst. Actu.*, **103**, 205–12.

Praetz, P. D. (1976). Maturity guarantees for benefits linked to the Australian Stock Market. *Bull. Inst. Actu. Australia and New Zealand*.

Waters, H. R. (1978). The moments and distributions of actuarial functions. *J. Inst. Actu.*, **105**, 61–75.

Wilkie, A. D. (1976) The rate of interest as a stochastic process—theory and applications. *Proc. 20th International Congress of Actuaries*, Tokyo 1976.

EXERCISES FOR CHAPTER SEVENTEEN

1 Derive (17.3).

2 (a) Prove that

$$\text{Var } a_{x:\overline{n}|} \text{ (obs.)} = \sum_{j=0}^{n-1} \{q_{x+j}/(p_{x+j}E_{x+j})\}(_jp_x v^j a_{x+j:\overline{n-j}|})^2.$$

(b) The value of $a_{60:\overline{10}|}$ at 5 per cent interest is required with mortality the same as that underlying the experience in Table 12.1. Calculate the variance of the estimate of $a_{60:\overline{10}|}$ obtained by using the observed survival rates $\{\hat{p}_x\}$.

3 Write down expressions for $\mathscr{E}A_x$, $\text{Var } A_x$ and $\text{Cov}(\ddot{a}_x, A_x)$ assuming a known fixed rate of interest, but a variable age at death.

4 What premium should the life office in example 17.4 charge so that the risk of making a loss on the block of new business is only 0·01?

CHAPTER EIGHTEEN

PRACTICAL ASPECTS OF MORTALITY

TABLES IN CURRENT USE

18.1 Some historical reference to mortality tables has been made in Chapter 1, and elsewhere specific references have been made to earlier tables where these served to illustrate method. It is proposed here to make no further reference to earlier tables but to deal only with those tables which are in common use in the United Kingdom at the present time. These are

1 English Life Tables 12 and 13.
2 Assured Lives A1949–52.
3 Assured Lives A1967–70.
4 Annuitants a(55).
5 *Impairments Study 1951; Build and Blood Pressure Study 1959.*

ENGLISH LIFE TABLE 12

18.2 The national life table is used for general demographic work. It is also used to some extent for industrial assurance because the policy-holders in this class have been traditionally regarded as close, in their mortality characteristics, to the general population. In recent years, however, the difference in mortality experience between ordinary life assurance and industrial life assurance has become less marked.

Data base

18.3 All deaths registered in England and Wales in the years 1960, 1961 and 1962 were included.

Calculation of population at risk

18.4 In previous national life tables the exposed to risk had been assumed to be sufficiently accurately measured by the population at the midpoint of the period as estimated by adjustment to the census population (for births, deaths and migration between the census date in April and 30 June of census years, the mid-years of the periods). On this occasion a more accurate method of deriving the exposed to risk was employed, as follows.

18.5 The census was taken on the night of 23–24 April 1961, i.e. 0·31 of a year after the beginning of 1961. If P_x is the population aged x last birthday enumerated at that date (i.e. x to $x+1$ exact), then on the assumption of an even spread of birthdays over the year, $0·31 P_x$ will have their xth birthdays spread between 1 January 1961 and census day and $0·69P_x$ will have their birthdays spread between 23 April 1960 and 31 December 1960, so that $0·31P_x$ are aged $x-0·31$ to x and $0·69P_x$ are aged x to $x+0·69$ on 1 January 1961. If we then go back one year to 1 January 1960 we have $0·31P_x$ at $x-1·31$ to $x-1$ and $0·69P_x$ at $x-1$ to $x-0·31$. Ignoring mortality and migration, for the moment, the contributions in years of these two groups to the exposed to risk in the period 1960–2 (rate interval = year of age x to $x+1$) would be as in Table 18.1.

18.6 If we were to repeat this analysis for $P_{x-2}, P_{x-1}, P_{x+1}, P_{x+2}$ and extract the exposures in 1960–2 at age x last birthday, we should obtain (by diagonal summation) $0·23805P_{x-2} + 0·95195P_{x-1} + P_x + 0·76195P_{x+1} + 0·04805P_{x+2}$.

18.7 This may be quickly verified by drawing the conventional exposure diagram (Figure 18.1). The line EF represents the census enumeration and the horizontal lines mark exact ages. The channels of ageing are at 45 degrees to the horizontal. We are concerned with how much of these channels lie within the rectangle ABCD, i.e. within age x last birthday in the period 1960–2. Only those enumerated at age x last birthday generate a complete parallelogram representing a whole person–year of exposure. As a fraction of this complete parallelogram, the exposures of the other age groups can be seen at a glance to be of the right order. It can also be seen geometrically that the fractions for P_{x-2} and P_{x+1} and for P_{x-1} and P_{x+2} (or any two ages separated by three years) must be complementary.

18.8 We have now to adjust this for those who died after 1 January 1960 but before census date, and who were therefore exposed to the date of death though not enumerated in P_x etc., and also for those who died after enumeration but before 31 December 1962, and who were not exposed for the full 3-year period.

18.9 Consider θ_x^{60}, the deaths in 1960 at age x last birthday. On 1 January 1960 some were aged $x-1$ and some aged x last birthday. Of the deaths occurring at time t years from the beginning of the year ($t<1$), a proportion $(1-t)$ may be assumed to have been aged x last

Table 18.1 Contributions to exposure

Age of exposure (last birthday) (1)	$A = 0{\cdot}31P_x$				$B = 0{\cdot}69P_x$			Grand total exposures (4)+(7) (8)
	Range of duration (2)	Average exposure (3)	Total exposure for A $(3)\times0{\cdot}31P$	Range of duration (5)	Average exposure (6)	Total exposure for B $(6)\times0{\cdot}69P$		
$x-2$	0·31 to 0	0·155	$0{\cdot}155\times0{\cdot}31P_x$					$0{\cdot}04805P_x$
$x-1$	1·0	1·0	$0{\cdot}31P_x$	1·0 to 0·31	0·655	$0{\cdot}655\times0{\cdot}69P_x$		$0{\cdot}76195P_x$
x	1·0	1·0	$0{\cdot}31P_x$	1·0	1·0	$0{\cdot}69P_x$		$1{\cdot}00000P_x$
$x+1$	0·69 to 1·0	0·845	$0{\cdot}845\times0{\cdot}31P_x$	1·0	1·0	$0{\cdot}69P_x$		$0{\cdot}95195P_x$
$x+2$				0 to 0·69	0·345	$0{\cdot}345\times0{\cdot}69P_x$		$0{\cdot}23805P_x$
Total		3·0	$3{\cdot}0\times0{\cdot}31P_x$		3·0	$3{\cdot}0\times0{\cdot}69P_x$		$3{\cdot}00000P_x$

[handwritten annotation in column (2): Age at 1.1.80 (x-2+1) ≤ (x-2)+1]

Note. See para. 18.5. P_x is defined as the population enumerated at the census at age x last birthday.

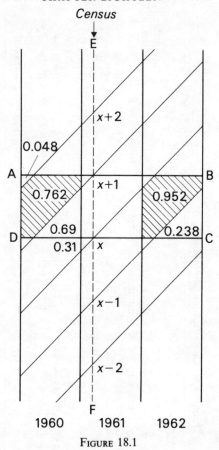

FIGURE 18.1

birthday at 1 January 1960. For each such death t years' contribution
to the central exposed to risk at age x last birthday should be added.
Of the same deaths at time t, the proportion aged $x-1$ at 1 January
1960 would be t with, again, t years' contribution to the exposure in
the calendar year of death. In this case, however, only $\frac{1}{2}t$ on average
would have been exposed at age x last birthday, the remaining $\frac{1}{2}t$ being at
age $x-1$ last birthday (assuming a uniform distribution of the xth
birthday between 0 and t from 1.1.1960).

18.10 The additional exposures for deaths in 1960 would therefore
be:

At age $x-1$ $\qquad\qquad \int_0^1 \frac{1}{2}t^2 dt = \frac{1}{6}$ years

$\qquad$ age x $\qquad \int_0^1 t(1-t).dt + \int_0^1 \frac{1}{2}t^2 . dt = \frac{1}{3}$ years

18.11 Considering the addition to exposure at age x last birthday, we must take $\frac{1}{3}$ year for each death of θ_x^{60} and $\frac{1}{6}$ year for each death of θ_{x+1}^{60}, that is exposed at $(x+1)-1$, i.e. aged x, a total of $\frac{1}{3}\theta_x^{60}+\frac{1}{6}\theta_{x+1}^{60}$. In dealing with the deaths of 1961 it is convenient to split these into θ_x^{61a} before census date and θ_x^{61b} thereafter. Once again assuming an even distribution of birthdays, we see that of the deaths aged x at time t in 1961 ($t<0\cdot31$), the first element of $(1-t)$ aged x last birthday at 1 January 1961 will have their xth birthdays centred at a point of time $\frac{1}{2}(1-t)$ from the end of 1960 $\left[\left(\frac{1+t}{2}\right)\text{ from date of death}\right]$ and so will add $(1-t)\dfrac{(1+t)}{2}$ at age x, while the second element of t with birthdays centred at $t/2$ from the beginning of 1961 will add $t\,.\,t/2$ at age x: an overall total of $\frac{1}{2}$ for each θ_x^{61a}, i.e. $\frac{1}{2}\theta_x^{61a}$. At age $x-1$ we shall have $\frac{1}{2}(1-t)(1+t)$ for the first element and $t\,.\,1$ for the second element: a total of $\frac{1}{2}(1+2t-t^2)$ for each dt, i.e.

$$\frac{1}{0\cdot31}\theta_x^{61a}\int_0^{0\cdot31}\tfrac{1}{2}(1+2t-t^2)dt \text{ or } 0\cdot639\theta_x^{61a}$$

At $x-2$ we have, for the second element above,

$$\frac{1}{0\cdot31}\theta_x^{61a}\int_0^{0\cdot31}t\,.\,\frac{t}{2}dt \text{ or } 0\cdot016\theta_x^{61a}$$

so that the corrections at age x become

$$+\tfrac{1}{2}\theta_x^{61a}+0\cdot639\theta_{x+1}^{61a}+0\cdot016\theta_{x+2}^{61a}$$

[It is not really necessary to deal with θ_x^{61a} in two elements, since if one assumes birthdays of those who die at time t to be centred at a point $(\frac{1}{2}-t)$ before 1 January 1961, the contribution to exposure is at x,

$$\frac{\theta_x^{61a}}{0\cdot31}\,.\,\int_0^{0\cdot31}\tfrac{1}{2}\,.\,dt;\text{ at age }x-1,\ \frac{\theta_x^{61a}}{0\cdot31}\int_0^{0\cdot31}(\tfrac{1}{2}+t)dt.$$

This yields a correction of $+\frac{1}{2}\theta_x^{61a}+0\cdot655\theta_{x+1}^{61a}$ which will be different from the more precise value given above only if θ_{x+1}^{61a} is significantly different from θ_{x+2}^{61a}. Note $0\cdot016\theta_{x+1}^{61a}$ is included in place of $0\cdot016\theta_{x+2}^{61a}$.] Similar reasoning is applied to θ_x^{61b} and to θ_x^{62} and the full corrections become:

$$\tfrac{1}{3}\theta_{x+1}^{60}+\tfrac{1}{6}\theta_{x+1}^{60}+\tfrac{1}{2}\theta_x^{61a}+0\cdot639\theta_{x+1}^{61a}+0\cdot016\theta_{x+2}^{61a}-0\cdot079\theta_{x-2}^{61b}$$

$$-0\cdot766\theta_{x-1}^{61b}-\tfrac{1}{2}\theta_x^{61b}-\tfrac{1}{6}\theta_{x-1}^{62}-\tfrac{1}{3}\theta_x^{62}$$

18.12 As a check we see that the coefficients for θ^{60} and θ^{62} add to $+\frac{1}{2}$ and $-\frac{1}{2}$ respectively; that the coefficients for θ^{61a} add to 1·155, i.e. the average of durations 1 and 1·31; that the coefficients for θ^{61b} add to 1·345, i.e. the average of durations 1·0 to 1·69.

18.13 In theory there should be a further adjustment for migration, but the net migration in any year is so much smaller than the number of deaths that no further correction was thought to be necessary.

18.14 The *Report* of the Government Actuary did not demonstrate, by comparison with the official mid-year studies for 1961, whether or not these correction procedures led to greater precision. The crude comparison in Table 18.2 was therefore prepared for males.

Table 18.2   *England and Wales—Males—1961*

Age	Exposed to risk as estimated by G.A.D. (000s)	G.R.O. 1961 mid-year estimate of Home population × 3 (000s)	Difference (per cent)
5–9(a)	5,040·8	5,014·2	−0·53
10–14	5,578·4	5,662·5	+1·51
15–19	5,010·2	4,944·3	−1·32
20–24	4,312·3	4,304·4	−0·18
25–29	4,352·6	4,347·0	−0·13
30–34	4,496·1	4,495·2	−0·02
35–39	4,839·0	4,818·3	−0·43
40–44	4,516·2	4,569·6	+1·18
45–49	4,707·5	4,713·0	+0·12
50–54	4,712·5	4,678·2	−0·73
55–59	4,245·3	4,243·8	−0·04
60–64	3,313·1	3,317·4	+0·13
65–69	2,469·2	2,459·7	−0·38
70–74	1,810·7	1,800·6	−0·56
75–79	1,175·7	1,168·5	−0·61
80–84	620·4	615·3	−0·82
85+	278·4	276·6	−0·65

The group (a) is the first quinary age group for which comparison can be made. The method described above did not give the exposed to risk at ages 0, 1 and 2, and at these ages the rates were calculated from records of births and deaths.

18.15 It will be seen that the discrepancies between the two sets of figures, in quinary groups, are rarely more than 1 per cent. However, the grouping would have considerable smoothing effects and it is likely that at individual ages the errors would be relatively larger. The group discrepancies are biased, it will be noted. The reader should be prepared always to justify extra complexity in adjustments of this kind, not only theoretically but also in terms of the improvement in accuracy relative to effort. In some cases the improvement may be only marginal and the detail unjustified.

Graduation

18.16　The form of mathematical curve of m_x used for E.L.T. 11 (see Chapter 14) was again applied. This was a combination of a logistic curve with a normal curve:

$$m_x = a + b[1 + \exp(-\alpha(x - x_1))]^{-1} + c[\exp(-\beta(x - x_2)^2)]$$

Don't learn actual formula. Know comb. of log. + normal

18.17　The fit of the curve was reasonably close to the data for females but for males it was not so good, mainly because the graduated curve cut through certain waves in the observed rates at ages between 32 and 52. As the *Report* points out, this graduation had to deal less with random errors (which must have been very small in such a large experience) than with systematic errors, owing to an inherent lack of precise correspondence between the deaths and the assumed exposed to risk.

18.18　To complete the graduation, it was necessary to obtain rates for the younger ages. Rates at ages 0–3 were obtained from the records of births and deaths in the years 1956 to 1962 rather than from the census enumeration. From ages 4 to 26 (for males) and 4 to 19 (for females) the rates of mortality are small (never much in excess of 1 per 1,000). It was found possible to produce smooth series of rates over these ranges for the two sexes by minor adjustments of the crude rates. The *Report* states that the hump in the curve of the rates for males at age 20 was regarded as attributable to the high accident rate among youths, and a genuine feature of the experience, which was therefore retained.

Further analysis

18.19　As is customary, rates of mortality were calculated according to marital condition for each sex, and an analysis was made of the differences between rates of mortality in the standard regions. An abridged life table was prepared for England, for Wales, and for

Greater London. The scope of the census and registration data available in a national investigation does permit detailed sub-division without any danger of relatively large sampling errors arising from small numbers.

ENGLISH LIFE TABLE 13

18.20   At the time of revision of this book, E.L.T. 13 had not been published. A copy has become available only just as the revised book is going to press. Detailed comment is therefore impracticable. It is clear, however, that the method used for estimating exposures was exactly the same as for E.L.T. 12. The shape of E.L.T. 13 rendered the graduation method of E.L.T. 12 inappropriate, and, instead, use was made of the spline No. 4 of the paper of McCutcheon and Eilbeck (1977).

18.21   A discussion of the spline functions and their use for graduation has already been provided in paras 16.21 to 16.42.

ASSURED LIVES 1949–1952 (A1949–52)

18.22   This table was compiled by the Joint Mortality Investigation Committee of the Institute of Actuaries and the Faculty of Actuaries in Scotland, to which most life-assurance offices in Great Britain regularly contribute data. Although this table is currently in use by some offices for valuation and surrender value purposes, it is being replaced by A1967–70, to which reference is made below.

Data base

The lives and deaths to be included in the Continuous Mortality Investigation (CMI) are carefully specified in instructions issued by the Joint Committee.

18.23   Deaths were included for the years 1949 to 1952 inclusive. The year 1952 had exhibited lighter mortality than 1945–50 but not as light as 1948; 1951 was a year of heavy mortality at middle and older ages on account of an influenza epidemic. It was thought that a combination of one heavy year, a fairly light year, and two moderate years would constitute an experience representative of the scale of year to year fluctuations in the mortality of assured lives. The exposed to risk was derived by the census method, i.e. from returns indicating policies in force by date of birth and curtate duration of assurance (0, 1, 2, 3, 4, and 5 and over years) at the start of each of the years 1949 to 1953 inclusive.

Scope

18.24 The data were originally sub-divided into eight classes of business, namely combinations of whole-life or endowment, with with-profit or non-profit, with medical or non-medical. It was found, as might be expected, that whole-life assurance mortality was heavier than that for endowment assurances, and that the mortality of non-medical policies was heavier than that for medical policies. No attempt was made to construct separate tables for whole-life and endowment assurances, despite the class selection, because the data were scanty in the whole-life class at young ages and in the endowment class at older ages. The next step was to decide whether or not to differentiate between medical and non-medical business. Here an interesting feature emerged, illustrating the need to analyse data sufficiently thoroughly to identify the real rather than the apparent source of class selection. Analysis showed that the major source of heterogeneity was variation between offices. In individual offices the difference in mortality between medical and non-medical business was very much diminished as compared with the data for all offices combined. The real reason for the apparently substantial class selection was that a high proportion of the total non-medical business was transacted by offices whose mortality experience was heavier than average in all classes. The overall non-medical experience was weighted with data from 'heavy' mortality offices. Differentiation according to participation in profits was also considered and rejected for the same reasons.

18.25 In view of these findings the obvious course to adopt was to concentrate on differentiating the 'light' and 'heavy' office experiences. With some intention of this kind in mind the Committee proceeded to construct a general table, based on the whole of the data, which would be representative of a 'medium' experience. Two exceptions were made:

1 At ages 50–70 the rates were made to adhere more closely to the data for whole-life assurances than to that for all classes combined, on the grounds that at those ages the sums at risk in life offices' portfolios were much greater for whole-life assurances than for endowment assurances (above age 70 endowment data virtually disappeared).

2 It was known that for many years the whole-life non-profit 'in force' data had contained paid-up policies under which all contact

had been lost with the lives assured. (In 1951 the offices were requested to exclude these paid-up policies from their returns.) This meant that the data for 1949–52 contained a substantial number of such policies, with a consequent appreciable understatement of mortality rates at extreme old age. Therefore, at ages over 80, attention was focused upon the whole-life with-profit (medical) class, while between 50 and 80 there was increasing weight given to the entire whole-life class and less to others.

Duration of selection

18.26 For examining selection the actual deaths at each duration from 0 to 4 were compared with the expected deaths according to the experience at durations 3 and over. Three features emerged. There was no rapid approach of the select rates to the ultimate. After an initial rise from duration 0 to duration 2 there was a marked flattening in the progress of the percentages from duration 2 to duration 4. In order to reach the ultimate limit it was necessary for the percentages to take a sharp upward turn at some point beyond duration 4. The factors contributing to these features were (a) prolonged initial temporary selection, (b) operation of selection by withdrawals, and (c) spurious selection caused by inherent inconsistency between the data at short and long durations. (Some of the 'heavier' offices bulked proportionately larger at duration '5 and over'.)

18.27 The Committee were inclined to reject select rates altogether and to produce only an aggregate table, but thought that this would not have been generally acceptable. They therefore compromised at a select period of two years. This experience illustrates how difficult it is, in the face of many sources of heterogeneity, to decide just how long true temporary selection really persists. It should never be imagined that the difference between $q_{[x]}$ and q_x is more than a crude estimate of the effects.

Graduation

18.28 As already indicated in Chapter 14, the need to accommodate (i) an almost flat level of q_x at young ages, (ii) a sharp upward turn between 40 and 55, and (iii) a flattening off in the upper part of the curve, suggested a Perks type curve. After experiment Beard derived a formula

$$q_x = (A + Bc^x)/(Ec^{-2x} + 1 + Dc^x)$$

The fitting of the formula was achieved empirically. Even if a 'best' fit based upon accepted techniques of statistical estimation had been desired, the complicated nature of the graduation formula would at the time have rendered the mathematical work intractable. The Committee maintained that the main object was not a statistically rigorous close fit but 'a smooth curve which would serve as a working instrument'. The parameters of the curve were therefore determined by trial and error. In the event, fidelity to the data was not sacrificed unduly. For the 'All classes' table (ages 21–95), for example, (a) 56 per cent of the values of $[\text{Actual deaths} - \text{Expected}]/\sqrt{\text{Actual}}$ were within the range 0–0·9 (assuming that the deviations followed a normal distribution approximately, it would be expected that 66 per cent would fall within this range); (b) the total deviations $\Sigma(A-E)$, irrespective of sign, amounted to 2,553 compared with $\Sigma\sqrt{A} = 2,433$; and (c) the deviations changed sign frequently up to age 55. Thereafter E tended to exceed A, but this was intentional since, as indicated above, increasing regard was to be given to the heavier whole-life with-profit (medical) experience.

18.29 This graduation is a very good example of a very effective compromise between two objectives, the elimination of irregularities and the achievement of a desired mathematical shape to the progression of q_x. While this shape was imposed, it was nevertheless designed to accommodate as faithfully as possible the well-defined features listed above, which emerged from a careful analysis of the data. This underlines the importance of experience and, above all, of thorough investigation of data as the prerequisites of reliable judgement.

ASSURED LIVES A1967–70

The data base

18.30 Apart from relating to a later period of time, the data base for the A1967–70 tables was essentially the same as for the A1949–52; essentially, that is, in the coverage of lives. The assured lives investigation was originally restricted to policies on male lives issued in the United Kingdom at standard rates of premium without surcharge, and was divided into two sections, viz. medical and non-medical. The medical section relates to lives which have been medically examined at entry and the non-medical section relates to lives accepted under a standard type of non-medical proposal form.

(In 1973 an investigation was begun of policies issued on female lives on the same basis as for policies of male lives.)

18.31 The investigation was carried out in select form, the period of selection studied being 5 years. The census method was employed and the contributing offices were asked to submit, annually, returns of the 'in force' on 1 January and of the deaths during the preceding year. Various classes of policy were excluded, e.g. policies issued outside the U.K., pure endowments, deferred assurances; a full list is given in C.M.I. *Report* No. 1 (1973). The underlying principle in the exclusions was that of consistency between deaths and 'in force'. Certain categories of death claim (e.g. suicide when the sum assured was not paid) were excluded from the returns of deaths in order to ensure that the derived tables of mortality would represent measures of the risk of death resulting in the payment of the sum assured. These categories are also set out in full in C.M.I. *Report* No. 1.

18.32 Printed forms were supplied to the offices for making the annual returns, and there were separate forms for medical and non-medical business. Individual columns were provided on the forms for durations 0 to 4, with a final column for durations 5 and over. For the 'in force' the duration at 1 January of year N was defined as— duration $= N - 1 -$ year of issue. The ages at which the policies in force were tabulated were intended to be the nearest ages on 1 January. However, various approximations were used by different offices according to their internal record systems. Deaths were to be recorded according to nearest age and curtate duration of death. Some approximation to age at death was allowed but *not* to duration.

Experience for 1967–70

18.33 The C.M.I. *Report* No. 1 provides a comparison between the experience of the period 1967–70 and that expected on the basis of A1949–52. This showed that while in the early 1960s the C.M.I. had noted some falling off in the rate of improvement of mortality as compared with previous years, the rate of improvement had reasserted itself. This was illustrated by the following relationship between observed q_x at durations 2 and over and the q_x of the A1949–52 ultimate table:

$$q_x(1967\text{–}70) = \cdot 84\, q_x\,(A1949\text{–}52) - \cdot 00016$$

$$q_x(1963\text{–}66) = \cdot 89\, q_x\,(A1949\text{–}52) - \cdot 0002$$

$$q_x(1959-62) = \cdot 91 \, q_x(A1949-52) - \cdot 0002$$

$$q_x(1953-58) = \cdot 95 \, q_x(A1949-52) - \cdot 0002$$

The improvements since 1949–52 were slightly better for assured lives than for the general population of Great Britain.

18.34 The C.M.I. *Report* No. 1 supplemented this account of improving mortality of assured lives by an analysis of mortality in 1967–70 according to cause of death. For each of several principal cause of death groups a comparison was given of the deaths expected on the basis of the rates of mortality by cause in the general population of England and Wales and those actually recorded among assured lives. Actual deaths as a percentage of expected were generally less than 100, but there were a few cause-of-death groups where the percentages were greater than the all-causes percentage. These were malignant neoplasms of bone, etc., malignant neoplasms of genito-urinary organs, malignant neoplasms of nervous system, neoplasms of lymphatic and haematopoietic tissue, acute myocardial infarction, cerebro-vascular disease (non-medical experience), other diseases of the circulatory system, and all the accident and violence groups with the exception of suicide in the non-medical experience.

Choice of select period

18.35 When the actual deaths for each duration and quinquennial age-group separately were expressed as percentages of the graduated rates for durations 5 and over, it was found that the percentages rose from duration 0 to duration 2 and were then roughly level until duration 4. This implied that at some later duration there would be a steeper rise to an ultimate level above 100 per cent. This was true of both medical and non-medical experience (and had been noted in the A1949–52 data). The difference between the '2 and over' and '5 and over' graduated rates was small, so that whole-life or endowment assurance functions would not differ substantially whether a 2-year or a 5-year select table was used, but the Committee thought that it might not be appropriate to use a two-year select table for the calculation of short-term temporary assurance rates. They therefore prepared graduated tables on both a 2-year and a 5-year select period. The view expressed by the Committee and confirmed in the discussion on the paper was that the 2-year select period table would be the most suitable as a basis for the construction of monetary tables. The 5-year table is, of course, available for those who wish to use it.

Graduation

18.36 Over almost the entire age range of the table a mathematical formula was fitted to q_x/p_x. This was

$$q_x/p_x = A - Hx + Bc^x$$

and since $q_x/p_x = f(x)$ transforms to $q_x = f(x)/(1 + f(x))$, this amounts to

$$q_x = \frac{A - Hx + Bc^x}{1 + A - Hx + Bc^x}$$

The parameters were derived by maximum likelihood estimation. The considerations leading to this choice of formula are set out in the paper submitted to the Institute of Actuaries and the Faculty of Actuaries in 1974 by the Joint Mortality Investigation Committee. [This paper and the following discussion is worth reading in full; it broke considerable new ground.] The main factors to be accommodated by the graduation were (1) while mortality rates increased almost exponentially from the late twenties to the upper end of the age range so that a Gompertz formula almost fitted, there was nevertheless an upward bulge, i.e. q_x plotted on logarithmic-linear paper followed not a straight line but a line slightly but significantly curved in the middle (bowed away from the abscissa); and (2) q_x declined with increasing age from the early teens to the early twenties.

18.37 Because the actual experience was erratic at the extreme ages, the curve was fitted only from $15\frac{1}{2}$ to $89\frac{1}{2}$. The fitted curve was cut off at age 17, and below this age an arbitrary series of q_x was constructed on the basis of population data; this procedure was adopted to deal with the paradox that the observed q's were higher for the age-group $15\frac{1}{2}$–$17\frac{1}{2}$ than for the group $18\frac{1}{2}$–$20\frac{1}{2}$, yet it was known that the bulk of the deaths were from vehicle accidents and that they should start to rise in incidence progressively from age 17, the minimum age for a driving licence. (Tests of the graduation are shown in the Institute and Faculty paper.)

TABLES FOR LIFE OFFICE ANNUITANTS a(55)

18.38 Since there is a need to make allowance for the future improvement in mortality rates when dealing with annuity business, these tables, though based on the then current experience of life-office annuitants, used a process of projection. The basic objective was a double-entry table in which the rate of mortality varied with both the attained age and the calendar year (in which the age would be attained). The main tables produced were those deemed to be appropriate for immediate life annuities purchased in 1955.

The baseline

18.39 The choice of a baseline for the projection for males presented some difficulty. The observed mortality of male annuitants at durations 5 and over in the period 1946–8 was exceptionally light at some age-groups and heavy at others, and the shape of the curve of death rates was unlike any normal pattern. It was not known whether this was due to class selection or to paucity of data. Examination of the data for durations 5 and over for other years of experience provided no better basis for a table. Examination of the data for durations 1 and over showed that, for the two years 1947–8, the rates were more consistent from one age-group to another (and these data were used for the single-entry table described below in para. 18.50). The double-entry table baseline was, therefore, derived by working backwards from a duration 1 and over to a hypothetical duration '5 and over' table. For this purpose it was assumed that the same relationships between the different durational rates at any age would apply to males as to females and that the ratios derived from female data (see below) could be used. (As the duration '1 and over' rates for males applied to 1947–8, they had to be slightly modified so that the duration '5 and over' would relate to 1947.) The duration '5 and over' rates thus obtained were graduated by the Perks formula:

$$q_x = (A + Bc^x)/(1 + Dc^x)$$

18.40 Below age 60 the data were scanty and unreliable, and the

Table 18.3

| Age | Duration t | |
x	0	1–4
50–75	0·60	0·83
80	0·63	0·85
85	0·67	0·88
90	0·72	0·91

graduated rates were further adjusted to make them consistent with the experience of assured lives in 1947–8.

18.41 The next step was to derive rates of mortality appropriate to durations 0–4 by asuming that $q_{[x-t]+t} = \phi(x,t).q_x$, where $\phi(x,t)$ varied with x and t. Values of $\phi(x,t)$ were derived, as already indicated, from inspection of the ratio of actual deaths in the experience for females at durations 0, 1, 2, 3, 4 to those expected on the basis of the duration '5 and over' rates, over the period 1921–48.

18.42 The values of $\phi(x,t)$ in Table 18.3 were used for both sexes.

18.43 It was further assumed that when q_x had been projected for future calendar years, this same value of $\phi(x,t)$ could be regarded as applicable to each calendar year.

18.44 To provide a baseline for females, the female annuitants' mortality experience at durations 5 and over for the period 1946–8 was graduated by a Makeham formula, with adjustments at the older ages. At ages below 60 the annuitants' experience did not contain adequate data to produce reliable rates, and the Makeham graduation yielded values at these ages that were relatively high in comparison with the rates for assured lives. Though, as we have seen, it was possible for males to determine the base-line at ages 40–59 by reference to assured lives experience 1947–8, there were no comparable data for females, and therefore it was decided to fix the baseline for females at ages 40–49 as 80 per cent of the baseline for males. The intermediate rates for ages 50–59 were then fixed to provide a smooth join with the Makeham graduation of the female annuitants' experience at age 60. (See Chapter 14 on blending.)

The projection

18.45 The basic projection formula was a simple geometrical progression. The value of q_x in year $(N+k)$ was assumed to be related to q_x in year N by the formula:

$$^{(N+k)}q_x = {}^{(N)}q_x r_x^k$$

where r_x was the annual reducing factor at age x. The construction of the double-entry table required the application of a series of factors r_x to the baseline values of q_x.

18.46 The data available for deriving the r_x series consisted of the mortality experience of immediate life annuitants for the following periods:

1 the British Offices experience 1863–93;
2 the British Offices experience 1900–20;
3 the Continuous Mortality Investigation 1921–48.

18.47 In order to minimize the effects of temporary initial selection, the experience of the first 5 years of duration was excluded. The projected rates in the double-entry table would therefore be appropriate to durations 5 and over.

18.48 There are two kinds of influence determining the changes over time in q_x for annuitants. On the one hand, there is the systematic progressive reduction in mortality arising from improvements in hygiene and in the level of living; on the other, there is the effect of financial conditions upon the class of life entering the experience. The second influence is less systematic and certainly not always in the same direction. It would be desirable to smooth it out of any process of estimating r_x, and this is why such an extensively long experience was used. From this experience average percentage rates of reduction per annum and corresponding annual reducing factors were first calculated for female lives over the period 1880–1945. To these factors the following formula was fitted:

$$r_x = 0.9784 + 0.0002x$$

18.49 When the experience for male lives was investigated, it was found that the average annual rates of reduction over the period 1880–1945 were substantially lower than for females. There was some doubt as to how far this was a reflection of the relatively slower rate of improvement in the mortality of males as compared with females (a general population feature) or to more intense class selection in male annuitants compared with female annuitants. In these circumstances there was reluctance to project, for males, lower reduction factors than for females, and it was decided to use the same values of r_x for males as for females.

The single-entry table

18.50 For practical use a table was needed, so that at any given age the rate of mortality would be an average of rates for different calendar years appropriate to the period over which annuity calculations were being made. The rate of mortality in this table was taken as the rate for the calendar year in which age x would be attained by persons aged x and under, taking out annuities in 1955.

One year was substituted for 5 years as the length of the select period.
18.51   The steps were as follows:

1   The determination of a baseline appropriate to durations 1 and over for the purpose of projection. For females: Continuous Mortality Annuitants' Experience 1946–8 quinary pivotal values $52\frac{1}{2}$–$97\frac{1}{2}$, obtained by King's formula applied to exposed to risk and deaths. For males: Annuitants' experience 1947–8, ages $52\frac{1}{2}$–$77\frac{1}{2}$; assured lives experience 1947–8 (durations 3 and over), $82\frac{1}{2}$–$97\frac{1}{2}$ (an experience lighter than that of annuitants at these higher ages).

2   Calculation of mean intervals taken by entrants in 1955 to attain each successive age of the life table, estimated from an inspection of the age distribution of the 'in force' at duration 0 in the period 1946–8. For example, for female entrants aged $x = 70$ and under, the average number of years before the attainment of age 70 was 7·0, to which must be added 8 years (the difference between the baseline and 1955 to obtain the number of years for which the value of q_{70} should be projected from the baseline.

3   Calculation of projected rates of mortality (pivotal values, ungraduated) using the annual reducing factors already employed in the double-entry table over the intervals estimated in stage (2), e.g. $q_{82\frac{1}{4}}$ for female lives is derived as follows:

Mean interval to attainment of $82\frac{1}{2}$ interpolated from above table	= 14·9
Add for interval 1947 to 1955	= 8·0
	22·9
$r_{82\frac{1}{4}} = 0\cdot9784 + 0\cdot0002(82\frac{1}{2})$	= 0·9949
$q_{82\frac{1}{4}}$ from 1946–8 female annuitants' experience at durations 1 and over	= 0·09386
Hence required $q_{82\frac{1}{4}} = 0\cdot09386(0\cdot9949)^{22\cdot9}$	= 0·08349

4   Such values were calculated for ages $52\frac{1}{2}$, $55\frac{1}{2}$ ... $97\frac{1}{2}$ and graduated by the Perks formula, $q_x = (A + Bc^x)/(1 + Dc^x)$. A similar procedure was followed for males.

5   Ratios of q_x had to be determined to complete the table by the addition of select rates for duration 0. This ratio was taken as 0·60 up to age 75, increasing to 0·63 at age 80 and 0·72 at age 90.

18.52   The monetary tables were thenceforward referrred to as the a(55) tables to indicate that they were appropriate to new entrants in 1955.

Other tables in preparation

18.53 It may be mentioned that other tables in preparation by the C.M.I. which are likely to come into general use are the following

1 Tables for male and female annuitants to replace the a(55) tables (which are described in para. 18.38). These will be based on the experience of immediate annuitants during 1967–70, the details of which are set out in C.M.I. *Report* No. 1. The graduation of the rates of mortality derived from this experience was achieved by fitting a polynomial to $\log(q_x/p_x)$, i.e.

$$\log(q_x/p_x) = \sum_{r=0}^{n} a_r x^r.$$

The reasons for this choice of curve are set out in C.M.I. *Report* No. 2. The C.M.I. are preparing a table for a particular calendar year in the future which will be broadly appropriate to the mix of business in force over the medium-term future. The year 1990 has been chosen, and the projection of the mortality is effectively to be by the application of a constant reduction factor applied to q_x/p_x. In practice there is to be a deduction from age approximating to this reduction factor. The reason for this choice of year and a full discussion of the method of projection is given in C.M.I. *Report* No. 3.

2 Tables of mortality after retirement for pensioners based on the experience of life office pensioners for 1967–70. These will also be forecast to 1990, and the methods of graduation and projection are the same as for the new annuitants' tables. The details are also given in C.M.I. *Report* No. 3. These tables will be based not on lives but on amounts of pensions, to take account of the facts that those with larger pensions have generally lighter mortality and that, as schemes increase in maturity in the future, average pensions (as a proportion of pre-retirement income) are likely to increase. Greater weight should therefore be given to the lighter mortality experience, and basing the rates on amounts of pensions achieves this.

3 Tables of sickness rates for permanent health insurance. These have already been discussed in Chapter 7.

IMPAIRMENTS

18.54 The survival prospects of people with particular recognizable and commonly occurring impairments (e.g. diabetes) are of interest not only to actuaries in life insurance, who have to decide the terms on which such people can be insured, but also to medical workers generally and to demographers. The only proper approach is that of the longitudinal study—following up a particular group of lives, specified at the outset of the study, and observing their mortality as it is experienced. While a number of *ad hoc* studies have been organized, the cost in manpower of keeping in touch with a group of people who, the better they feel the more reluctant they are to maintain contact, and who in any case change their addresses during the course of the follow-up, makes such studies formidable undertakings. The life offices have the advantage that the machinery of insurance both facilitates the specification of the groups (among those medically examined before acceptance) and the subsequent follow-up (premiums have to be paid, and, except in rare circumstances, someone applies for the sum assured on the death of the policy-holder). Life-insurance records provide, therefore, an important source of data.

18.55 The general method is as follows:

1 Define a sufficiently homogeneous group satisfying observable criteria and ensure that this group is identified in the life-office records.
2 Observe the deaths in each year of experience.
3 Calculate the related exposed to risk to allow for entrants and exits in the normal way.
4 Apply a standard mortality table to calculate the expected deaths.
5 Compare stages 2 and 4, usually expressing 2 as a percentage of 4.

18.56 The comparison is normally made separately for the two sexes and within reasonably narrow age-groups (it is sometimes important to know whether the impairment effect is uniform over all ages or whether there is an age gradient in the effect). Strictly the standard table used to calculate expected deaths should relate to unimpaired lives. It is not always possible to produce such a table, and it may be necessary to use a table based on lives accepted at standard rates of premium; these will include some with impairments not considered serious enough to warrant a surcharge.

18.57 There are two standard works of reference. The first is the *Impairment Study 1951*. This was based on the records of twenty-seven offices in the U.S.A. and Canada and covered an average duration of exposure of more than 6 years for 725,000 impaired lives. Mortality differentials were assessed for a large range of impairments, e.g. heart murmurs of various kinds, epilepsy, asthma, duodenal ulcer, diabetes and goitre, to mention only a few. Generally the assessment was made, as indicated above, by comparing actual deaths with those expected on the basis of a standard table for the same ages and durations of policy. This was followed in 1960 by the *Build and Blood Pressure Study 1959*, again compiled by the Society of Actuaries. It covered the ordinary life insurance experience of twenty-six companies in the U.S.A. and Canada between 1935 and 1954. The build study covered 4,900,000 lives and the blood pressure study 3,900,000 lives. The same technique of comparing actual and expected deaths was employed. The data were grouped according to sex, age, weight, height, and the presence or absence of minor impairment and blood pressure, and the mortality differentials were related to these variables both singly and in combination. A further study is currently in course of preparation and will be published partly in 1979, under the title of *Build Study 1979*, and partly in 1980 under the title of *Blood Pressure Study 1979*. There has been some striking improvement in the relative mortality of the overweights and hypertensives as a result of favourable developments in medicine and underwriting.

18.58 The Society of Actuaries have also published a book entitled *Medical Risks—Patterns of Mortality and Survival*, which has digested and converted a variety of clinical and other mortality studies into a uniform life-table format of mortality rates, survival rates and mortality ratios. The data were known to exist but they were in many published articles scattered throughout the medical literature. The statistics refer to risk factors identified in groups of people under follow-up observation. The term 'risk factor' is used to include the history or presence of a specific disease or continued exposure to a hazardous occupation or habit, the presence of an abnormal finding on physical examination, or an abnormal medical test result. Almost all these risks, therefore, are of a medical nature. The abstracts of the studies are classified in broad disease categories, with associated chapters of interpretative text. Trends in mortality and new methods of treatment are commented upon where information is available, and references are given to additional papers which may be of interest. Only one-third of the abstracts are based on insured-lives data. Many of the abstracts relate to diseases for which no insured-lives data exist, and it is therefore possible to evaluate

some risks which hitherto have been considered uninsurable, and to consider extending insurance cover to more severely impaired lives.
18.59 Reference should also be made to the only extensive British Study on which a report by the investigators (Preston and Clarke, 1966) appeared under the title 'An investigation into the mortality of impaired lives during the period 1947–63'. This investigation is a continuing one based on the records of a single large life office. The investigation was designed to measure the mortality experienced within specified classes of impairment with a view to developing bases for assessing future ratings. There are nine main groups of impairment (circulatory, stomach and intestines, nervous disorders, tuberculosis, endocrine, underweight and overweight, respiratory (excluding tuberculosis), urinary, tumours) but these are sub-divided by other factors. For example, the circulatory disease group is sub-divided according to weight and blood pressure, and family history of cardio-vascular disease. Other groups are divided both according to the specific disease entity and some measure of severity. For each group, actual deaths and those expected on the basis of the mortality of assured lives accepted at standard rates of premium are given. A further investigation by R. D. Clarke, covering the years 1964–73, has been published (1979). Mention might also be made of the Birmingham Actuarial Society's study of the mortality of diabetics (Hayward and Lucena, 1965).

REFERENCES

Clarke, R. D. (1979). The mortality of impaired lives 1964–73. *J. Inst. Actu.*, 106.

Continuous Mortality Investigation (1953). a(55) Table for Annuitants. Preference to tables. Institute of Actuaries and Faculty of Actuaries.

Continuous Mortality Investigation *Reports*, No. 1 (1973), No. 2 (1976), No. 3 (1978). Institute of Actuaries and Faculty of Actuaries.

General Register Office (1969). *English Life Table 12. Decennial Supplement England and Wales, 1961*, H.M.S.O.

Hayward R. E. and Lucena B. C. (1965). An investigation into the mortality of diabetics. *J. Inst. Actu.*, **91**, 286.

Institute of Actuaries (1956). Mortality of assured lives. *J. Inst. Actu.*, **82**, 3.

Joint Continuous Mortality Investigation Committee (1974). Considerations affecting the preparation of standard tables of mortality. *J. Inst. Actu.*, **101**, 133; and *T.F.A.*, **34**, 135.

McCutcheon, J. J. and Eilbeck, J. C. (1977). Experiments in graduation of the English Life Tables (No. 13) data. *T.F.A.* **35**, 281–96.

Office of Population Censuses and Surveys (1979). *English Life Table 13.* H.M.S.O.

Preston, T. W. and Clarke, R. D. (1966). An investigation into the mortality of impaired lives during the period 1947–63. *J. Inst. Actu.*, **92**, 27.

Society of Actuaries (1954). *Impairment Study 1951.*

Society of Actuaries (1960). *Build and Blood Pressure Study 1959*, 2 vols.

EXERCISES FOR CHAPTER EIGHTEEN

1 In a certain country there is a complete system of death registration, deaths being registered at age last birthday, and censuses are held on 7 August every 10 years, the population being enumerated at individual ages. Life tables are constructed from the population enumerated at the census, and the deaths in the calendar year of the census and in the preceding and following calendar years.

Derive an expression for the exposed to risk of death (in central form) at age x, in terms of the census population and the deaths in the three years. Define clearly any symbols you use.

2 Show how all the constants in Barnett's graduation formula $q_x/p_x = A + Hx + Bc^x$ can be derived.

3 Explain in general terms how mortality was projected for the a(55) tables. Is the same procedure being adopted for the a(90) tables?

4 What method of graduation was used for the a(55) tables?

5 What was the duration of selection for the A1949–52 tables? What were the considerations leading to this decision?

6 What method of graduation was used for the A1949–52 tables and how was it justified?

7 What method of calculation of exposures has been used in the calculation of rates of mortality for the A1967–70 tables and how has the choice of select period been justified?

8 Give an account of the considerations leading to the choice of Barnett's graduation formula for the A1967–70 tables.

CHAPTER NINETEEN

SOCIAL AND ECONOMIC FACTORS IN MORTALITY

19.1 Social, economic and cultural factors are as important in influencing mortality differentials, especially for specific medical causes of death, as the more commonly (and more easily) measured factors of age, sex and marital condition.

19.2 The main difficulties in measurement are (1) assessment of cause of death, and especially of that element in the chain of morbid events leading to death at which the influence of environmental factors can be recognized, (2) recording of the social and economic characteristics of the population during life and death, and (3) relating, within each axis of classification, deaths to the specific population at risk.

19.3 Death is the end result of a chain of events which may occupy a short space of time as in sudden death in a road accident, or may be prolonged over a number of years, even decades, as in some degenerative conditions. The internationally accepted system of certification, and therefore of classification, of cause of death calls for the assessment of an underlying cause of death, i.e. a condition which may be regarded as the first of the chain of events leading to death. What is identifiable as the primary condition may not be recognized until quite late in a period of illness of which death may be an inevitable end result. Measurements of mortality must be conducted within the framework of available statistical analysis. Such measurements must therefore be in terms not of the whole continuum of events leading to death but of those, summarized in the death certificate, which can be recognized in medical practice.

19.4 The human body is a complex organism in continual reaction with the environment in which it exists, and it is a matter of some difficulty to isolate those features of the environment which may have a bearing either on the inception of the fatal chain of events or on the events themselves, especially when the events observed may only be those medically recognizable in a terminal phase. The illness leading to death may occur when the person is in a social environment quite different from that which perhaps in some subtle way has predisposed him to the observed illness. Factors affecting this predisposition may go back further still; they may not be environmental but genetic.

19.5   Quite apart from those factors which affect mortality and which are clearly seen to operate from outside the human body—for example, injury, exposure, infection—there are others which covertly disturb bodily function or affect bodily wear and tear; they may operate only to alter the rate of growing old and the speed of degeneration.

Definition of social and economic factors

19.6   We are concerned with a broad spectrum of elements which determine man's interaction with external conditions: his resistance to the inimical forces of nature, his approach to the economic struggle to supply himself with living needs, his position in society, participation in group behaviour, and attitude to social mores. We regard this whole process of adaptation to external stresses as reflective of health; we regard failure to adapt as ill-health; we focus upon this process as the mechanism of mortality variation. There are numerous distinct elements in the environment which influence this process of adaptation: the mode of employment and the associated working conditions; intelligence and educational attainment; and other elements in the level of living—nutrition, clothing, housing, access to medical care and other services which foster well-being, even entertainment and sport—most of which are purchasable and are therefore related to income. Then, too, there are the influences of cultural background, religion, social customs, art forms and modes of emotional exprssion.

19.7   The impact of community values on the implementation of programmes of health improvement or disease prevention has been well illustrated in the case-studies collection by Paul and Miller (1955). In health education there is always the obstacle presented by cultural features which reflect the fundamental moral code of social conduct. Even the comparatively simple process of improving the consumption of cow's milk may be obstructed by the antithetical association, heavily charged with emotion, of cattle with witchcraft. In the sphere of psychiatry the irrational fear and suspicion of the abnormal is often a barrier to the rehabilitation of the mentally ill within the community. Even the introduction of such a simple habit of rural hygiene as boiling drinking water can be opposed by quite complicated behavioural patterns.

19.8 In some instances the connexion between the isolated factor and economic conditions may seem to be rather remote, but it is nevertheless real. For example, atmospheric pollution, though widespread over a geographical area, has to be more endured by those whose economic circumstances are such as to prevent them from moving their domicile or their employment to more salubrious areas. In general those who dwell in atmospherically polluted industrial areas of the north of England are of lower socio-economic groups than those who dwell in the south, and they have a higher incidence of respiratory disease (General Register Office, 1954). Similarly it very often is the case that the risk of accidental injury or other occupational hazard is greater for those employments into which the more necessitous members of the community have been forced.

The measurement of social and economic factors

19.9 If observation of the cause of death is necessarily superficial, observation of the variation in social, economic and cultural environment is equally lacking in specificity, for in describing the surroundings of man we are dealing with a whole complex of elements of which we are well aware but which are difficult to quantify over the large groups in which the related mortality variations are to be observed. In the individual person it is practicable to measure or record employment, nutrition, housing conditions, ventilation, exposure to elements, urbanization, position in family, educational attainment, religion, attitudes to people and social aspirations, domestic situation, participation in household life, social and physical habits, sleep, access to medical services, attitude to hygiene, intelligence and adaptability. Some of these records will be descriptive and not susceptible to statistical or group measurement. For many of the others it is not possible to obtain specific masurements for defined groups of persons.

19.10 What is more important, it is not possible in relation to social and economic factors to treat human beings as if they were forms of plant life capable of being subjected to designed factorial experiments to test environmental influences. One cannot submit a specific group of persons to a defined set of economic circumstances, not even in the least benevolent of totalitarian regimes. Apart from the ethical problem, there are practical difficulties. Economic and social conditions emerge from the interaction of people of diverse characteristics living together in groups; the economic and social conditions both determine and are determined by the behaviour and movement of the individuals in the group. It would be extremely difficult at one and the same time to create a stable set of economic circumstances and to separate a particular segment of the social group to be subjected to these circumstances.

19.11 The next best thing is to discover, in the population, segments which are existing naturally and which are homogeneous in relation to specific factors, so that they would, as it were, lay themselves out as a factorial design. For example, if one wanted to investigate the independent effects of socio-economic level (as measured, for example, by the percentage of the economically active population in the employer, managerial and professional groups) and housing density (persons per room in dwelling), one could proceed to attempt to choose administrative areas $a,b,c,d,...$ (where the symbols stand for the names of the areas) according to Table 19.1.

Table 19.1

Socio-economic level (percentage of economically active population in employer, managerial, professional groups)	Housing density, category				
	1	2	3	4	5
0–4	a	m	e	c	
	h	x	j	u	
	l				
5–9	n	b			
	w	k	etc.		
10–14	etc.				

19.12 The population of areas b and k form a group uniquely specified in relation to socio-economic group and housing density. Other groups are also uniquely defined in relation to different combinations of socio-economic status and housing density. It would then be possible to make comparisons of mortality between groups of areas, vertically to hold housing density constant, or horizontally to hold socio-economic status constant; or alternatively a multiple regression analysis could be made in order to measure the relative contributions of the two factors to the explanation of the inter-area variance in mortality rates.

19.13 It is, however, rarely possible to obtain either a sufficient diversity of areas or even to make such a prior selection of areas. More often the data are limited to a number of adjacent areas for which the necessary population and death statistics are furnished, and it is necessary to make what one can of the diversity of indicators available. An important difficulty here is that the social index (whatever it may be) will be an average value which may conceal considerable heterogeneity within the area (since the areas have not been selected on the grounds of homogeneity). An example of the difficulties of interpretation that arise in such conditions of heterogeneity has been given by Benjamin (1965).

The level of living

19.14 If we are to be forced back upon rather general measures of social conditions, we come to a problem of growing importance and one of great difficulty though it is slowly yielding to treatment—the measurement of levels of living.

19.15 The United Nations has concerned itself very much with this problem, and has organized studies and conferences, culminating in a report of a Committee of Experts convened by the Secretary General (1954). The UN report, which has received further and developing study by international organizations, was couched in general terms and proposed twelve components: health, food and nutrition, education, conditions of work, employment situation, aggregate consumption and savings, transportation, housing, clothing, recreation, social security, and human freedom. The following paragraphs provide comments on some of the components.

Nutrition

19.16 A great deal is now known about diseases arising from specific excesses or deficiencies in diet, and about the mortality that is likely to ensue. It is necessary to distinguish between a situation where, as a result of lack of economic development, war or catastrophe, supplies of food are generally scarce or of poor quality, and a situation where food supplies are generally ample in quality but either because of poverty, ignorance or bad housekeeping (often engendered by bad housing) nutritional diseases arise.

19.17 There are still vast areas of the world where population pressure is an obstacle to emergence from primitive agriculture of low productivity; where marginal improvements in productivity are absorbed by a greater growth in the number of mouths to feed; where attempts to promote urban industrialization only make matters worse by transferring labour from the land; or where there is a shortage of capital to sustain economic development—a shortage which cannot be filled by personal savings because per capita income is desperately low. As a consequence there are hundreds of millions of people who do not get enough of anything, let alone the right things, to eat. In these parts of the world mortality is relatively high—from subnutrition rather than malnutrition.

19.18 As regards qualitative as distinct from quantitative deficiencies, there are diseases like kwashiorkor (protein deficiency), rickets (lack of calcium), scurvy (lack of ascorbic acid), beri-beri (vitamin and other deficiencies), and pellagra (lack of tryptophan required for the synthesis of nicotine acid in the body); but it is difficult to measure their contribution to mortality because the countries in which they are rife are those less-developed countries where mortality records are necessarily poor, or non-existent. (It is worth remembering that, at present, only one-third of the world's population is covered by enforceable systems of vital registration.)

19.19 It is even more difficult to assess the role of those nutritional deficiencies, most of them associated with adverse social conditions, that do not give rise to disabling symptoms but nevertheless result in a general lowering of well-being. It is generally believed, for example, that—aside from the advent of new drugs and antibiotics, changes in the virulence of organisms, and advances in mass immunization—some part of the dramatic reduction in mortality from infectious disease in children in Britain in the past 30 years can be attributed to improved resistance following a general rise in the nutritional level.

19.20 Here again we are prevented from making any specific assessment of the role of nutrition by the interference of other associations; nutritional deficiency is associated with relative poverty, with which also is associated poor parental care, insanitary housing conditions, and higher incidence of respiratory and other infections. The grossly undernourished die with specific signs of their dietary deficiency; the less obviously ill-nourished may deteriorate on this account more rapidly than their more fortunate fellows, but at their deaths the evidence may be overlaid by the marks of other factors.

19.21 At the other end of the scale there is over-feeding and obesity. Here the picture is a little clearer. Excessive body weight subjects the cardiovascular system to excessive strain; in addition, there is a specific association between obesity and diabetes mellitus. There are other physical consequences of excessive fat: bronchitis, abdominal hernia, gall-bladder disease, arthritis of the hips and knees, and restricted movement leading to higher risks of accidents.

19.22 Though the relationship between obesity and mortality is clear, the operation of social and economic factors is not so clear. While there is considerable variation in metabolism and in activity from one individual to another, so that one person would grow fat on a diet that would leave another person slim, it remains true that for any one person obesity results from eating more calorific food than is required to support actual activity. It is also true that overfeeding can be, and is, indulged in by those whose incomes permit it; that is by the rich rather than by the poor. However, to the extent that poor people may substitute cheaper carbohydrates for dearer protein in their diets, obesity is often also associated with poverty.

19.23 There is commonly a somewhat complicated situation in which affluence, by increasing total intake, and poverty, by affecting the dietary consitutents of a lowered intake, may both encourage the development of obesity and of higher mortality risk.

Occupation

19.24 For a proper study of the effect of occupation as such on mortality, we need to know not only the number of deaths from each cause by age and sex in each occupation (and if possible by duration of engagement in the occupation) but also the relative population at risk, i.e. the average numbers engaged in the occupation, similarly classified. On a national basis it is not practicable to attempt to obtain information of duration of engagement in the occupation either at a population census or at death registration. Details of occupation are recorded at the population census and, apart from the omission of the durational element, this enables populations at risk in particular occupations applicable to periods of time close to the census date to be derived. Occupation of the deceased is routinely furnished by the 'informant' at death registration, and it is customary for the registration authorities in some countries to tabulate this information for years surrounding the census, and to prepare reports on occupational mortality. The most recent investigation in England and Wales (General Register Office, 1978) relates to the period 1970–72.

19.25 It is usual in the investigations carried out by the Registrar

General of England and Wales to restrict consideration to the occupied and retired population of ages 15–64, and to allow for varying age structure within the range by standardization. Separate examination is made of males, single women and married women. In studies prior to the most recent investigation of 1970–72 the married women were classified by the occupation of their husbands. This was to provide a means of obtaining an indication of real occupational factors. It was considered that if wives showed the same excess mortality as the husbands for a particular occupation, it was implicit that a general environment or socio-economic factor was the cause rather than a true occupation hazard. However, this technique is no longer justified, since a much larger proportion of the married women are now in paid employment, with occupational risks of their own. Moreover it has been shown in the report of the 1970–72 investigation that occupations of husbands and wives tend to be closely correlated, so that they have similar working environments.

Difficulties of interpretation

19.26 The interpretation of occupational mortality data is much more difficult than the calculation of the indices.

19.27 Occasional vagueness in the entry of occupation in census returns and death registers places a strain upon the capacity of the coding clerk to make a 'reproducible' assignment to an occupation unit, i.e. an assignment that would be made by any other coder faced with the same description; there is thus no guarantee that in such circumstances the same assignment would be made for the same person both at census and death. Nor is it certain that in the event of death soon after the census date the same description will be used as at the census, since the informant may refer to the occupation carried out for the greater part of the lifetime of the deceased rather than to the occupation in which the deceased was most recently engaged. For example, a police sergeant who retires comparatively early in life may take up a clerical occupation of a relatively minor character to supplement his pension and give him an active interest; at his death it is very likely that the widow or other relative will still consider him to be a 'retired police sergeant'.

19.28 There is also a natural tendency for a householder completing a census schedule to elevate the status of his occupation, and for relatives to do the same at the registration of his death. This may take the form of using a description which implies a higher degree of skill or of supervisory capacity than is in fact applicable. If there were the same degree of elevation at both census and death registration, there would be errors in the statistics of an absolute character but differentials would not be distorted. However, it has been found that the conditions under which the census is carried out—the prior propaganda, the instructions and examples on the census schedule, the fact that the occupation entry is only part of a more extended discipline (including reference to industry and work place)—tend to make the census occupation entries more accurate than those made at registration.

19.29 If it is thought that the net result of discrepancies between the information source of the numerator of the death rate (the death registration) and that of the denominator of the death rate (the census record) is likely to be important, these can be eliminated by carrying out a matching of the two records before the calculation of the specific occupational death rates. This has been done in the United States of America (Hauser and Kitagawa, 1961) in connexion with the occupational mortality investigation associated with the 1960 population census. However, such an operation is expensive, since in order to permit analysis of specific occupational groups, a large number of deaths (500,000 in the U.S. investigation) has to be matched. Bearing in mind that, for reasons given below, this type of investigation is only a crude instrument for detecting occupational risks and that, for broad socio-economic comparisons, the errors are not so important, this degree of refinement would usually have to be weighed very carefully against other demands upon statistical resources.

19.30 The studies of occupational mortality are also handicapped by the fact that the information both at census and at death is related in most cases to the immediately antecedent occupation. While the census information probably gives a fair approximation to the mean numbers at risk in the different occupations, the deaths will be biased in the direction of lighter occupations to the extent to which failing health may lead workers to forsake heavier for lighter employment. For example, the high mortality apparently associated with such occupations as machine-minding, basket-making or newspaper selling, is probably entirely due to this factor of self-selection: these lighter occupations being taken up as an adaptation to pre-existing chronic illness or disability or to illness emerging during a former and more strenuous occupation. The extent of this error is not known; it is probably corrected to some extent by a tendency, noted above, to refer back to the occupation with which the deceased was associated for most of his life. Ideally, as we have already said, deaths and numbers at risk should be classified by duration of employment, but the difficulties of obtaining accurate information even at the census, let alone at death registration, are too great to be overcome with present resources.

19.31   Finally, there is the overriding difficulty of deciding whether excess mortality is due to occupational risk or general social environment. The occupational mortality index can therefore do no more than establish a prima facie case for closer study within the particular occupation.

Limitations of occupational mortality investigations

19.32   Having regard to these difficulties, it must be appreciated that the occupational mortality investigation associated with the census is a very crude diagnostic tool, giving no exact or final answers but throwing into relief differentials worthy of closer study by more precise methods. In this way the investigations have proved of great value in the past. It is probable that, in the future, longitudinal studies (viz. following up groups of workers throughout their period of employment) in particular industries under the close supervision of medical field workers will be more efficient in revealing true occupational risks. Such studies would not be confined to mortality risks but would embrace also sickness absence, i.e. they would begin at a point nearer the onset of the occupational influence on health. Research of this kind has already been carried out by the nationalized industries, especially by the National Coal Board (Liddell, 1973).

Occupational differences

19.33   The occupations with the twenty highest Standard Mortality Ratios (all causes) among 220 occupational groups in the 1970–72 investigation in England and Wales are given in Table 19.2.

19.34   Occupations with the twenty lowest Standard Mortality Ratios (all causes) are given in Table 19.3.

19.35   There are some curious contrasts in these two tables. Why should electronic engineers have high mortality while electronic fitters have low mortality. Could it be that the deaths have been divided between the two groups in a manner different from that of the allocation of the populations? Perhaps a man who died, having

Table 19.2

	S.M.R. (15–64) (both sexes)
Electrical engineers (so described)	317
Bricklayers', etc., labourers	273
Deck and engine-room ratings, barge and boat men	233
Deck, engineering officers and pilots, ship	175
Fishermen	171
Steel erectors, riggers	164
Foundrymen in engineering and allied trades	160
Coalmine workers, above ground	160
under ground	141
Shoemakers and shoe-repairers	156
Machine-tool operators	156
Publicans, innkeepers	155
Watch and chronometer makers and repairers	154
Leather products workers	147
Electronic engineers	145
Rolling, tube mill operators, metal drawers	144
Printers (so described)	144
Brewers, winemakers and related workers	143
Tailors, dress, light clothing workers	140
Stevedores, dock labourers	140

recorded himself in the census as a 'fitter', was described flatteringly by his widow as an 'engineer'? Printers (so described) have high mortality but printing workers (not elsewhere classified) have low mortality. Is this again a result of the deaths and populations being divided in a different way? The most obvious example of different treatment of numerator and denominator of the death rate is the contrast between high mortality of 'electrical engineers' (so described) and the low mortality of 'electrical engineers' defined as those who require training of a university standard. After the death of her husband it is probable that the widow, not having any knowledge of the rules of the official occupation classification, would simply record her husband as an 'electrical engineer', but the census data from which the populations are derived would be subject to more vigorous inspections of the presence or absence of university or professional qualifications. The deaths of qualified engineers would be understated; the deaths of 'electrical engineers' (*sic*) would be overstated; but the populations would probably be correct (the census authorities do have access to records of membership of

Table 19.3

	S.M.R. (15–64) (both sexes)
Electrical engineers (only those requiring training of university standard	42
Coke-oven and gas workers	46
Foremen, engineering and allied trades	47
University teachers	49
Paper products workers	50
Managers, building and contracting	54
Physiotherapists	55
Local-authority senior officers	57
Mechanical engineers	58
Typists, shorthand writers and secretaries	59
Company secretaries and registrars	60
Ministers of the Crown, M.P.s and senior government officials	61
Printing workers (not elsewhere classified)	62
Public-health inspectors	64
Office managers	64
Office machine operators	65
Managers, engineering and allied trades	65
Primary and secondary school teachers	66
Electrical and electronic fitters	67
Radiographers	69
Managers, mining and production	69
Social welfare workers	69

professional organizations and they also have knowledge of the approximate numbers of persons with various university degrees, or their equivalent). Discrepancies such as those described above would require closer scrutiny before the mortality could be properly assessed. We have a classic example of what happens when correspondence between the numerator and the denominator of a death rate is not complete.

19.36   The main specifically occupational differentials remarked upon in the report of the 1970–72 investigation were the following: confirmation of the direct association of higher mortality from pneumoconiosis with dusty work such as that performed by coalminers, stonemasons and slate workers; confirmation that the higher mortality from bronchitis in dusty trades is not merely due to inferior socio-economic conditions but is due to dust itself; higher mortality from cancer of the lip and skin among farmers, foresters and fishermen; higher mortality from cancer of the nose for woodworkers, and higher mortality from cancer of the scrotum for machine-tool operators; and an association between mortality from mesothelioma (a rare form of cancer mainly in the lining of the lung) and the work of metal plate workers and riveters, and gas and electric welders (owing to asbestos exposure). These associations were already well established, but some new pointers emerged. Butchers experienced higher mortality from cancer of the lung and maxillary sinus, possibly, as in the case of woodworkers, from exposure to sawdust; and higher mortality from lung cancer was found among electroplaters and dip platers (it was already known that chrome platers suffered higher mortality from this cause). An example of how the occupational analyses may identify general influences on health was given by occupations such as watchmakers, precision-instrument makers, tailors and various other groups who relied on their hands for performing precision work. Each of these groups had higher mortality from arthritis (a condition which does not usually cause death) as well as from anaemia. A possible explanation for these higher rates is that people with severe arthritis are treated with drugs such as butozolidin and phenyl-butozone, which are known to produce anaemia as a side-effect. The connection with occupation may reflect the effort of the work itself, or perhaps the tendency of arthritics who do this kind of work to be treated more frequently or with more powerful drugs, or it may be that this is the type of work selected by disabled people. Here are clues to be followed up and evaluated by special studies.

19.37 Other occupational risks have emerged from specific investigations. For example, in the study of carcinogens certain occupational associations have been found. The high incidence of skin epithelioma in cotton mule spinners in Britain some 50 years ago led to investigations which corroborated the suspicion that the lubricating oil used was carcinogenic. This finding was followed by protective action, viz. the use of oils of different composition, and modification of machinery to prevent oil splash. Cancer of the scrotum was at one time prevalent in chimneysweeps, owing to the concentration of soot in the skin (one clear example of the value of soap and water—as Clemmesen (1951) remarked, 'The Danish Chimney Sweepers Guild which in 1778 ruled that journeymen and their apprentices should have a daily bath, may, whatever their motives, have done more to prevent human cancer than many research workers'). Tumours of the urinary bladder in certain sections of the chemical industry have been found to be associated with specific aromatic hydrocarbons—in one important instance the isolation of the agent, an anti-oxidant used in the rubber industry, led to its immediate voluntary withdrawal and the cessation of its manufacture, but in other instances, too, there has been modification of handling processes or abandonment of production as a result of these clear statistical analyses. Another example is provided by the high incidence of lung cancer in those working with arsenic, asbestos dust or chromatic dust.

Urbanization

19.38   One of the strongest influences militating against health in the past has been the increasing gravitation of the population into crowded cities. By 1851 about half the population of England and Wales had become aggregated in towns. In 1921 only 20·7 per cent of the population were left in rural districts and in 1961 this proportion had fallen slightly to 20·0 per cent. By 1961 two-fifths of the population were concentrated in the six major conurbations of Tyneside, West Yorkshire, South East Lancashire, Merseyside, West Midlands, and Greater London. (The term 'conurbation' is given to certain large agglomerations of urban areas which represented towns that had outgrown their administrative boundaries.) Progressive urbanization has continued. In earlier days, when the process of town expansion was not accompanied by the provision of public-health or other environmental services as we now know them, town life was associated with many inimical factors—streets instead of fields; damp, dark and ill-ventilated dwellings instead of country cottages; dust and belching smoke and noise instead of clean air and quiet; a preponderance of indoor occupations; crowding together of the population with enhanced opportunities for the transmission of infectious disease; bad drainage and risks of contamination of water supplies; and importation of food from areas far distant from sources of supply, with consequently increased opportunities for its infection and decay. Many of the worst elements of town life have been removed or mitigated by enlightened local government and by the general rise in standards of hygiene in the day to day life of the community at large. Many town dwellings are superior in space, heating, ventilation and sanitation to the country cottage. The town often has the advantage of more extensive medical services. Indoor occupations still predominate but factory and office conditions are immeasurably better. The dust, the noise and the herding together remain, however; and if modern medicine and improved nutrition have together greatly lessened the mortality from infectious disease, more rapid and more voluminous traffic has not only increased the speed with which epidemics spread within a town or from one town to another, but also has provided greater opportunities for fatal or disabling accidents.

19.39 That the urban-rural differential in mortality still exists may be seen from the following age-standardization death rates per 1,000 in 1971 in England and Wales:

Conurbations	12·5
Areas outside conurbations	
Urban areas with population of 100,000 and over	12·5
Urban areas with populations 50,000 and under 100,000	11·4
Urban areas with populations under 50,000	11·4
Rural districts	10·5

19.40 However, it still remains true that health is not only related to bricks and mortar and to medical services but is also dependent on mode of occupation, personal habits (in turn determined by intelligence and educational background) and nutrition; in fact, to the whole life-style and the level of living (which, in turn, is associated with the level of income). We are brought back to the problem of trying to disentagle the separate influences of particular elements in the general complex of social conditions when these elements are all interdependent. Those who can afford an expensive house can also afford to be well-fed and well-clothed, and by the same token are rarely in dirty or unhealthy occupations; they are usually well-educated and know how to take care of their health. One condition implies all the others.

Housing

19.41 In so far as housing conditions directly affect health, they normally do so by affecting the incidence of infectious disease. The more a household (of a particular size) is crowded into small or few rooms, the greater the opportunity for infection to spread by droplet or direct contact from one to another. This increase in the facility of transmission of infection is even greater when bedrooms have to be shared by members of the same family or where rooms are used both for living and sleeping; it is also greater, especially for diarrhoeal diseases, where more than one family are compelled to share the same sanitary arrangements (water closet or washing-up facilities).

Classification of housing conditions

19.42   There have been several attempts to reduce the many aspects of housing conditions that have to be taken into account in any general evaluation into a single-figure index. This is done by awarding 'points' or 'scores' to the various aspects and adding up the total score.

19.43   The immediate difficulty is that while the population, which forms the denominator of the death rate, may be classified according to these housing characteristics at the population census, it is not possible to enquire about housing conditions when deaths are registered, and so the numerators of death rates specific to housing differentials cannot be directly determined. We are therefore forced back once again to the device of isolating populations each sufficiently homogeneous in relation to a particular level of housing conditions and comparing the death rates of these populations.

1944   There is also the difficulty, to which reference has already been made, of isolating the effect of housing conditions from that of other factors with which housing conditions are highly correlated.

19.45   Generally the direct effect of bad housing conditions (as distinct from the general level of living) upon mortality has in the past been demonstrable only in infectious disease, especially tuberculosis. The incidence of tuberculosis is now generally low, and the incidence of many of the once common fevers is kept low by mass immunization; on the other hand, enteritis is still a problem associated with poor housing.

Climate and geography

19.46   The influence of climate can only be separated with difficulty from that of other conditions of environment. No useful comparison bearing on this point can be made between the general death rate of communities possessing fairly good vital statistics but living in different climates. Australia, New Zealand, South Africa and Canada all furnish instances of remarkably low death rates associated sometimes with sub-tropical summers and extremely cold winters. Where a country is notoriously unhealthy, this is usually due in a large measure to the endemicity of malaria or of other insect-borne diseases, often along with parasitic diseases, e.g. anchylostomiasis. These causes can be removed and are being removed.

19.47 Climate has a marked influence on the prevalence of particular diseases, e.g. malaria or yellow fever where a high temperature is needed for effective multiplication of the vectors of infection. Diphtheria and scarlet fever prevail little in tropical countries. The prevalence of tuberculosis in some tropical areas is not a product of the climate but of other social factors, coupled with racial susceptibility or lack of immunological protection. The common cold and influenza are found the world over, but respiratory disease other than tuberculosis is not prevalent in dry sunny climates.

Education and culture

19.48 Those in professional and managerial employment have lighter mortality than unskilled workers. The former are also better educated, in health and in all matters, than the latter. Does education have an effect independently of socio-economic conditions? Is it possible to separate the two effects? General experience suggests that both questions should be answerable in the affirmative. The impact of the inimical forces of nature is clearly different for different economic levels, but clearly individuals at the same economic level may react differently and take different decisions in response to external stimuli according to their cultural background.

19.49 Very little progress has been made in this area of mortality study, except in relation to perinatal mortality, where the cultural background of the families is under observation and not that of the individuals whose mortality is being studied, for infants have no educational background. Poor mothercraft has long been recognized as an important factor in infant mortality.

19.50 It is worth recalling the experience of England and Wales at the beginning of this century, when infant mortality was high. The causes of death, which were emphasized by public-health workers at that time, were poverty, uncleanliness, overcrowding, alcoholic indulgence, poor water supply, unsatisfactory food storage, conservancy disposal as distinct from water-carriage of excreta, inefficient scavenging, and, most of all, abandonment of breast-feeding without adequate cause. It was known that breast-feeding was associated with lower incidence of infectious disease, especially enteritis.

19.51 It was these factors which the public-health authorities then attacked. Under the influence of French medicine, infant welfare centres gradually appeared on the scene. A beginning was made with the establishment of milk depots to provide clean cow's milk to mothers unable to breast-feed. A school for mothers was opened in London in 1904, and another in 1907. The generations of women then passing through their child-bearing life were the first to benefit from compulsory education under the Act of 1870, so that health education was receiving ready acceptance. An infant welfare centre (so called) was opened in London in 1913. By 1917 London had 100 such centres. In 1918 the Government made these centres a compulsory function of public-health authorities. About the same time a personal approach to education in maternal care was intensified through health visitors, who were, from 1907, notified of all births in order that they might make early contact with the mother. Health visitors established a bond of confidence between themselves and the vast majority of mothers and succeeded in conveying to mothers the simple truths of asepsis, nutrition and physical development. A third contemporary advance was a rise in the standard of midwifery, following the establishment of the Central Midwives Board in 1902. As a result infant mortality plunged downward, from 156 per 1,000 live births in the period 1896–1900 to 90 for the period 1916–20 and 55 for 1936–40. With the establishment of the National Health Service, progress has continued, and the rate in 1975 was 16 per 1,000.

The mode of living

19.52 Until recently a striking feature of mortality trends in some developed countries has been the failure of mortality at older ages in men to improve, in contrast to the steady decline in death rates for women at all ages. Two causes of mortality stood out as contributory to increasing numbers of deaths, which more than offset reductions in numbers of deaths from other causes—cancer of the lung and bronchus and arterial heart disease. That this was happening only in males and only in some countries suggested that some feature of the way of life of men in these countries might be responsible. Prospective studies identified cigarette smoking as the major cause of higher mortality from lung cancer; and in addition to cigarette smoking a number of other factors (see para. 19.55)—principally over-eating and under-exercising—were shown to be associated with higher mortality from arterial heart disease.

19.53 The evidence in relation to smoking was well brought together by the Royal College of Physicians in the United Kingdom in a report of a special committee (1960). The committee summarized the situation in the following way: 'Several serious illnesses, in particular lung cancer, affect smokers more often than non-smokers. Heavier smokers have a higher death rate than lighter smokers: those who continue to smoke have a higher death rate than those who stop: cigarette smokers have a higher death rate than smokers of pipes or cigars. There is no doubt of the truth of these statements; dispute continues only about their interpretation.' There is now little dispute. In a world review of levels and trends of lung-cancer mortality, Benjamin (1977) has remarked on three elements of tragedy:

(a) rising death rates from lung cancer contrast with levelling off or falling death rates from cancer of other sites;

(b) after a delay, women are following the experience of men in incurring increasing mortality of cancer of the lung;

(c) atmospheric pollution plays a part and there are some dust exposed occupations that have special risks, but cigarette smoking is the factor to which lung cancer is not only strongly related but related in a rising gradient with the amount of smoking. A priori the disease is preventible given the will to do so; but smoking is addictive and the will is that much harder to create. Nevertheless public awareness of the smoking hazard is increasing and the lung cancer story may yet end as a success story for preventive medicine.'

19.54 Lung cancer is not the only risk incurred by cigarette smokers. They may develop bronchitis, tuberculosis, coronary heart disease or cancer of some sites other than the lung, and cigarette smoking is known to impair the rate of healing of peptic ulcers.

19.55 The causes of mortality from cardiovascular disease were less clear. There was some evidence of dietary influence: it was considered that a diet rich in animal fat meant the ingestion of saturated fatty acids, which led to a high cholesterol level and might also inhibit fibrinolysis. In turn this led to arterial deposits and coronary thrombosis, occlusion, ischaemia and cardiac failure. However, the mechanism was not firmly established. The report by the Director General of the World Health Organisation to the 23rd World Health Assembly in 1970 identified the following factors as increasing the risk of coronary heart disease: high blood pressure, obesity, diabetes, raised blood cholesterol levels, physical inactivity, impaired lung function and personality type. Cigarette smoking is related to coronary heart disease independently of all these factors. Longitudinal studies in Framingham, Massachusetts (probably the most authoritative to date) have indicated cholesterol, cigarette smoking, E.C.G. abnormality, and blood pressure as the most important risk factors, aside from age itself (Truett, Cornfield and Kannel, 1967).

19.56   There is an association between sedentary occupations and above-average mortality from ischaemic heart disease, but it is overlaid by social differentials—the ability of those with higher incomes to secure and to understand better health care. In the 1970–72 investigation in England and Wales the standardized mortality ratios (to 100 for all occupied and retired males) at age 15–64 for ischaemic heart disease were those given in Table 19.4.

Table 19.4

Employers in industry, etc.	108
Managers in industry, etc.	93
Professional workers (self-employed)	82
Professional workers (employees)	90
Ancillary workers and artists	88
Foremen and supervisors (non-manual)	82
Junior non-manual	118
Personal service	122
Foremen and supervisors (manual)	90
Skilled manual	112
Semi-skilled manual	110
Unskilled manual	112
Own account (non-professional)	80
Farmers—employers and managers	89
Farmers (own account)	54
Agricultural workers	79
Armed forces	147
Other or indefinite	47

At least it is clear that farmers and agricultural workers who live an active outdoor life have lower than average mortality from ischaemic heart disease, while clerical workers have higher than average mortality.

19.57   More recently the picture has become more sombre. In Britain and in many western countries the gap between rates of mortality for adult men and those for adult women has ceased to widen, not because the mortality of men has begun to improve again but because the mortality of women has ceased to improve. The figures for England and Wales in Table 19.5 are illustrative:

Table 19.5   *Death rate per 1,000 of women aged 45–54*

1941–45	6·43
1946–50	5·51
1951–55	4·89
1956–60	4·46
1961–65	4·42
1966–70	4·34
1971	4·32
1972	4·44
1973	4·37
1974	4·40
1975	4.28

19.58   The causes of death are those which have been responsible for the lack of improvement in the mortality of adult men of middle and older ages—heart disease and respiratory disease, especially cancer of the lung. Death rates per 100,000 women aged 45–64 in England and Wales for a few selected causes are shown in Table 19.6 for the years 1955, 1960, and 1965 to 1975.

Table 19.6

Cause of death	1955	1960	1965	1966	1967	1968	1969	1970	1971	1972	1973	1974	1975
Cancer of trachea, bronchus and lung	18	22	30	30	33	33	35	36	38	41	40	43	45
Ischaemic heart disease	88	101	118	117	114	113	117	116	117	126	126	127	125
Bronchitis	22	18	20	22	18	22	25	21	20	22	19	19	18
All other diseases	610	547	527	527	510	529	538	524	511	519	504	504	494
Total—all diseases	738	688	695	696	675	697	715	697	686	708	689	693	682

19.59 The higher mortality of those who habitually consume substantial quantities of alcohol is well established. We have already noted (para. 19.33) the higher mortality of those whose occupations are associated with the sale of alcoholic drinks. The predominant cause of death is cirrhosis of the liver. Death rates per 100,000 males for this cause are shown for a few selected countries in Table 19.7.

Table 19.7

Country	Rate	Year
America		
Canada	15·7	1973
Chile	51·6	1971
Mexico	31·8	1973
United States	21·3	1973
Europe		
Austria	45·5	1973
England and Wales	3·9	1973
France	47·7	1970
Germany F.R.	34·6	1972
Italy	46·6	1972
Netherlands	5·0	1972
Norway	5·3	1972
Scotland	5·7	1973
Asia		
Egypt	17·3	1972
Japan	19·1	1973
Sri Lanka	7·3	1968

In looking at these figures it should be borne in mind that in countries where a severe social stigma attaches to alcoholic indulgence a certifying medical practitioner might use a form of words which avoids reference to cirrhosis. However, standards of certification have been rising and this kind of error has tended to be much reduced. It is possible that the absolute levels of mortality from cirrhosis of the liver shown above are understatements; it is unlikely that the comparison between individual countries is grossly distorted.

Socio-economic groups

19.60 We have seen that the correlations between the various social, economic and cultural factors are so strong that it is dangerous and can be misleading to study any one in isolation. For this reason many workers have regarded it as an economy of effort to concentrate on a single indication of the general level of living with which all other factors are associated in the same general direction. This indication is usually derived from the one objective characteristic which is most easily, most commonly and most accurately recorded, namely occupation. Sometimes industry, status (employer, manager, foreman, etc.) and whether or not economically active are also incorporated in the one indicating classification.

19.61 The occupational classification used, for example, in England and Wales comprises some 200 unit groups to which one or more individual occupations are assigned, depending upon the description on the census schedule (General Register Office, 1978).

19.62 Each unit, however, will be broadly homogeneous in respect of the job performed (e.g. manual or non-manual, machine or hand, skill necessary), and the conditions in which it is performed (indoor or outdoor, clean or dirty, sedentary of ambulant, hot or cold, long or short hours, seasonal pressure, etc.). For presenting differentials associated with general levels of living, however, it is more practical to group units together. The earliest attempts to do this were made by the General Register Office of England and Wales and gave rise to 'social classes'.

I   Professional etc. occupations.
II Intermediate between I and III.
III Skilled workers.
IV Intermediate between III and V.
V   Unskilled workers.

19.63 The method here is to attribute to each of the occupations distinguished in the classification a ranking based either on social values (for example, that of standing within the community, as in General Register Office practice from the 1911 census onwards) or on a score derived from a battery of such values (as in the United States Census of 1960). This has three disadvantages:

1 There is a likelihood that the ranking will be influenced by preconceived notions of just those differentials of health or behaviour which the groupings are to be used to discover.
2 It is difficult to provide an economic interpretation of the

interrelationships of the groups and other social characteristics because of the abstract and subjective character of the ranking.

3   The socio-economic homogeneity of the so-called 'social classes' is limited by the fact that whole occupational units only are assigned to a group irrespective of the circumstances of individual workers coded to that unit.

19.64 Nevertheless the 'social classes' served their purpose in effecting a broad division of the occupied population by economic and social circumstances which were more difficult to describe than to recognize, at a time when even if characteristics could be described, they could not be measured.

19.65 To mitigate the difficulties described in para. 19.64 as applying to 'social classes', new 'socio-economic groups' were introduced by the General Register Office at the 1961 Census as an alternative grouping to social classes. They represented an improvement in environmental homogeneity.

19.66 The method, which was developed in France (Brichler, 1958) and standardized in a European Working Group on Population Censuses convened by the Economic Commission for Europe, is to derive groups automatically from a cross-tabulation of the four economic classifications normally used in the population census: (1) type of activity (active or inactive and in the latter event the type of inactive group, e.g. hospital inmate, housewife, etc.); (2) occupation; (3) employment status (employer, manager, etc.); and (4) branch of economic activity (industry).

19.67 The individual cells of such a cross-tabulation represent groups with substantial homogeneity of social and economic characteristics, and these can be grouped into broader groups to the extent of contraction in numbers of groups that may be desired. An important feature of these groups is the fact that they are not necessarily ranked in any preconceived order; it is claimed only that they are economically different, not that any one group has higher social standing than another. Clearly in material terms the level of living is higher for one group than another, so that some degree of economic ordering is inevitable.

19.68 If deaths can be similarly classified by social class or socio-economic groups, the mortality differentials can be examined. If this can be done within the national vital registration system, the statistical investigation can be carried out on a large scale. It must be admitted immediately that this is more difficult for socio-economic groups which require for their identification more characteristics than are normally recorded at the registration of death; it is, for example, easier to obtain from the informants particulars of the deceased's occupation than details of his branch of economic activity. But if this form of analysis cannot be applied to a combination of census data (populations) and vital registration records (deaths) on a routine basis, it can be applied in ad hoc studies; in England and Wales such studies are carried out on a national basis, and covering a period of a few years (usually 3) surrounding the census year.

19.69 At the 1970–72 investigation (General Register Office, 1978) the social class gradient in mortality (all causes) discernible for men was as shown in Table 19.8. I = professional, II = employers and managers, IIIN = intermediate and junior non-manual, IIIM = skilled manual, including foremen and supervisors and own account non-professional, IV = semi-skilled manual and personal service, and V = unskilled manual.

Table 19.8   *Standardized mortality ratios for men, ages 15–64 (all causes)*

	Social Class				
I	II	IIIN	IIIM	IV	V
77	81	99	106	114	137

19.70 The social class gradients differed both in steepness and in direction for different causes of death. Causes for which mortality rose steeply with social class (i.e. with less favourable economic circumstances) are listed in Table 19.9 to which has been added three examples of an opposite gradient.

19.71 There were very few diseases for which in 1970–72 the mortality declined consistently from Social Class I to Social Class V. At first sight this may seem surprising, since in the investigation of 1949–53 it had been found that mortality from coronary heart disease, cerebro-vascular disease, diabetes and suicide showed just such a downward gradient. However, the danger of over-eating, under-exercising, cigarette smoking and over-worrying (factors associated with at least two of these diseases) have been central themes of health education for a long time, and it may well be that it has been heeded. There is evidence that there has been a decline in cigarette smoking in the higher social classes (Benjamin, 1977). Moreover it

Table 19.9

	S.M.R.s (males 15–64)					
	I	II	IIIN	IIIM	IV	V
Respiratory tuberculosis	26	41	84	89	124	254
Bronchitis, emphysema, asthma	36	51	82	113	128	188
Pneumonia	41	53	78	92	115	195
Ulcer of stomach	54	53	99	102	117	209
Malignant neoplasm, stomach	56	66	79	118	125	147
Malignant neoplasm, trachea, bronchus and lung	53	68	84	118	123	143
Cerebro-vascular disease	80	86	98	106	111	136
Hypertensive disease	71	85	104	104	112	141
Nephritis, nephrosis	58	83	103	103	109	152
Motor-vehicle traffic accidents	77	83	89	105	121	174
Leukaemia*	113	100	107	101	104	95
Other lymphatic neoplasm*	123	101	105	103	106	96
Cirrhosis of liver*	104	145	108	80	87	120

*Causes apparently associated (in 1970–72) with comparative affluence.

must be borne in mind that we are discussing mortality from diseases, not their incidence. It could well be that the more affluent experience a higher incidence of a disease but can command, and are better educationally and economically equipped to co-operate with, timely medical care and adjustment to their general life-style so as to reduce the risk of death from that disease.

19.72 The 1970–72 investigation in England and Wales also provided standardized mortality ratios (all causes) for ages 15–64 for men in different socio-economic groups (Table 19.10). The social and economic differentials are very clear. For example, the mortality of the self-employed is lighter than the employed both for professionals and for farmers; and the mortality of unskilled manual workers compares unfavourably with that of their foremen. These differentials apply to many specific causes of death, especially cancer of the trachea, bronchus and lung; anaemias; meningitis; heart disease;

Table 19.10

Employers in industry, etc.	102
Managers in industry, etc.	80
Professional workers, self-employed	69
Professional workers, employees	79
Ancillary workers and artists	75
Foremen and supervisors, non-manual	67
Junior non-manual workers	106
Personal service workers	134
Foremen and supervisors, manual	79
Skilled manual workers	113
Semi-skilled manual workers	115
Unskilled manual workers	139
Own account workers (other than professional)	77
Farmers, employers and managers	99
Farmers, own account	61
Agricultural workers	103
Members of armed forces	147
Inadequately described occupations	86

cerebro-vascular disease, all forms of respiratory disease; peptic ulcer; and accidental deaths.

19.73 From all that has been previously discussed in this chapter about the difficulties of definition of social factors and the near impossibility of separating the individual contributions to mortality of these factors (because of their inter-correlation), it does appear likely that the attempt to take mortality analysis to a greater stage of refinement than these socio-economic groups may bring only marginal improvement to set against a very great increase in labour. It is clear that, given a sufficient degree of homogeneity, these groups provide a powerful tool for the study of social differentials in mortality. Of course it is necessary to be sure of the social, economic and cultural characteristics of the groups and intensive studies are necessary. These studies can be carried on independently of the mortality analysis. Brichler (1958) has given examples of a wide range of factors which in France have been differentiated among the socio-economic groups—alcohol consumption, sickness absence, school-leaving age, radio and television habits, possession of household equipment (refrigerators, washing machines, etc.), expenditure and savings, housing conditions, size of family, religious belief, etc. An innovation in the England and Wales occupational mortality investigation of 1970–72 was the use of data from the General

Household Survey to examine differences between social classes in the possession of certain home amenities (bath, w.c., central heating) and of telephone, television, washing machine, refrigerator, one car or more; and also to examine differences in smoking habits between major occupational groups. This method of looking at social and economic factors in mortality would seem to be as satisfying and as simple as any approach so far devised to the exploration of mortality data normally derived from census and vital registration records as well as those derived in ad hoc retrospective studies.

Prospective studies

19.74 Retrospective studies have had their major successes and there is often no alternative to the retrospective approach, but this is not the ideal research method. The scientific method which forms the basis of productive research requires that hypotheses (in the present context about relationships between various social factors and mortality) should be constructed and validated or invalidated by experimental evidence. The information requirements of such experimentation are unlikely to be exactly fulfilled by what has already been recorded in respect of deaths which have occurred in the past and before the hypotheses could influence the system of recording. Moreover, once deaths have occurred and have been recorded, it is difficult to add to the record by any supplemental enquiry. The evidence grows cold very quickly; it may never have existed.

19.75 For these reasons the prospective or longitudinal enquiry seems superior to the retrospective study. The prospective inquiry demands the following through of a group of lives suitably selected to meet experimental requirements (if only to be representative of the general population) and their observation over the course of time during which their deaths and the essential evidence specifically related to the testing of hypotheses are recorded.

19.76 Two of many examples may be quoted. First, the Framingham Study (Dawber *et al.*, 1959). At this town in Massachusetts, the U.S. National Heart Institute has been conducting a prospective study of factors related to the development of cardiovascular disease. A random sample of two-thirds of the adult population aged 29–62 years was selected for observation. The subjects, all initially free of any cardiovascular symptoms, have been brought in for regular clinical examination. Already much useful information has been gathered about the role of hypercholesterolaemia and hypertension, and many other factors are under study, for example, geographical distribution, educational status, smoking and drinking habits. Here the actual development of disease in subjects initially free of disease is under observation in individual environments which are carefully charted. Another example is that of Doll and Hill (1964), who followed up a representative group of medical practitioners in order to relate their smoking habits to mortality from cancer of the lung and other diseases. This represents a classical example of the prospective study, both in respect of the careful statistical organization applied and the thoroughness with which possible sources of bias were eliminated in the final analyses.

19.77 There is another important reason why the longitudinal study represents the more profitable development for future research. This takes us back to the difficulty of extending evidence of association between social factors and mortality to hypotheses about causation and to the problem of the long chain of events leading to death. Longitudinal studies provide the opportunity of observing the emergence of the first symptoms of disease in those initially free of disease. The point of observation is therefore much farther back than the terminal condition of death, and much closer to the actual conditions associated with the onset of disease. An important advantage is that the deaths emerge from a defined exposed to risk, a basic consideration in mortality measurement.

19.78 This chapter has discussed mortality differentials, but clearly the same principles apply to the observation of differentials in sickness or retirement rates or in fertility, namely (1) separation of groups which are as far as possible homogeneous in respect of the factor under investigation, and (2) correspondence in this respect (and in respect of exposure to risk) between the numerator and the denominator of each rate. Not only do the same principles apply but the same difficulties and pitfalls present themselves.

REFERENCES

Benjamin, B., (1965). *Social and Economic Factors in Mortality*, Mouton, Paris.

Benjamin, B., (1977). *Levels and Trends in Lung Cancer Mortality*, World Health Statistics 1977, No. 2, W.H.O., Geneva.

Brichler, M. (1958). Classification of the population by social and economic characteristics. *J.R.S.S.*, Series A, **121**, 161.

Clemmeson, J. (1951). Etiology of some human cancers. J. Nat. Cancer Inst., **12**, 1.

Dawber, T. R., Kannel, W. B., Revotskie, N., Stokes, J., Kagan, A., and Gordon, T. (1959). Some factors associated with the development of coronary heart disease. Six years follow-up experience in the Framingham Study. *Amer. J. of Pub. Health*, **49**, 1349.

Doll, W. R., and Hill, A. B. (1964). Lung cancer and other causes of death in relation to smoking. *Brit. Med. J.*, **i**, 1399.

General Register Office (1954). *Annual Statistical Review of the Registrar General of England and Wales, 1950*. Text Medical, HMSO, 19.

General Register Office (1978). *Decennial Supplement 1970–72*, No. 1, *Occupational Mortality*, HMSO.

Hauser, P. M. and Kitagawa, E. M. (1961). Social and economic mortality differentials in the U.S.A., 1960. *Proc. Social Statistics Section*, 1960, American Statistical Association, Washington, D.C., 116.

Paul, B. D. and Miller, W. B., eds. (1955). *Health, Culture and Community*, Russell Sage Foundation, New York, 493.

Liddell, F. D. K., (1973). Morbidity of British Coal Miners in 1961. *Brit. J. Industrial Med.*, **30**, 1–24.

Royal College of Physicians (1960). *Smoking and Health*, Pitman Medical Publishing Company, 70.

Truett, A., Cornfield, J. and Kannell, W. B. (1967) A Multivariate Analysis of the Risk of Coronary Heart Disease in Framingham. *J. Chronic Diseases*, **20**, 511.

United Nations (1954). *Report on International Definition and Measurement of Standards and levels of Living*, UNO, 65.

EXERCISES FOR CHAPTER NINTEEN

1   What are the exposed to risk problems in any attempt to assess the relative effects of social and economic factors on mortality?

2   Are the problems referred to in exercise 1 any less difficult to resolve in relation to fertility?

3   In studying the effect of occupation on mortality what are the problems of statistical interpretation as distinct from exposed to risk problems?

4   How are the socio-economic groups used by the Office of Population Censuses and Surveys defined? Do you consider them to be superior to the original social classes? If so, why?

5   It has been suggested that the hair dyes used by women *may* be a health risk. If you were invited to organize a national survey to investigate this suggestion in relation only to mortality, what kind of analysis would you propose and what data would you wish to obtain?

6   Name three diseases in respect of which there is an excess mortality in the lower socio-economic strata of the population. Can you suggest reasons for this differential?

CHAPTER TWENTY

NON-LIFE INVESTIGATIONS

20.1 There are many situations in commerce and industry where we are concerned to observe the 'life' of inanimate objects. Classical examples are electric light bulbs, refrigerators, motor cars, television sets; these are the more common-place examples of the general problem of estimating the actual durability of the so-called consumer durable. The investigations sometimes deal with 'life' in the sense of duration of full operational capability; sometimes they are concerned with 'life' in a more restricted sense of duration in a particular condition, e.g. in stock and unsold, unused or not yet an obsolete model.

20.2 These investigations are usually part of the data-gathering for the application of operational research techniques to problems of maintenance or renewal of stock or of production process control. These mathematical techniques themselves are outside the scope of this book but it is important to bear in mind that the investigations will be part of the larger task of identifying the bounds of a complete system and of measuring the operating characteristics of this system (this is what operational research is all about). In practice it is essential to look at the system as a whole before deciding just what decrement rates are required, but we shall assume for the purpose of this chapter that this has been done.

20.3 The measurement, for example, of the risk of the termination of the useful life of a motor car does not introduce any new principles. The time scale is different and the rate interval is often very much shorter than in the investigation of the mortality of human lives, but the basic principle of identifying the exposed to risk from which the 'deaths' have arisen remains unchanged. There is the same need to distinguish between the rate interval and the total period of the investigation. This will be illustrated by the following examples.

Example 20.1

An urban authority (population 200,000) is concerned about the costs of maintenance of bulbs in the electric street lighting which was instituted 6 years ago. Full records of the replacement of light bulbs exist, and the authority is already aware of considerable variability in the life of bulbs. It desires to have an estimate, based on past experience, of the expected life of a new bulb and the expected cost of replacements in the coming year. A neighbouring authority which is contemplating the institution of a similar system wants to know whether it can use the results of these enquiries to estimate its likely initial replacement costs.

The first step is to calculate bulb-failure rates. A convenient unit of time for durational rates will have to be decided upon. This must not be so short as to restrict the data applicable, nor so long that it obscures the durational changes in the risk of failure. There will be some interest in the point of time, if there is one, when the risk rises sharply. Moreover, if the duration intervals are too long, then the average rate for the interval cannot be used for a fraction of that interval, as it could if the change were more gradual. Nor could the failures, say θ_x in the interval x to $x+1$, be assumed in such circumstances to be evenly distributed over the interval, and this will cause difficulty in the calculation of expected lifetime, because later in this example we shall use the approximate formula for expected lifetime which implies that assumption. (The point has been laboured because it is of very general application). In this case we assume that an examination of the data has indicated (a) that a unit of 3 months will be likely to be satisfactory, and (b) that the whole 6 years' data may be used, since there have been no changes in the construction of the light bulbs or in extraneous conditions. It is also assumed that all replacements are made with *new* bulbs.

Tabulations will be required of

N = the total number of bulbs installed during the 6 years.

θ_x = the number of failures after x but before $(x+1)$ quarters of use. The rate interval is from x exact to $(x+1)$ exact.

P_x = the number of bulbs now in use and installed between x and $x+1$ quarters ago (as at the end of the 24 quarters), i.e. of curtate duration x.

Let E_x be the exposed to risk of failure after x but before $x+1$, the failures being exposed for the full quarter in which they occurred, i.e. we are considering a q-type rate. Then, on the assumption (which would need to be tested) that the average duration in use of P_x is $x+\frac{1}{2}$, we can write:

$$E^0 = N - \tfrac{1}{2}P_0$$

$$E_1 = E_0 - \theta_0 - \tfrac{1}{2}(P_0 + P_1)$$

$$E_x = E_{x-1} - \theta_{x-1} - \tfrac{1}{2}(P_{x-1} + P_x)$$

The failure rate for duration x (for the interval x to $x+1$) will be $\mathring{q}_x = \theta_x/E_x$, and x will have integral values 0 to 23.

It may be necessary to graduate these rates to reduce sampling errors. Although the example refers to a fairly large town and 6 years may seem therefore to be a large sample, θ_x may be a small number at some or all durations and, assuming a binomial distribution, the error, approximately $\sqrt{\theta_x}$, may be relatively large.

We can then, using a suitable radix (i.e. to keep the d_x of the table integral), construct a life table for electric bulbs. This would show d_x the number of failures between x and $x+1$ (exact) $= l_x \cdot q_x$ and l_{x+1} the number surviving to exact duration $x+1 = l_x - d_x$. This table would extend to l_{24}.

Unless l_{24} is virtually zero, $\mathring{e}_x$ cannot be calculated without some assumption about values of l_x above $x = 24$. Some attempt would normally be made to extrapolate l_x, having regard to its trend prior to $x = 24$.

Strictly

$$\mathring{e}_0 = \int_0^w l_t \, dt / l_0,$$

where w is the limit of useful life. If l_t can be regarded as linear over each quarter,

$$\mathring{e}_0 = \left(\tfrac{1}{2}l_0 + \sum_1^w l_t \right) / l_0.$$

We can assume that the cost of replacement (bulb, labour, transport, etc.) is known and is constant.

Assuming that the average duration of P_x is $x + \tfrac{1}{2}$, the number of failures in a year will be estimated as

$$\sum_{x=0}^{x=24} P_x(l_{x+\frac{1}{2}} - l_{x+4\frac{1}{2}})/l_{x+\frac{1}{2}} = F, \text{ say.}$$

Some of the replacements will themselves fail during the years and allowance should be made for these. If we assume that, on the average, replacements take place in the middle of the quarter, the following allowance should be made for failures before the end of the year:

$$\tfrac{1}{4}(F/l_0)[4l_0 - l_{\frac{1}{2}} - l_{1\frac{1}{2}} - l_{2\frac{1}{2}} - l_{3\frac{1}{2}}]$$

$$\frac{F}{l_0}\left[\tfrac{1}{4}(l_0 - l_{3\frac{1}{2}}) + \tfrac{1}{4}(l_0 - l_{1\frac{1}{2}}) + \tfrac{1}{4}(l_0 - l_{2\frac{1}{2}}) + \tfrac{1}{4}(l_0 - l_{\frac{1}{2}})\right]$$

If the shape l_x warrants it, it may be possible to use $F(l_0 - l_2)/l_0$ as a sufficient approximation.

Some of the further replacements will fail before the end of the year, but this contingency can probably be ignored.

The cost of replacements is then obtained by multiplying by the unit cost.

The extraneous conditions which have been assumed to be invariant (in their effect on bulb lifetime) include voltage levels, conditions of lamp mounting, vandalism, road-traffic vibration, atmospheric conditions, hours of use depending on duration of daylight. (Hours of use might be a more appropriate measure of 'age' but, in practice, this would be difficult to record for individual bulbs.) These factors vary both seasonally and generally, and their variations may or may not affect bulb life. We are getting near to the same problem that we discussed under 'class selection'. If there were enough data we should like to investigate the separate 'mortality' effects of these factors and to allow for the more important of them. The neighbouring authority will have to consider whether these factors operate at the same intensity in their area and, if not, what allowance should made for any known differences in their influences.

The unit cost may be changing if only as a result of general inflation, but perhaps as a result of purely local changes in labour or storage costs, and a forecast value of the unit cost might be made. This aspect is not, however, relevant to our main interest in this textbook, viz. 'mortality' measurement.

Example 20.2

A transport company has for many years maintained a fleet comprising a large number of lorries, each of which runs the same mileage every day under broadly the same road and traffic conditions. Every 4 weeks, tests of engine performance are carried out, and in the event of failure to pass this test, the lorry is taken out of service and permanently removed from the fleet. Lorries are also taken from the fleet if they are damaged in an accident of defined severity (such accidents are not uncommon). You are asked, on the basis of records to be maintained over one year, to estimate the expected fleet life of a lorry and the separate accident and engine failure removal rates in each year of duration from entry into the fleet (year to year changes in model can be ignored). Each lorry is reserved for the use of one particular driver throughout its life, and the management wish to know whether lorries have a longer life if handled by older drivers. What records would you require? Show how you would assemble the data and indicate your method of calculation. How would you present your results?

First we recognize that there are two sources of decrement, one of which (accident damage) will probably occur randomly and will be spread fairly evenly over any interval of time, while the other (engine failure) will occur at integral number of months from the start of service of a lorry.

The rate interval will be a 4-week period and the unit of duration or 'age' will be 4 weeks. It will be assumed that the period of investigation runs from 1 January 1978 to 31 December 1978.

The basic record required for every lorry will comprise:

1   date of entering service;
2   date of birth of driver;
3   date of permanent removal from service;
4   reason for permanent removal.

It is possible that these items are already part of the standard maintenance record and may be on punched cards or even magnetic tape (if the fleet is very large).

The records will be scheduled to show separately for three age-groups of drivers, e.g. under 35, 35–54, 55 and over, as at 1 January 1978:

b_x = no. of lorries of age x in completed 4-week periods at 1 January 1978.

e_x = no. of lorries of age x in completed 4-week periods at 1 January 1979.

n = no. of lorries coming into service during the year of investigation

w_x^a = no. of removals from fleet as a result of accident during year of investigation at age x in completed 4-week periods.

w_x^f = no. of removals from fleet as a result of engine failure during year of investigation at age x 4-week periods *exact*

(engine failures must, by definition, occur at exact ages).

Assuming that $\mathring{E}_x$ excludes those removed by engine failure at the xth test, i.e. at age x exact, then

$$\mathring{E}_x = \mathring{E}_{x-1} + \tfrac{1}{2}(b_{x-1} + b_x) - \tfrac{1}{2}(e_{x-1} + e_x) - w^a_{x-1} - w^f_x$$

$$aq^a_x = w^a_x / \mathring{E}_x$$

$$aq^f_x = w^f_{x+1} / \mathring{E}_x$$

From these rates we can develop a service table in which

$$ad^a_x = al_x \times aq^a_x$$

$$ad^f_x = al_x \times aq^f_x$$

$$al_x - al_{x+1} = ad^a_x + ad^f_x$$

(note that ad^f_x are exits at the end of this interval and are aged $x+1$ exact at exit).

When we come to calculate the expected life, we have to remember that w^f_x is not evenly spread over the 4-week period of age x to $x+1$ but occurs at the end of that interval. We have therefore to calculate

$$e_0 = [(1 . ad^f_0 + 2 . ad^f_1 + 3 . ad^f_2 + \text{etc.})$$
$$+ (\tfrac{1}{2}ad^a_0 + 1\tfrac{1}{2}ad^a_1 + 2\tfrac{1}{2}ad^a_2 + \text{etc.})]/al_0$$

$$= \left[\sum_0^w al_x - \tfrac{1}{2}\sum ad^a_0 \right]/al_0 \quad \text{(4-week periods)}$$

It will probably suffice to present the results in the form of three separate life tables for the three age-groups of drivers if they are significantly different, or as one consolidated table if there are no significant differences. However, in testing differences between sets of accident or engine-failure rates, dependent rates will have to be converted to independent rates.

We would use

$$q^a_x = (aq^a_x \quad \text{(all } ad^f_x \text{ are fully exposed to } q^a_x)$$

$$q^f_x = aq^f_x(1 - aq^a_x) \quad \text{(all } ad^a_x \text{ are not engine-tested)}$$

Up to this point we have worked with 4 weeks as the unit interval for x. Rates were requested for each year of duration. If the rates do not change rapidly from one 4-week period of age to another, it will be easy from the service table to aggregate 12 months of decrement to produce annual dependent rates and thence to derive independent rates. If the rates do vary, and especially if the gradient of variation changes, it may be necessary to advise the management that annual rates would conceal these important variations and that it would be better to concentrate upon 4-weekly rates.

For testing differences between groups of drivers it would be assumed that, at any age, failures or accidents are binomially distributed. The tests should be performed on ungraduated rates. In practice one would look at the graduated rates (largely, therefore, free of sampling errors) and ignore small differences between groups of drivers. The ungraduated rates would be tested only in marginal cases, i.e. where a large difference between rates might be due to residual sampling error. It will be borne in mind that the management will be concerned with age differentials only to the extent that they may be commercially or administratively important. If the age differentials are such as to suggest that an age effect might come in suddenly at a particular age (for example, if the 55 and over group produces an entirely different pattern of rates from that for the younger drivers), it may be necessary to go back to the crude data and to reschedule in narrow age-groups to pinpoint such a critical age. In such circumstances it may be necessary to ask for the accumulation of records over a longer period than one year in order to obtain sufficiently large numbers.

Example 20.3

The chief librarian of a local authority which serves a population of 250,000 and maintains several branch libraries wishes to examine the amount of time books of different types and of different ages spend on loan in each year. The period of the investigation consists of the three calendar years 1974–76 inclusive. There are twenty categories of books and all books are already marked with the number of the category to which they have been assigned. The age of the book is defined as the difference between the year of first publication and the year of observation as a new purchase, or as taken on loan or as existing in the library, as the case may be. The year of first publication has been carefully marked on the flyleaf of every book. During the period of investigation, as each book was returned to the library, a clerk completed a slip with the following information:

No. of category of book.
Age of book.
Date of start of loan.
Date of completion.

At the beginning and end of the investigation similar slips were prepared for all books on the shelf, indicating the date of listing (1.1.74 or 31.12.76) and the category and age of book. All these records have been transferred to computer tape.

You are now invited to complete the investigation.

It will be appreciated that this is very similar to a sickness investigation. It will be necessary to calculate the central rate of borrowing, and, further, to disaggregate the rate into its true components, (a) the frequency of spells of borrowing, and (b) the average length of spell. This will be done for each category of book and, within each category, for each age of book.

Define b_x = no. of books on the shelf or on loan at 1.1.74 aged x.

e_x = no. of books on the shelf or on loan at 31.12.76 aged x.

n_x = new books reaching the shelves during the investigation period at age x.

w_x = books withdrawn from circulation during the investigation period at age x (owing to obsolescence, damage, loss, etc.).

s_x = No. of spells of borrowing terminating during that period for books of age x (at start of loan).

d_x = total days of borrowing for spells terminating in the period for books age x (at start of loan).

It is assumed that loans ending in 1974 but beginning in 1973 (which are included in the investigation) are exactly balanced by those beginning in 1976 but ending in 1977 (which are excluded).

The central exposed to risk

$$E^c_{x+1} = E^c_x + \tfrac{1}{2}(b_x + b_{x+1}) - \tfrac{1}{2}(e_x + e_{x+1})$$
$$- \tfrac{1}{2}(w_x + w_{x+1}) + \tfrac{1}{2}(n_x + n_{x+1})$$

or we could use the census method and take $E^c_x = \tfrac{1}{2}[b_x + e_x]$. Then number of spells per year at age $x = s_x / E^c_x$.

average duration of spell $= d_x / s_x$

total days of borrowing per year at age $x = d_x / E^c_x$.

General insurance

20.4 Such investigations as have been described in this chapter are particularly important in the practice of general insurance—marine, fire, motor, liability insurance, etc. There are, however, added complications and a number of statistical problems (some of them in the realm of risk theory) which are outside the scope of this textbook. (For a description of the general insurance market and the actuarial principles involved in the conduct of general insurance see *General Insurance* by B. Benjamin, published by Heinemann, 1977.) Suffice it to say that we have to deal not only with the probability of occurrence of an accident or other event leading to an insurance claim but also the conditional probability that, a claim having occurred, its amount will lie within specified limits (the distribution of amounts of claims is commonly very skew). There are administrative factors also to be taken into account: litigation or other delays may mean a long time interval between the event giving rise to a claim and the actual payment of a claim.

20.5 All this, however, concerns the assessment of the reserve funds needed to preserve solvency. We are interested here only in the measurement of the probability of occurrence of a claim. For this purpose we have to bear in mind that:

1   Except in cases of total loss, an event causing a claim does not remove the insured property or person from exposure to further risk of claim during the period for which a premium has been paid.

2   The exposures (on a rate or time basis) are very heterogeneous in relation to factors affecting the risk of a claim. In motor insurance mileage covered is an obvious source of heterogeneity. This usually means that the distribution of the number of claims in a period is not a poisson or binomial distribution but a negative binomial or compound poisson. It also means that to establish the force of these factors, exposures and claims need to be subjected to considerable statistical analysis. If the vehicle–year were to be used in motor insurance as the unit of exposure, there would need to be subdivision of the data into classes which are sufficiently homogeneous in relation to cylinder capacity, age of car, mileage, age of driver, business use, etc.

20.6 These considerations bring us to the main problem (in relation to the subject of this textbook), namely, the choice of the unit to be used to measure exposures. In earlier chapters we have always used what will doubtless be regarded by the reader as the natural measure—a specified number of *objects* (living or non-living) at risk of a specified event which will give rise to claim, each object being classified by its origin (e.g. existing, new entrant, exit, etc.) and by any other factor affecting risk, e.g. sex age, medical selection (of a life) or age, type of product, type of use (of an inanimate object), and weighted by the *length of time at risk*.

20.7 In general insurance it is simply not possible to record sufficient information to measure exposure on this basis, i.e. 'life-time' at risk, of the insured object. Nor is this necessarily always the most appropriate basis. For example, in fire insurance one policy may cover a number of sites, each site comprising a different number of buildings with different insured values. The building itself is unsatisfactory as a unit, not only because of different monetary values attaching to buildings, but also because of the different types, sizes, designs and uses of buildings. In motor insurance the time spent off the road represents time at minimal risk; time on the road or, even better, mileage covered would be a better measure of exposure than time insured. It would, however, be impracticable—certainly too costly even if possible—to record mileage covered.

20.8 We have therefore to consider using alternative units of exposure which can serve as proxies for the units that might, in ideal circumstances, be preferred as being directly the origins of events giving rise to claims.

20.9 Before considering these possible alternative units we must pause to consider the acceptability of the concept of a claim frequency related not, for example, to motor cars or their passengers but to, say, written premiums (those due as a result of new policies written or policies renewed). In life assurance the object of exposure is the insured life and the unit of exposure is the person–year (when an annual rate is to be derived). The numerator of the rate is the number of deaths during the investigation period, and the units of exposure, to form the denominator of the rate, are calculated by attributing to each person (either exactly or approximately) the time during which he or she is exposed to risk during the same investigation period, and within the category of person to which the rate is to apply. In subsequent experience multiplication of the actual numbers of life-years at risk within the category by this derived rate provides an estimate of the number of deaths to be expected. Since the main object of the exercise is to obtain this estimate, any consistent combination of unit of exposure and multiplier could be used—consistent, that is, in using the same unit in the denominator of the multiplier (or rate) and as the

Table 20.1

Class of insurance	Unit of exposure
Employers' liability	Turnover
	No. of employees
	Payroll
	Premium
Marine	No. of voyages
	Ship-miles
	Sum insured
	Premium
Aviation	No. of take-offs
	Plane-miles
	Passenger-miles
	Passenger flying time
	Sum insured
	Premium
Motor	Vehicle-years
	Policy-years
	Premium
Pecuniary loss	Sums insured
	Full value
	Premium
Personal accident	Person-years
	Premium
Property	
Fire	No. of buildings
	Sum insured
	Maximum expected loss
	Premium
Householders	
	No. of buildings
	Sum insured
	Premium
Reinsurance	
	Premium—of reinsured
	—of reinsurer

multiplicand for estimating deaths. Premiums could be used as the unit of exposure for life assurance, but since this would give greater weight, within the age or other category, to those with larger sums assured, the efficiency of the multiplier as an estimator would be affected by changes in the mix of sum assured from time to time. The life happens to be the easiest, as well as the best, estimating unit to use for life assurance.

20.10 Bearing in mind, then, this point about consistency, we can proceed to consider the possible units of exposure for general insurance. Table 20.1 gives examples. The net risk premium earned is commonly favoured as a unit, not only because it is relatively easy to ascertain but because it must give weight to the various factors influencing risk. The 'earned premiums' are defined as the product of the written premiums (some written in earlier years) and the proportion of the policy term at risk in the period of investigation.

20.11 One disadvantage of using a convenient proxy unit of exposure (e.g. vehicle-years) instead of a more specific measure (e.g. vehicle-miles) is the submerged heterogeneity which is then introduced (some vehicles travel much larger mileages in a year than others). This may be largely overcome by standard statistical procedures, i.e. separate claim rates (the multipliers of para. 20.9) may be computed for different categories within a particular class of insurance, the categories being such as to separate the different sources of heterogeneity. For example, in motor insurance different levels of mileage may be separated by classifying policies according to use (especially if used for business purposes or commuting), or location of garage (town users have different average mileages from country users), or age of policy-holder (old drivers tend not to drive so far as younger drivers), and these factors are of interest in themselves as sources of differential exposure.

20.12 A further disadvantage of using the premium as a unit of exposure is that premiums are relative to a rating structure which may change from time to time. It is therefore desirable to adjust premiums to a common reference structure, otherwise heterogeneity arising from structure changes will be introduced into the data. Furthermore premiums incorporate loadings for commission and expenses; these may vary between classes and also between risks within a class of insurance, and this will introduce additional bias unless it is avoided by the use of the net risk premium.

20.13 When the unit of exposure has been chosen and defined, the calculation of the total amount of exposure to form the denominator of the claim rate is straightforward and employs the same counting principles as in life-assurance mortality investigations. Both policy-year and calendar-year aggregation is used in general insurance. The basic principle is that whatever aggregation is used for units of exposure must also be used for claims.

20.14 The calendar-year or calendar-accident-year method groups together all units of exposure and all claims within the calendar year or years under investigation (and within any specific categories, e.g. age of driver in motor insurance). The policy-year method allocates units of exposure and claims to the policy years beginning within the calendar years of investigation. This allocation requires a little more data-processing to achieve. It is claimed as a disadvantage of the policy-year aggregation that the information is more out of date than in the calendar grouping, because of the need to await the end of the policy years. However, any trend in rates can be projected unless the experience is changing too rapidly or too violently for this to be a reliable procedure, and in the latter case the calendar-year grouping would also give results that would be unreliable for further use. Moreover there is in both methods a delay in processing because of the need to allow for the delay in reporting claims.

20.15 The calendar-year method is, on the whole, simpler, because only premiums (if used as units of exposure) have to be apportioned for the parts of the policy years which are divided between two consecutive calendar years, and it is to be preferred unless there are compelling reasons for requiring a reference to the policy year. In employers' liability and third-party policies it is sometimes possible that the total premium is not known until the end of the policy year; this happens when a deposit premium is paid at the beginning of the policy year on an estimated basis and an adjustment is made at the end of that year when the exact turnover or wage roll can be ascertained. In reinsurance it is frequently found that the premium is not fully received for perhaps 3 years.

20.16 In both the calendar-year and policy-year methods account has to be taken of any changes in effective exposure during the policy year. There are not often cancellations during a policy year but there may be endorsements, increasing sums insured, adding items to the schedule of insured properties or changing the motor vehicle covered by the policy.

20.17 Where, as in most modern offices, the statistical system is computerized, each policy can be given an exact period of exposure within the year of investigation. If a computer is not available, then it is possible to use an approximate method of aggregating periods of exposure. The methods generally in use are given below.

1   *8ths basis.* If it is assumed that the annual policies written in a quarter are uniformly distributed over the quarter (with no bias in location according to size of premium, etc.), then it may also be assumed that these policies, as a group, start on average at the midpoint of the quarter. Thus, policies written in the consecutive quarters of the calendar year contribute 7/8th, 5/8th, 3/8th, 1/8th years respectively to the exposure within that calendar year and 1/8th, 3/8th, 5/8th 7/8th respectively to the following calendar year. Endorsements which are effective for a fraction of a policy year are either ignored (on the assumption that they balance out) or some estimate of their general effect must be made.

2   *24ths basis.* The principle here is the same for the 8ths basis, but a month rather than a quarter is used as the operative counting unit of time. Policies written in the month of May are assumed to contribute 15/24 years to the current year and 9/24 years to the following year. If there is a uniform distribution of policy dates over each month but not over the quarter, the 24ths basis will give a closer approximation to the exact exposure count than the 8th basis. If there is no such uniform distribution, then the 24ths basis may not be more accurate. Both methods will give biased results, the bias depending on the actual distribution of policy dates over the year. In order to conform to the insured's financial year many commercial policies are renewed at 31 March or 31 December. To take an extreme example, a distribution of policies equally shared between these two dates would, on the 8ths basis, lead to overstatement of exposure, in the year in which the policies were written, by 1/8 year for each policy; and on the 24ths basis by 1/24 year for each policy. In practice such an extreme case would not arise, but it would nevertheless be a necessary precaution at least to examine the renewal date distribution of a random sample of policies in each category of exposure so that more appropriate approximation formulae could be designed to reflect these distributions.

3   *The census method.* As in mortality investigations, a weighted average of counts of policies in force at terminal and intermediate

dates can be used to calculate the total exposure. In general the census method is the simplest and quickest to use. The greater the number of censuses, the closer the approximation to exact measurement, but the law of diminishing returns applies and there is usually insufficient gain of accuracy to justify the cost of carrying out censuses more frequently than quarterly, i.e. one at the beginning and end of each quarter, giving equally spaced censuses over each calendar year with weights of 1/8, 1/4, 1/4, 1/4, 1/8 in averaging. The census method has the advantage of implicitly taking account of the effect of endorsements and also of cancellations.

20.18   As an example of the calculation of exposures by the different methods, consider the four motor policies in Table 20.2.

Table 20.2

	A	B	C	D
Renewal date	9.1.76	1.5.76		3.12.76
Inception date			23.9.76	
Claim date		15.2.76		
No claim discount (NCD) status:				
1976 renewal	2 years	2 years	1 year	2 years
1975 renewal	1 year	4 years	—	1 year

20.19   All other factors are assumed to be the same for each policy and unchanged throughout. The total exposure for the four policies in 1976 for each N.C.D. level and for all other factors together is shown

Table 20.3

Method	Exact	8ths		24ths		Census	
	days	years	/days	years	/days	years	/days
NCD level 1 year	444	$1\frac{3}{8}$	502	$1\frac{7}{24}$	471	$1\frac{3}{8}$	502
2 years	630	$1\frac{5}{8}$	593	$1\frac{15}{24}$	593	$1\frac{5}{8}$	593
4 years	121	$\frac{3}{8}$	137	$\frac{9}{24}$	137	$\frac{3}{8}$	137
All other factors	1,195	$3\frac{3}{8}$	1,232	$3\frac{7}{24}$	1,201	$3\frac{3}{8}$	1,232

in Table 20.3 for each of the four methods of calculation, exact, 8ths, 24ths and five quarterly censuses.

20.20 As might be expected, quarterly censuses give the same result as the application of the 8ths rule in straightforward cases (no endorsements and cancellations); as might be expected also, the 24ths rule is more accurate than the other two approximations. The four cases have been deliberately designed to strain the accuracy of the approximate methods (even so, the largest error is only 3 per cent). In practice, with a large number of policies and renewal dates well spread over the year, the errors in the approximate methods would be relatively insignificant. Nevertheless, given computer availability, exact counts would be quicker and more reliable, especially if the risk group classification is at all complicated.

Claims

20.21 The risk classification is an important aspect when we come to consider the numerator of the claim rate. As in mortality investigations, it is a fundamental rule that the numerator and the denominator used in the calculation of the claim frequency should correspond. The coding used for claims must be the same as that used for exposures. Precautions have to be taken in data-processing to ensure this correspondence, e.g. the derivation of exposure and claim data from the same file. There is also a need to have a firmly established definition of a claim and its reference date (normally the date of the incident giving rise to the claim). This definition must be consistent throughout the office statistical system and consistent with the use to which the calculated claim frequencies are to be put. Application of these rates in future experience will reproduce any errors or bias in the identification of past claims for the numerators of claim frequencies. Bias can arise from delays in notification and in processing into the filing system of claims, new policies, endorsements, cancellations. It must be stressed that the input to the statistical system should be directly derived from day to day transactions as these take place, so as to minimize the delay in recording policies, changes of status, claims, etc. It is also necessary to see that sufficient historical detail is retained on the file for each policy in order to ensure that it is possible to refer back to the true insurance position as it existed at an earlier date. This will make it possible to be sure that all contributions of the policy to exposure in different statuses (especially N.C.D. status in motor insurance) have been correctly counted.

20.22 This last point is important because, in measuring claim frequencies according to N.C.D. category, we require to classify the claims according to the N.C.D. category at the renewal date (or entry date) preceding the date of the accident, and, if using the census method, to classify the policies in force according to N.C.D. category at the renewal date (or entry date) preceding the census date.

20.23 In considering what to do about delays it is certainly not safe to ignore them on the assumption that the same proportional error will be introduced into both exposures and claims.

Delays in claim reporting

20.24 Delays in reporting claims can be very long—dependent on the class of insurance—so that claim frequencies cannot in the ordinary way be reliably estimated until sufficient time has elapsed to encompass this delay; at least until a date at which the number of incurred but not reported claims is likely to be a negligible proportion of the total incurred claims. While motor claims may nearly all be reported within 3 months of being incurred, employers' liability and products liability claims may not be reported until years after actual incurrence. Reinsurers suffer from delays in reporting claims because the direct insurer may initially expect settlement within his own retention, but may eventually have to call upon the reinsurers because the final claim amount proves to be greater than the initial estimate (either from monetary inflation before settlement or because injuries prove to be greater than initially diagnosed).

20.25 If allowing sufficient time to pass to encompass these delays means that the claim-frequency analysis (counting all claims related to exposures) is too out of date to be relevant to current experience, then an attempt must be made to project the eventual total of claims for a particular year of origin from the durational distribution of those which have already occurred. The process is analogous to the use of the d_x column of the life table (up to age t) to estimate the value of l_0. The radix of the table l_0 (births in the life table) is the total claims in the origin year, and the decrements d_x are the numbers of claims (incurred in year 0) but reported in development year x, $l_0 - l_x$ of claims $= \Sigma d_x$ being the total number reported by year x. The unit of time may be smaller than a year for shorter-term classes of insurance.

For motor insurance the unit may be a week. The table resulting from this process is called a delay table.

20.26 Given such a delay table, based on recent experience, the total claims N_0 to be expected when N_x have been reported in x units of time is $N_x(l_0/l_0 - l_x)$.

20.27 Table 20.4 is an example of the use of the method.

Table 20.4

Delay table				Reported by	Estimated
Unit of time			Month of	end of	total no.
(months)	l_x	d_x	occurrence	December	of claims
			January	974	974
0	1,000	556	February	964	964
1	444	284	March	955	957
2	160	53	April	1,040	1,047
3	107	37	May	1,037	1,031
4	70	28	June	969	990
5	42	15	July	971	991
6	27	10	August	989	1,047
7	17	7	September	965	1,059
8	10	6	October	893	1,031
9	4	4	November	880	1,261
10	0		December	535	1,924
				11,124	13,262

The total claims arising from September (for which we have $N_{3\frac{1}{2}} = 965$, on the assumption that the occurrences are spread over the month of September) will be

$$N_0 = N_{3\frac{1}{2}} \cdot (l_0/l_0 - l_{3\frac{1}{2}}) = 965 \cdot (1,000/911 \cdot 5) = 1,059$$

It will be seen that the estimated total claims arising from the year, at 13,262, is some 19 per cent above the total reported by the end of the year.

20.28 The delay table would be monitored regularly to see that it continued to be appropriate. One way of doing this is to estimate from the table the number of later notifications which should follow from any month of origin. For example, if the 971 claims arising in July and reported by the end of the year represent $[(\Sigma_0^4 d_x) + \frac{1}{2}d_5]/l_0$ of the total, then the numbers of late reports arising from July, in the months of

January, February and so on of the next year, would be expected to be $\frac{1}{2}(d_5 + d_6)$, $\frac{1}{2}(d_6 + d_7)$, $\frac{1}{2}(d_7 + d_8)$, etc. multiplied by ·971 or 12, 8, 6, 5, 2. Obviously with such small numbers there would be large sampling deviation from expectation. To increase the size of the numbers the test would probably be of *all* late notifications in January, February, etc. arising from the preceding year, against expectations. The total expectation for January (which the reader should check) will be 1,157. If d_x is binomially distributed and we can use the poisson approximation, this will have a standard error of approximately $\sqrt{1,157}$ or 34. A figure outside the range of two standard errors either way, i.e. 1,089–1,225 would suggest another look at the delay experience.

20.29 The calculation of the 'life table' for claim reporting is itself a straightforward mortality-type investigation. Given a statistical system that can readily relate claims to their period of origin, the only problem is the choice of a unit of time which is neither so long that the table is too short for reliable prediction (inadequate sub-division so that all reports are exhausted in d_0 or d_1, for example) or so short that there is unnecessarily detailed arithmetic in the application of the table.

20.30 In general insurance, especially motor insurance, there are many possible sources of heterogeneity with regard to risk of claim; we refer to these as risk factors. Some examples of risk factors have been mentioned in para. 20.11. If there are risk factors attaching to policies each at defined levels of intensity which differ from policy to policy, then an aggregate claim rate derived from one period of experience will not be applicable subsequently, if, as is likely, the mix of levels of the risk factors in the total portfolio of policies were to change. In the following paragraphs we shall refer specifically to motor insurance to illustrate methodology.

Motor insurance as an illustration

20.31 What we need, therefore, is a sub-division of the portfolio into a matrix of numbers $p_{i,j,k}$ ... of policies subject to risk factor 1 at level i, risk factor 2 at level j, etc., and a matrix of claim frequency rates $f_{i,j,k}$ ... applicable to each combination of levels of risk factor. To derive this matrix of rates, standard methods of multivariate analysis may be used. These methods are treated fully in the statistical textbooks and can be dealt with only briefly here. (A useful reference is Kendall, 1972.)

20.32 The first problem is to decide upon the extent of sub-division of experience that is necessary. The true risk factors are not all known, and some that are thought certainly to be significant are not directly measurable because it would be impracticable to record the necessary data (e.g. actual mileage travelled). It would be necessary to consider the likely risk factors and then to decide whether their levels could be recorded on policy files, or whether some other factors which are directly recordable could be used to indicate their levels. The experience of underwriters will be invaluable in these considerations, which are largely empirical. The larger the number of risk factors to be investigated, the more complicated the investigation, the smaller the numbers in individual cells of the matrices (so that broad groupings required may defeat the object of analysis), and the less the predictive reliability of the results. As in similar statistical exercises in other fields, this is the stage when hard thinking in concert with experienced underwriters can bring valuable dividends in simplicity and practicality.

Levels of risk factor

20.33 Even when the number of factors has been reduced to the minimum considered to be essential, there is a further problem. Unless a particular risk factor is capable of being graded (and measured) at increasing levels of intensity, its use in a rating structure will be limited to a 'present' and 'absent' role. There will be an unknown element of heterogeneity in either group; to put it another way, the factor is unlikely to be more than a rather crude discriminant of risk (this does not mean that the differences between the two groups will be small). The following paragraphs may make this need for 'levels' of risk factors clearer.

A model of risk variation

20.34 To provide as much information as possible to enable the variation of risk associated with the different factors to be fully taken account of in rating, it would be desirable to construct a model of the risk process which expressed the departure of the claim frequency of a specific group from the overall mean frequency as a function of the quantified intensity of presence of the risk factors that are identifiable. Such a model may be *additive*:

$$f_{i,j,k,l,m,\,\cdots} = \mu + a_i + b_j + c_k + d_l + e_m \qquad (20.1)$$

where $f_{i,j,k,l,m} \ldots$ is the claim frequency for the sub-group of policies at levels i, j, k, l, m, etc. respectively of risk factors A, B, C, D, E, etc., and a_i, b_j, c_k, d_l, e_m, etc. are the values of the parameters associated with the factors and express the departure of $f_{i,j,k,l,m} \ldots$ from μ, a base frequency when no risk factors are operating: or it may be *multiplicative*:

$$f_{i,j,k,l,m} \ldots = \mu \cdot a_i \cdot b_j \cdot c_k \cdot d_l \cdot e_m \ldots \qquad (20.2)$$

the parameters having different values from those of formula 20.1 above.

The multiplicative model means of course that $\log f$ is expressible as an additive model. Johnson and Hey (1971) have used an additive model, while Bailey and Simon (1960) and Mehring (1964) have used a multiplicative form.

20.35 The usual procedure for fitting such a model to the values of $f_{i,j,k,l,m}$, derived from experience, is to apply multiple regression techniques. These are set out in standard statistics textbooks. The first step is to derive a matrix of the zero order correlations between each pair of the risk factors A, B, C, D, E, etc. This enables the degree of independence of the factors to be assessed. Clearly there would be no point in introducing the further complication of a fifth factor E if it is so highly correlated with B as to be adequately represented by B; b_j would account for the greater part of the influence of E, and since the 'free' variation of E (undetermined by B), would be small, e_m would be of little significance. This first step then is a precaution against unnecessary complication of the model. The next step is to fit the model by least squares, i.e. by minimizing $\Sigma (C - n \cdot f)^2 / n$, where n is the exposure and C is the number of claims, and the summation is carried out over all $i, j, k, l, m \ldots$ This gives rise to a set of normal equations which may be solved to yield values of the parameters $a, b, c, d, e \ldots$ Standard computer programs are available for the necessary matrix inversion. Alternatively, and less laboriously, one could minimize $(C - n.f)^2 / n.f.$, using $(C - n.f)^2 / C$ as an approximation, and solve the equations iteratively. It is then possible to produce a standard table to give expected claim frequencies for different combinations of the various risk factors. In practice, as Johnson and Hey (1971) point out, it is advisable to refine the model continually by comparing actual with expected claims and adjusting the parameters to conform to experience. Johnson and Hey also point out that, having obtained the parameters, it is possible to increase all the a_i and decrease all the b_j

simultaneously by the same constant without affecting f. They found it convenient to introduce the constant parameter μ and to make it equal to the overall claim frequency of the portfolio, and to adjust the values of a_i, b_j, etc., so that the total contribution from each factor is approximately zero. This is likely to remain true unless the composition of the portfolio changes markedly.

20.36 Up to this point we have been talking of the total claims frequency of a particular group without considering whether the claims are produced by a number of policy-holders having one claim each, or a few policy-holders having several claims, i.e. we have not considered the possible heterogeneity of a group which might be a mixture of groups with different underlying claim risks.

20.37 The mixture would not be a problem in itself, provided that its constituency remained stable and the average experience thus remained also stable. No group, however well-defined in terms of the separation of known risk factors, is ever pure. We may use our model to reduce heterogeneity but we cannot entirely eliminate it. The problems lie in the likelihood that the heterogeneity may change from year to year, thus gradually invalidating the claim-frequency model.

20.38 Johnson and Hey have suggested that heterogeneity can be examined by looking at the relative frequencies of 0, 1, 2, ... etc. claims by an individual policy-holder during a defined interval of time. As might be expected, such a distribution is highly skew. The figures in Table 20.5 are taken from the paper by Johnson and Hey.

This distribution fits closely to a negative binomial with the same

Table 20.5

Number of claims in year	Frequency among those exposed throughout the year
0	370,412
1	46,545
2	3,935
3	317
4	28
5	3
All	421,240
Mean	·1317
Variance	·1385

mean and variance. This might also be expected, since in early work on what was then supposed to be accident proneness, the negative binomial was developed as the appropriate distribution for the relative frequency of accidents to an individual person, given that the risk varied from person to person but for an individual person remained constant over the period of observation (Greenwood and Yule, 1920). The concept of accident proneness has largely been abandoned, but the concept of a risk distribution remains. It has been shown that the risk distribution associated with the negative binomial claim number distribution is of the Pearson Type III form (also highly skew).

20.39 To recapitulate, then, the principles brought into play in the derivation of the exposures and claims for the measurement of claim rates in general insurance are essentially the same as those in life insurance. There is, inherently, a great deal more heterogeniety in general insurance, and therefore a greater need for multi-factorial analysis, but here again the statistical methods are general and are not peculiar to general insurance. What is peculiar to general insurance is the need to provide for delay both in the reporting of claims and in the reporting of changes in the status of policies before the commencement of the rate interval. While the first kind of delay can, as we have seen in para. 20.26, be allowed for by statistical methods, the second kind of delay cannot— it has to be avoided by making sure that changes of status are speedily recorded.

REFERENCES

Bailey, R. A. and Simon, L. J. (1960). Two Studies in Automobile Insurance Rate-Making. *The Astin Bulletin*, **1**.

Beard, R. E. (1957). Analytical Expressions of Some of the Risks Involved in General Insurance. *Trans. 15th International Congress of Actuaries*.

Beard, R. E. (1959). Some Statistical Aspects of Non-Life Insurance Statistics. *J. Inst. Actu. Students' Society*, **13**.

Beard, R. E. (1964). Some Statistical Problems Arising from the Transaction of Motor Insurance Business. *J. Inst. Actu. Students' Society*, **17**, 279.

Beard, R. E. (1967). On the Compilation of Non-Life Insurance Statistics. *J. Inst. Actu.*, **93**.

Greenwood, M. and Yule, C. U. (1920). An Inquiry into the Frequency Distributions of Multiple Happenings. *J.R.S.S.*, **83**, 233–79.

Johnson, P. D. and Hey, G. B. (1971). Statistical Studies in Motor Insurance. *J. Inst. Actu.*, **97**, 199.

Kendall, M. G. (1972). *Multivariate Analysis*, Griffin, London.

Mehring, J. (1960). Die Versicherung von Kraftfahrschaden in der Bundesrepublik Deutchland. *Trans. 16th International Congress of Actuaries*, B1, 5.

Mehring, J. (1964). Ein Mathematisches Hilfsmittel fur Statistikund Tariffragen in der Kraftfahrtversicherung. *Blatter der Deutschen Gesellschaft fur Versicherungs-mathematik*, **VII**.

Scurfield, H. H. (1968). Motor Insurance Statistics. *J. Inst. Actu. Students' Society*, **18**, Part 3.

EXERCISES FOR CHAPTER TWENTY

1 An engineering firm making high quality machinery uses for the production of a particular part, a machine tool which must be taken out of service as soon as tolerances in the product increase beyond a prescribed level. These tolerances are tested daily. The management of the firm would like to know how the risk of failure of the machine tool increases with its age, partly because the tool is expensive and they wish to budget for future replacements, and partly because testing increases costs and they would like if possible to reduce the frequency of testing. The machine tools are in constant use. There are twenty such machines and the shop-floor impression is that they fail after about 10 months. How would you proceed to investigate the failure rate and what information would you aim to present to the management?

2 In respect of example 20.2 the information in Table 20.6 is available for a particular age group of driver.

Table 20.6

Completed 4-week periods of service	Lorries in service at		Removals in 1978 for	
	1 January 1978	31 December 1978	accident	failure to pass test
0	110	120	15	0
1	111	99	14	0
2	100	114	10	0
3	102	98	13	0
4	88	92	8	2
5	101	87	14	6
6	79	93	16	15
–	–	–	–	–
–	–	–	–	–
–	–	–	–	–

Construct a table for the first six 4-week periods of service for lorries, showing the numbers out of a suitable radix which go out of service by accident or failure.

3   What are the main differences in exposed to risk and claim frequency estimation as between life assurance and general insurance?

4   What do you understand by the term 'risk factor' in general insurance?

5   How would you investigate risk factors in fire insurance?

HISTORY OF LIFE TABLES

The life table, as a concept, goes back 300 years to the publication of John Graunt's 'Natural and Political Observations ... upon bills of Mortality'. Graunt provided a new idea, an idea pregnant with developments certainly, not all of which he can have foreseen. The idea he presented was of a group of births followed through life and gradually reduced in number by deaths. (In those days it was not so gradually: two-fifths were dead before the age of six.) His numbers of survivors (see below) formed a crude life table which, although incorrectly calculated, represented a tremendous leap forward from the simple death rate to a new and graphic method of representing the age pattern of mortality: 'of the said 100 conceived there remain alive at six years end 64, at fifteen years end 40, at twenty-six 25, at thirty-six 16, at forty-six 10, at fifty-six 6, at sixty 3, at seventy-six 1, at eighty 0'.

From this beginning the life table was developed as a refined tool of mortality measurement. The first complete life table was constructed by Edmond Halley (1656–1742) and was based on the death records of Breslau for 1687–91. Males and females were not distinguished in it, and, like the Northampton table (below), it was based on deaths alone. It is fair to add, as has been pointed out by Greenwood (1948), that Halley realized the population was not stationary and made some correction for the excess of births over deaths. James Dobson (of Equitable fame), who was associated with the beginnings of life assurance in Britain, made use of a life table which he calculated from London Bills of Mortality, 1728–50, to work out premiums. The first life table widely used for the purpose of determining the rate of premium to be used for life assurance was Dr Price's Northampton table, published in 1783. This was based on the death returns for a parish in Northampton in 1735–80. Dr Price was under the misapprehension that the population of this parish was stationary, judging by the number of infantile baptisms. However, at the time the data were recorded there were a large number of Baptists in Northampton, who repudiated infantile baptism. The consequence of this oversight was that the living were understated and Dr Price assumed the mean duration of life to be 24 years, when it was really about 30 years. Dr Price, however, also constructed a correct life table from the population and deaths in Sweden, which was the first national life table ever made.

The Carlisle table was constructed in 1815 by Milne, from the observations of Dr Heysham, upon the mortality of two parishes in that town in the years 1779–89, and two enumerations of their population in 1779 and 1787. It represented an advance in life-table technique, being based on a proper estimate of the population at risk. At the time it was constructed it showed results too favourable for the whole country but, owing to the decrease of mortality which followed, it later became more applicable.

The Carlisle table, although based on scanty and uncertain data, was largely employed in assurance work for many years. Later, many individual assurance offices investigated their mortality experience, alone or in combination with other offices.

In 1843 the *Seventeen Offices' Experience* was published, and later the *Twenty Offices' Experience*. The last-named was published in 1869, and included the Healthy Males (H$^{[M]}$) table. This table, compiled by the Institute of Actuaries, soon became a standard, and remained so until the issue of the British Offices' Tables, based on data relating to the period from 1863 to 1893, which were supplied by sixty British offices. The work of compilation was carried out by the Institute of Actuaries and the Faculty of Actuaries jointly. The O$^{[M]}$ table of this work for male lives took the place of the H$^{[M]}$ table. Government Annuitants' tables were published first on the experience of 1875–1904 and later on the years 1900–20. After the 1914–18 war the Institute of Actuaries and the Faculty of Actuaries in Scotland undertook the joint collection of life-office statistics of the mortality of annuitants from 1900 to 1920, and in 1924 produced the a(f) and a(m) tables, which were of special interest in that they forecast the mortality considered likely to be appropriate to those purchasing annuities in 1925.

Under the same auspices the Life Offices again combined to produce statistics and tables (A1924–29), relating to the mortality of assured lives in the years 1924 to 1929. Two further tables, a Light and a Heavy table, were used to indicate the range of variation between different offices. About the same time a permanent organization was set up (The Continuous Mortality Investigation Bureau—C.M.I.) for the continuous collection of data. Further annuitants' tables, the a(55), considering males and females separately and based on the experience of 1946–48, were issued in 1953. These forecast the mortality considered likely to be appropriate to those purchasing annuities in 1955. In 1956 an assured lives table based upon the experience of 1949–52 was also prepared. More recently there have been a new series of tables in preparation; one for assured lives based on the years of experience 1967–70 has already appeared and others for annuitants and pensioners are in production (see Chapter 18).

The national experience of England and Wales has been made the subject of a series of life tables published by the Registrar General.

Dr Farr constructed English Life Table 1, based on the census returns of 1841 and the deaths of the same year (Registrar General's Fifth Report). Thinking, however, that the records of one year's deaths might be open to challenge owing to the short time embraced by them, he constructed the English Life Table 2. This was founded on the census enumerations of 1831 and 1841, and the deaths of 7 years, viz. those in 1841 and the 3 previous and 3 subsequent years. The difference between these two English Life tables is slight.

The English Life Table 3, constructed by Dr Farr, was based on the census enumerations of 1841 and 1851, and upon the deaths registered in the 17 years 1838–54.

The near agreement between the results obtained by these three English Life Tables is very remarkable, and shows that, notwithstanding annual fluctuations, there was a fairly stationary level of mortality during 1838–54 (which continued up to the year 1871). This stability in the level of mortality led Dr Farr to abandon his intention of constructing a fourth English Life Table relative to experience in a period ending in 1872.

The Healthy District Life Table was constructed by Dr Farr on the basis of the mortality during the 5 years 1849–53 in sixty-three selected English districts, which showed, during the decennium 1841–50, a mean annual death rate not exceeding 17 per 1,000 persons living. As pointed out by Dr Farr, it expressed 'very accurately the actual duration of life among the clergy and other classes of the community living under favourable circumstances'. It represented also a standard of healthiness already attained, and was therefore a realistic yardstick. This table is printed in the Thirty-third Annual Report of the Registrar General.

The English Life Table 4 by Dr Ogle, published in the Supplement to the Thirty-fifth Annual Report of the Registrar General, dealt with the national experience in the decennium 1871–80, and those (5 and 6) by Dr Tatham with the corresponding experiences of 1881–90 and 1891–1900.

The New Healthy Districts Life Table by Dr Tatham gave a valuable index of sanitary and social progress. Thus, whereas in 1849–53, the period dealt with by Dr Farr's Healthy Districts Life Table, 'less than 6% of the total population lived in districts the crude death rates in which were below 17·5 per 1,000; in 1881–90, on the other hand, no less than 25% of the population lived in districts the crude death rate in which fell below 17·5 per 1,000 and 4½% in districts the crude death rate in which did not reach 15·0 per 1,000'. When differences of age and sex constitution were allowed for by obtaining death rates in a standard population, it was found that about one-sixth of the entire population had death rates below 15 per 1,000 in 1881–90. This new Healthy Districts Table was therefore calculated on 46 million years of life, a basis more than nine times as great as that of the older table. In the corresponding Healthy Districts Life Table for 1891–1900 it was found practicable to utilize the experience of an aggregate population of 4·4 million in 260 districts, the crude death rates in which did not exceed 14 per 1,000.

For the decennium 1901–10 much more abundant information was supplied. The making of national life tables for this period was entrusted to George King, an actuary. In this report the following life tables are given:

1   Life tables for England and Wales for males and females respectively, based on the experience of the 10 years 1901–10 (No. 7) and corresponding to the English Life Table 6 for the decennium 1891–1900.
2   Life tables for England and Wales, for males and females, based on the census of 1911 and the deaths of the 3 years 1910–12 (No. 8).
3   Life tables for females only, according to marital condition, single, married or widowed, based on the census of 1911 and deaths in 1910–12.
4   Sectional life tables, for males and females, respectively, for:

   (a)   The administrative county of London.
   (b)   The aggregate of county boroughs.
   (c)   The aggregate of urban districts.
   (d)   The aggregate of rural districts.

These were based on the deaths in 1911 and 1912, and on the estimated population in the middle of each of these years.

Life Tables No. 9 for 1920–2, No. 10 for 1930–2, No. 11 for 1950–2, No. 12 for 1960–2 and No. 13 for 1970–2 were prepared by the Government Actuary. For E.L.T. 9 and 10 the census populations and deaths grouped in 5-year age periods were graduated to remove irregularities due to errors of age statement, etc., and rates of mortality were derived at quinary age points; rates for individual ages were obtained by interpolation. In connexion with English Life Table 9 an extensive analysis was made of variation of mortality between different geographical areas, and complete sets of rates were given for County Boroughs in Northumberland and Durham (Heavy mortality) and Eastern Counties Rural Districts (Light mortality). Full life tables were provided for Greater London. In the 1931 Decennial Supplement regional comparisons were made; rates for individual ages 0–84 for each sex were given for Northumberland and Durham County Boroughs and for the Eastern Regional Rural Districts; and life tables for Greater London were given. Mortality rates at quinary age points were compared for single, married and widowed women. E.L.T. 11 broke new ground in that King's method was abandoned in favour of fitting a mathematical curve to the crude death rates; this was a combination of a logistic curve with a symmetrical normal curve. This new form of graduation was repeated in E.L.T. 12. For E.L.T. 13 a spline graduation was preferred (see Chapter 18).

REFERENCE

Greenwood, A. (1948) *Medical Statistics from Graunt to Farr*, Cambridge University Press, Cambridge.

ANSWERS TO EXERCISES

Chapter 1

1. (i)

	Values of m_x	
Age	Area A	Area B
0–14	0·0040	0·0020
15–44	0·0020	0·0015
45–64	0·0200	0·0150
65–84	0·0850	0·0740
85+	0·3000	0·2560

(ii)

	Standardized mortality rates
Area A	0·0233
Area B	0·0193

Chapter 2

3.

Age	$\mathring{m}_x$	$\mathring{q}_x$
55	0·0120	0·01192
56	0·0125	0·01242
57	0·0132	0·01311

4.

						Age last birthday			
Case	Classification	53	54	55	56	57	58	59	60
A	b_{55} e_{60}			$\frac{1}{2}$	1	1	1	1	$\frac{1}{2}$
B	b_{53} w_{55}	$\frac{1}{2}$	1	$\frac{1}{2}$					
C	n_{60} w_{60}								$\frac{1}{2}-\frac{1}{2}=0$
D	b_{55} θ_{58}			$\frac{1}{2}$	1	1	$\frac{1}{2}$		
E	b_{53} e_{58}	$\frac{1}{2}$	1	1	1	1	$\frac{1}{2}$		
F	n_{59} w_{59}							$\frac{1}{2}-\frac{1}{2}=0$	
G	b_{55} θ_{55}			$\frac{1}{2}-\frac{1}{2}=0$					
	Totals E_x^c	1	2	$2\frac{1}{2}$	3	3	2	1	$\frac{1}{2}$

5.

Age last birthday	b_x	n_x	w_x	θ_x	e_x	E_x^c
53	BE					1
54						2
55	ADG		B	G		$2\frac{1}{2}$
56						3
57						3
58				D	E	2
59		F	F			1
60		C	C		A	$\frac{1}{2}$

Chapter 3

1.
Age x	θ_x/E_x
25	0·00448
26	0·00480
27	0·00505

3.
A	0·00917
B	0·01055

Chapter 4

2. (a) $\mathring{q}_{40} = 0·00221$

$\mathring{q}_{41} = 0·00244$

(b) $\mathring{q}_{55} = 0·0111$

$\mathring{q}_{56} = 0·0127$

$\mathring{q}_{57} = 0·0144$

$\mathring{q}_{58} = 0·0171$

$\mathring{q}_{59} = 0·0195$

3.
Age x	b_x	n_x	w_x	θ_x	e_x	E_x
42		2(AL)				1
43		2(DM)				3
44	2(GK)	2(HI)				7 6
45	2(BN)	1(E)	3(GHN)	1(B)		9
46	1(C)		1(C)	2(DI)	3(AEL)	4·5
47						2
48					1(M)	1
49					1(K)	0

$q_{44} \doteqdot \theta_{45}/E_{45} = 1/9$

4. (a) 0·01350

(b) 0·01452

(c) 0·01363

Chapter 5

1. $E^c_{[30]2} = 250·5$

$E^c_{33} = 1746·5$

2. Cases included
A	b_{71}	e_{76}
C	$b_{[38]+1}$	$w_{(38)+1}$
D	b_{39}	θ_{42}
F	$n_{[27]}$	e_{32}

Chapter 6

2.
Age x	l_x	d_x	w_x
25	100,000	170	11,358
26	88,472	156	8,845

4.
Age x	bl_x	bd_x	bm_x	ml_x	md_x
25	100,000	619	4,109	0	10
26	95,372	616	4,072	4,009	31
27	90,684	619	3,911	8,050	54
28	86,154	595	3,673	11,907	79

ee Errata

Chapter 8

1.

Age x	No. of spinsters living at exact age x	Central rates		Marriages	Withdrawals
		Marriage	Withdrawal		
20	10,000	·2436	·0385	2,135	337
21	7,528	·2721	·0272	1,782	178
22	5,568	·3043	·0217	1,457	104
23	4,007	·3000	·0167	1,038	58
24	2,911	·3063	·0180	767	45
25	2,099				

INDEX